D1064763

# THE
# OXFORD ENGINEERING SCIENCE SERIES

*General Editors*

E. B. MOULLIN      SIR DAVID PYE

SIR RICHARD SOUTHWELL

# MODERN DEVELOPMENTS IN FLUID DYNAMICS
## HIGH SPEED FLOW

*Composed under the aegis of the*

FLUID MOTION SUB-COMMITTEE OF THE
AERONAUTICAL RESEARCH COUNCIL

*and edited by*

## L. HOWARTH

*with the assistance of*

H. B. SQUIRE *and* THE LATE C. N. H. LOCK

VOLUME II

OXFORD
AT THE CLARENDON PRESS

*Oxford University Press, Amen House, London E.C.4*

GLASGOW  NEW YORK  TORONTO  MELBOURNE  WELLINGTON
BOMBAY  CALCUTTA  MADRAS  KARACHI  LAHORE  DACCA
CAPE TOWN  SALISBURY  NAIROBI  IBADAN  ACCRA
KUALA LUMPUR  HONG KONG

FIRST EDITION 1953
REPRINTED 1956, 1964

REPRINTED LITHOGRAPHICALLY IN GREAT BRITAIN
AT THE UNIVERSITY PRESS, OXFORD
BY VIVIAN RIDLER
PRINTER TO THE UNIVERSITY

# CONTENTS

# XI

## EXPERIMENTAL METHODS

### SECTION I

### WIND TUNNELS AND MOVING BODIES

## § 1. Introduction

AN aerodynamic experiment is regarded as a high-speed one if the Mach number somewhere approaches or exceeds unity. The velocity of sound, $a$, is given by

$$a = \sqrt{\left(\frac{\gamma p}{\rho}\right)} = \sqrt{(\gamma \mathscr{R} T)}. \tag{1}$$

For air with $\gamma = 1 \cdot 40 \qquad a = 65 \cdot 8 \sqrt{T}$,

where $a$ is the velocity of sound in feet per second and $T$ is the absolute temperature in Kelvin degrees. At $288°$ K., $a = 1,115$ ft./sec., so that the velocities associated with compressibility phenomena in air at normal temperatures are of the order of 1,000 ft./sec.

Although it is immaterial whether fluid flow past a body is due to the motion of the body or to that of the fluid, there are a number of reasons for which it is advantageous to keep the object under examination at rest. In particular, it is very much more convenient to mount and use stationary instruments than moving ones. Moreover, where high speeds are desired, it is often easier to circulate a quantity of fluid with enormous kinetic energy than it is to propel even a small test object under control and to stop it without damage. These considerations explain the continuing importance of high-speed wind tunnels in spite of limitations which will be described later, but the alternative methods are more advantageous in certain circumstances.

## § 2. High-speed wind tunnels

The most important aerodynamic variables of high-speed flow are usually the Mach number and the Reynolds number. Wind tunnels may be classed first of all as 'supersonic' or 'subsonic' depending on whether or not operation is possible at free-stream Mach numbers in excess of unity. A separate classification depends on whether the

Reynolds and Mach numbers are independently variable, or, in practice, whether or not the stagnation pressure is variable.

When the stagnation temperature and pressure are held constant, the Reynolds number $R$ varies quite widely with the Mach number $M$. Thus, using Sutherland's formula† to relate the temperature $T$ and viscosity $\mu$, the Reynolds number for a length $l$ in a flow obtained by homentropic expansion from rest at conditions 0 is easily shown to be given by

$$R = \frac{Ul\rho}{\mu} = \frac{a_0 l\rho_0}{\mu_0} \frac{M}{\{1+\frac{1}{2}(\gamma-1)M^2\}^{(2-\gamma)/(\gamma-1)}} \left(\frac{T_0/\{1+\frac{1}{2}(\gamma-1)M^2\}+C}{T_0+C}\right) \quad (2)$$

where $U$ is the velocity, $\rho$ the density, and $C$ is Sutherland's constant.† Fig. 129 shows the variation of Reynolds number per foot length with $M$ for a stagnation pressure of 14·7 lb./sq. in. abs. and for a variety of temperatures.

Since the Reynolds number is proportional to the pressure at constant Mach number and temperature, high Reynolds numbers can be attained in small wind tunnels by operating at high stagnation pressures. In practice, however, it is generally difficult to use stagnation pressures above one atmosphere for aircraft models because the stresses and deflexions due to aerodynamic loading become excessive, and the supports and their interference introduce increased uncertainties. The alternatives of securing low kinematic viscosities by operating at very low temperatures or by using gases other than air have quite great potential advantages.

Although experiments on the walls of a wind tunnel itself can take full advantage of the Reynolds numbers of Fig. 129, at near-sonic speeds the stream is so sensitive to any obstruction that the size of the test model is limited in a way which is considered later (see Fig. 144) in relation to wind-tunnel wall corrections, and the Reynolds number is thereby reduced.

The wind tunnels of Fig. 130 (a), (b), and (c) are of the constant stagnation pressure type. The convenience of building a tunnel to take in air directly from the atmosphere is offset by the fact that, at speeds approaching the speed of sound, the static temperature may fall sufficiently to cause condensation of the water vapour in the air, with consequent changes in flow. Control of the cooling-air

† See Chap. X, § 7.

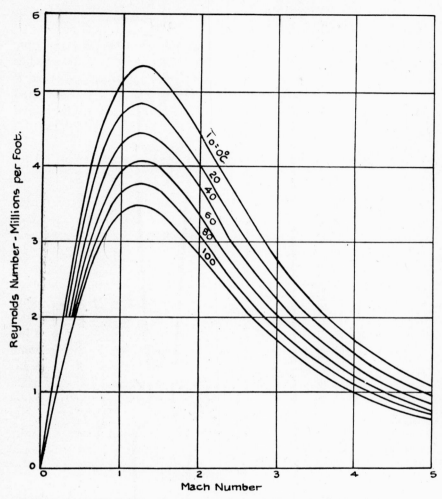

Fɪɢ. 129. Variation of Reynolds number with Mach number and stagnation
temperature (stagnation pressure = 14·7 lb./sq. in. absolute).

circulation between zero and 20 per cent. of the tunnel flow allows
a return-flow tunnel† of the D.V.L. kind (Fig. 130 (a)) to run hot
enough to avoid condensation for most atmospheric conditions,
though at some loss in Reynolds number as Fig. 129 shows. In the
same way, the relative humidity in a wind tunnel of the jet-engine

---

† Göthert and Matt, 'The D.V.L. high-speed wind tunnel', *Lilienthal-Ges. Luftfahrtforsch.*, No. L.G.L. 127 (1940), *Rep. Aero. Res. Coun.*, No. 9,149 (1945).

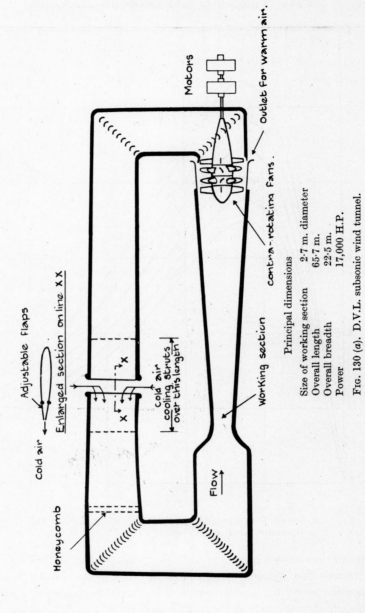

Honeycomb

Cold air

Adjustable Flaps

Enlarged section on line X X

Cold air cooling struts over this length

Flow

Working section

contra-rotating Fans.

Motors

Outlet for warm air.

Principal dimensions

| | |
|---|---|
| Size of working section | 2·7 m. diameter |
| Overall length | 65·7 m. |
| Overall breadth | 22·5 m. |
| Power | 17,000 H.P. |

Fig. 130 (a). D.V.L. subsonic wind tunnel.

induced type† (Fig. 130 (b)) can be reduced by mixing with the inflow a fraction of the hot, though moist, exhaust gases. At the higher speeds reached by the W.V.A. tunnel‡ (Fig. 130 (c)), however, the intake air is drawn through a bed of silica gel which reduces the

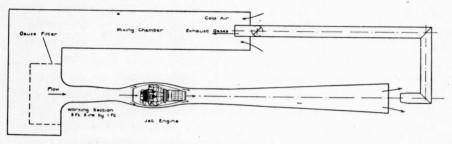

FIG. 130 (b). A high-speed tunnel driven by a jet engine.
(The English Electric Co., Ltd.)

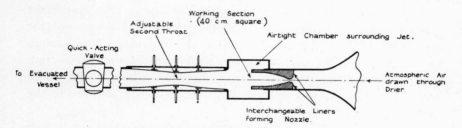

FIG. 130 (c). Intermittent supersonic tunnel at the W.V.A.

absolute humidity to about 0·5 g. water per kg. of dry air. Driers of this type using silica gel or alumina are most appropriate to short-duration intermittent wind tunnels. Although silica gel adsorbs an amount of water of the order of 25 per cent. of its dry weight, a large quantity is required for drying the flow of a continuous straight-through tunnel.

There are many circumstances in which it is advantageous to separate the effects of Reynolds number and Mach number varia-

† Ellis, 'Industrial wind tunnels', *J. Roy. Aero. Soc.* **53** (1949), 797.
‡ Owen, 'Note on the apparatus and work of the W.V.A. Supersonic Institute, Part I', *Rep. Aero. Res. Coun.*, No. 9,281 (1945), *Tech. Notes Roy. Aircraft Estb.*, No. Aero. 1,711.

tions. While it is usually possible to construct models of different scales, there is usually some doubt about the precision of similarity of such models, and changes in size imply changes in wall corrections unless the tunnel size is changed too. For these reasons many wind tunnels are completely closed so that the stagnation pressure and Reynolds number can be varied independently of the speed. The tunnels illustrated in Fig. 130 (d),† (e),‡ and (f),§ have this advantage. With a closed circuit the drying problem is comparatively trivial, but the cooling system needs to remove the heat equivalent of the whole driving power. In the R.A.E. tunnel‡ shown in Fig. 130 (e) a refrigeration system with brine storage serves both to remove the water vapour from the incoming air and to provide a large thermal capacity for cooling. Starting supersonic tunnels under reduced pressure lessens the violence of buffeting as the tunnel shock wave passes through the working section during the starting process, and so permits the use of smaller supports with reduced interference.

In the induced-flow tunnel‖ shown in Fig. 130 (g) dry compressed air is supplied to a pressure chamber and escapes through injector slots downstream of the working section, thus inducing a flow through the tunnel. The air is then ducted back into the working section apart from a quantity, equal to that injected, which is allowed to escape through the exit valve in order to keep the pressure in the tunnel constant.

Fig. 130 (h) illustrates a type of wind tunnel suitable for testing cascades of aerofoils representative of the blading of compressors or turbines. In order to reproduce the conditions in an infinite cascade reasonably closely, such tunnels are commonly made to hold eight or ten blades, or arrangements are made, as in this instance, for removing the boundary layers in the end passages. Other tunnels for testing cascades are described†† by Todd.

† Ackeret, 'Windkanäle für hohe Geschwindigkeiten', *Atti Accad. d'Italia* (*5th Volta Congr.*) *Rome* (1935); *Rep. Aero. Res. Coun.*, No. 8,239 (1944).

‡ Thompson and Mair, 'The R.A.E. high-speed tunnel and a review of the work accomplished in 1942–45', *Rep. Memor. Aero. Res. Coun.*, No. 2,222 (1946).

§ Millikan, 'High-speed testing in the Southern California Co-operative wind tunnel', *Aero. Conf. Lond.* (1947), p. 137.

‖ Holder and North, 'The 9×3 in. N.P.L. induced-flow high-speed wind tunnel', *Rep. Aero. Res. Coun.*, No. 12,387 (1949).

†† Todd, 'Practical aspects of cascade wind tunnel research', *Proc. Instn. Mech. Engrs.* **157** (1947), 482; 'Some developments in instrumentation for air-flow analysis', ibid. **161** (1949), 213.

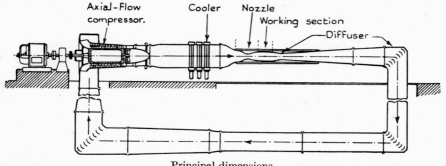

### Principal dimensions

| | |
|---|---|
| Overall length | 22·9 m. |
| Overall breadth | 8·8 m. |
| Size of working section | 40 cm. × 40 cm. |
| Power | 950 H.P. |

FIG. 130 (*d*). Zürich supersonic wind tunnel.

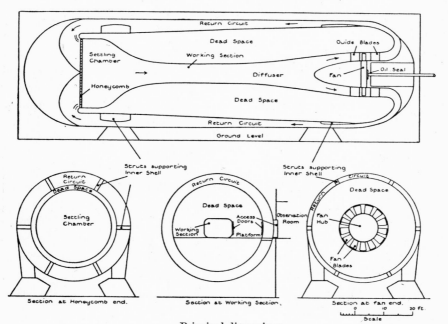

### Principal dimensions

| | |
|---|---|
| Overall length | 130 ft. |
| Diameter | 37 ft. |
| Size of working section | 10 × 7 ft. |
| Pressure range | $\frac{1}{10}$ to 4 atm. |
| Power | 4,000 H.P. |

FIG. 130 (*e*). Subsonic wind tunnel at the R.A.E.

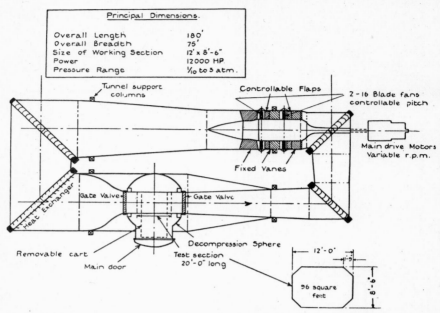

FIG. 130 ($f$). Southern California Co-operative subsonic wind tunnel.

## § 3. High-speed wind-tunnel design

In a large part of the circuit of a high-speed tunnel the air speeds are far below the speed of sound and low-speed tunnel design methods suffice.

*Contraction design.* In a low-speed tunnel a large contraction ratio is required to give a uniform steady flow in the working section. In a high-speed tunnel an additional reason† for a large contraction is to reduce the speed and pressure drop through coolers and driers‡ placed across the settling chamber upstream.

The shape of the contraction should be so designed that large adverse pressure gradients are avoided at the walls; such pressure gradients may cause boundary-layer separation and unsteady flow. Papers describing methods of design are listed in the bibliography at the end of the chapter.

---

† This requirement arises to a lesser extent in low-speed tunnels also because it is necessary to keep the speed through the gauze damping screens low.

‡ The speed through a silica gel or alumina drying bed should not normally exceed about 5 ft./sec.

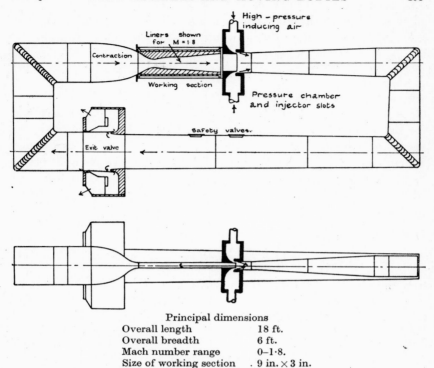

Principal dimensions
Overall length           18 ft.
Overall breadth          6 ft.
Mach number range        0–1·8.
Size of working section  . 9 in. × 3 in.

FIG. 130 (*g*). N.P.L. 9 in. × 3 in. induced-flow tunnel.

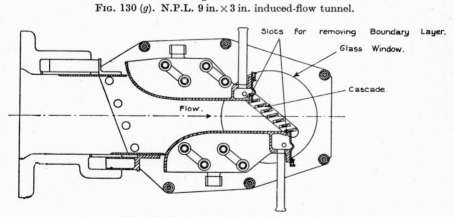

FIG. 130 (*h*). A tunnel for testing cascades.

## § 4. Throats and nozzles for supersonic tunnels

In the case of supersonic wind tunnels, the Mach number in the working section depends on the ratio of the cross-sectional area there to that at the 'throat'. On the assumption of one-dimensional homentropic flow, the relation would be (see Chap. VI, eqn. (30))

$$\frac{A}{A_t} = \frac{1}{M}\left[\frac{1+\frac{1}{2}(\gamma-1)M^2}{1+\frac{1}{2}(\gamma-1)}\right]^{(\gamma+1)/2(\gamma-1)}, \tag{3}$$

where $M$ is the Mach number in the working section whose area is $A$, $A_t$ is the area of the throat, and $\gamma$ is the ratio of specific heats for the air or other gas in the tunnel. In fact, the flow through the throat is faster near the walls than in the centre and by an amount which depends on the wall shapes.[†] Design purposes are well served by the following comparatively rough estimate due to Sauer.[‡]

*Flow through a two-dimensional throat.* Taking the $x$-axis positive in the direction of the flow and as the line about which the flow is symmetrical, the equation of motion is

$$\frac{\partial U}{\partial x}\left(\frac{U^2}{a^2}-1\right)+\frac{\partial V}{\partial y}\left(\frac{V^2}{a^2}-1\right)+\frac{2UV}{a^2}\frac{\partial U}{\partial y} = 0, \tag{4}$$

and Bernoulli's equation may be written

$$\frac{U^2+V^2}{2}+\frac{a^2}{\gamma-1} = \text{const} = a_t^2\left[\frac{1}{2}+\frac{1}{\gamma-1}\right]. \tag{5}$$

Putting $U = a_t(1+u)$ and $V = a_t v$, where $a_t$ is the velocity of sound at the throat, and taking the origin as the point where this velocity is reached on the $x$-axis, we find that

$$(\gamma+1)u\frac{\partial u}{\partial x}-\frac{\partial v}{\partial y} = 0 \tag{6}$$

approximately.[||] Then the velocity potential, for which

$$u = \frac{\partial\phi}{\partial x}, \qquad v = \frac{\partial\phi}{\partial y},$$

can be expressed by the series

$$\phi = f_0(x)+y^2 f_2(x)+y^4 f_4(x)+\dots. \tag{7}$$

If, for example, $u = \alpha x$ for $y = 0$, substitution of eqn. (7) in eqn.

[†] Taylor, 'Flow of air at high speed past curved surfaces', *Rep. Memor. Aero. Res. Coun.*, No. 1,381 (1930); Hooker, 'Flow of a compressible fluid near the throat of a constriction in a circular wind channel', *Proc. Roy. Soc.* A, **135** (1932), 498; Fox and Southwell, 'Flow of gas with velocities exceeding the speed of sound', ibid. A, **183** (1945), 38; Emmons, 'The numerical solution of compressible flow problems', *Tech. Notes Nat. Adv. Comm. Aero.*, No. 932 (1944).

[‡] 'General characteristics of the flow through nozzles in the neighbourhood of the critical velocity', *Rep. Aero. Res. Coun.*, No. 9,499, *Tech. Memor. Nat. Adv. Comm. Aero.*, No. 1,147 (1947).

[||] Cf. Chap. VIII, § 18.

(6) leads to the following values of the coefficients in eqn. (7):

$$f_0(x) = \frac{\alpha x^2}{2},$$

$$f_2(x) = \frac{\gamma+1}{2}\alpha^2 x,$$

$$f_4(x) = \frac{(\gamma+1)^2}{24}\alpha^3, \quad \text{etc.}$$

Then

$$\left.\begin{aligned}
u &= \alpha x + \frac{\gamma+1}{2}\alpha^2 y^2 + \ldots, \\
v &= (\gamma+1)\alpha^2 xy + \frac{(\gamma+1)^2}{6}\alpha^3 y^3 + \ldots.
\end{aligned}\right\} \tag{8}$$

From eqn. (5)     $(1+u)^2 + v^2 = \dfrac{\gamma+1}{\gamma-1} - \dfrac{2}{\gamma-1}\dfrac{a^2}{a_t^2}.$

But     $\dfrac{a^2}{a_t^2} = \dfrac{1+\frac{1}{2}(\gamma-1)}{1+\frac{1}{2}(\gamma-1)M^2},$

so that

$$(1+u)^2 + v^2 = \frac{(\gamma+1)M^2}{2+(\gamma-1)M^2} \tag{9}$$

$$= K, \text{ say, a constant for constant Mach number } M.$$

On substituting from eqn. (8), and neglecting terms involving higher powers of $y$ than $y^3$, it is found that

$$y^2 = \frac{(K-1)-\alpha^2 x^2 - 2\alpha x}{(\gamma+1)\alpha^2[1+\alpha x+(\gamma+1)\alpha^2 x^2]}. \tag{10}$$

It follows that the curves of constant Mach number are approximately parabolas having the $x$-axis as common axis.

The directions of the streamlines relative to the $x$-axis are given by the relation

$$\tan\theta = \frac{v}{1+u} = \frac{(\gamma+1)\alpha^2 xy + \frac{1}{6}(\gamma+1)^2\alpha^3 y^3}{1+\alpha x+\frac{1}{2}(\gamma+1)\alpha^2 y^2}. \tag{11}$$

It is seen, for example, that the streamlines are parallel to the $x$-axis when $v = 0$, i.e. when

$$x = -\frac{\gamma+1}{6}\alpha y^2,$$

and the radius of curvature of the streamlines when $v = 0$ is

$$\frac{[1+\frac{1}{3}(\gamma+1)\alpha^2 y^2]^2}{(\gamma+1)\alpha^2 y}.$$

## TABLE 1

*Flow through a Throat.   Curves of Constant Mach number.   $\gamma = 1.40$*

| Mach number 0·90 | | | Mach number 1·00 | | | Mach number 1·10 | | |
|---|---|---|---|---|---|---|---|---|
| $x$ | $y$ | Direction of flow | $x$ | $y$ | Direction of flow | $x$ | $y$ | Direction of flow |
| −1·038 | 0·000 | 0·00 | 0·000 | 0·000 | 0·00 | 0·987 | 0·000 | 0·00 |
| −1·042 | 0·202 | −0·20 | −0·004 | 0·200 | 0·00 | 0·984 | 0·201 | 0·18 |
| −1·057 | 0·404 | −0·40 | −0·019 | 0·400 | 0·00 | 0·973 | 0·403 | 0·36 |
| −1·078 | 0·606 | −0·61 | −0·037 | 0·600 | −0·01 | 0·954 | 0·605 | 0·54 |
| −1·109 | 0·808 | −0·83 | −0·063 | 0·800 | −0·03 | 0·927 | 0·806 | 0·70 |
| −1·148 | 1·010 | −1·07 | −0·100 | 1·000 | −0·06 | 0·896 | 1·007 | 0·88 |
| −1·198 | 1·213 | −1·32 | −0·142 | 1·200 | −0·10 | 0·856 | 1·208 | 1·01 |
| −1·254 | 1·417 | −1·59 | −0·194 | 1·401 | −0·17 | 0·806 | 1·408 | 1·13 |
| −1·322 | 1·621 | −1·90 | −0·254 | 1·601 | −0·25 | 0·750 | 1·609 | 1·25 |
| −1·402 | 1·826 | −2·23 | −0·325 | 1·801 | −0·37 | 0·684 | 1·810 | 1·32 |
| −1·493 | 2·032 | −2·61 | −0·404 | 2·001 | −0·51 | 0·613 | 2·010 | 1·38 |
| −1·594 | 2·238 | −3·04 | −0·490 | 2·203 | −0·69 | 0·533 | 2·209 | 1·42 |
| −1·704 | 2·447 | −3·51 | −0·587 | 2·405 | −0·93 | 0·448 | 2·409 | 1·43 |
| −1·827 | 2·658 | −4·06 | −0·691 | 2·606 | −1·16 | 0·351 | 2·608 | 1·38 |
| −1·968 | 2·870 | −4·69 | −0·806 | 2·808 | −1·47 | 0·244 | 2·807 | 1·30 |
| −2·119 | 3·084 | −5·40 | −0·931 | 3·013 | −1·83 | 0·132 | 3·007 | 1·18 |
| −2·287 | 3·302 | −6·19 | −1·066 | 3·218 | −2·25 | 0·009 | 3·205 | 1·00 |
| −2·471 | 3·524 | −7·12 | −1·214 | 3·424 | −2·75 | −0·120 | 3·405 | 0·78 |
| −2·676 | 3·748 | −8·16 | −1·381 | 3·634 | −3·34 | −0·260 | 3·605 | 0·50 |
| −2·900 | 3·975 | −9·40 | −1·561 | 3·845 | −4·04 | −0·408 | 3·805 | 0·15 |
| −3·151 | 4·210 | −10·84 | −1·754 | 4·061 | −4·84 | −0·572 | 4·007 | −0·29 |

| Mach number 1·20 | | | Peak curve ($v = 0$) | |
|---|---|---|---|---|
| $x$ | $y$ | Direction of flow | $x$ | $y$ |
| 1·923 | 0·000 | 0·00 | −0·001 | 0·200 |
| 1·920 | 0·206 | 0·37 | −0·005 | 0·400 |
| 1·908 | 0·412 | 0·73 | −0·012 | 0·600 |
| 1·889 | 0·618 | 1·09 | −0·021 | 0·800 |
| 1·863 | 0·824 | 1·45 | −0·033 | 1·000 |
| 1·832 | 1·029 | 1·79 | −0·047 | 1·200 |
| 1·793 | 1·234 | 2·12 | −0·065 | 1·400 |
| 1·746 | 1·438 | 2·44 | −0·084 | 1·600 |
| 1·693 | 1·642 | 2·74 | −0·107 | 1·800 |
| 1·628 | 1·845 | 3·01 | −0·132 | 2·000 |
| 1·560 | 2·048 | 3·26 | −0·159 | 2·200 |
| 1·485 | 2·250 | 3·48 | −0·190 | 2·401 |
| 1·402 | 2·451 | 3·68 | −0·223 | 2·601 |
| 1·313 | 2·652 | 3·83 | −0·258 | 2·801 |
| 1·213 | 2·851 | 3·94 | −0·297 | 3·001 |
| 1·106 | 3·050 | 4·02 | −0·337 | 3·202 |
| 0·992 | 3·249 | 4·05 | −0·381 | 3·403 |
| 0·871 | 3·447 | 4·04 | −0·428 | 3·604 |
| 0·742 | 3·644 | 3·99 | −0·477 | 3·805 |
| 0·605 | 3·841 | 3·86 | −0·529 | 4·007 |
| 0·460 | 4·038 | 3·67 | | |

The direction is measured in degrees from the $x$-axis.

TABLE 2

*Flow through a Throat.   Coordinates of Streamlines.   $\gamma = 1\cdot40$*

The table gives the values of $y$ corresponding to fixed values of $x$ for evenly spaced streamlines

| Sonic width | $x = -2\cdot0$ | $x = -1\cdot6$ | $x = -1\cdot2$ | $x = -0\cdot8$ | $x = -0\cdot4$ | $x = 0\cdot0$ | $x = 0\cdot4$ | $x = 0\cdot8$ | $x = 1\cdot2$ | $x = 1\cdot6$ | $x = 2\cdot0$ |
|---|---|---|---|---|---|---|---|---|---|---|---|
| 0·2 | 0·2067 | 0·2043 | 0·2024 | 0·2011 | 0·2003 | 0·2000 | 0·2003 | 0·2011 | 0·2024 | 0·2042 | 0·2066 |
| 0·4 | 0·4134 | 0·4085 | 0·4047 | 0·4021 | 0·4005 | 0·4000 | 0·4006 | 0·4021 | 0·4047 | 0·4084 | 0·4133 |
| 0·6 | 0·6199 | 0·6126 | 0·6070 | 0·6031 | 0·6007 | 0·6000 | 0·6009 | 0·6032 | 0·6072 | 0·6128 | 0·6200 |
| 0·8 | 0·8263 | 0·8166 | 0·8092 | 0·8040 | 0·8009 | 0·8000 | 0·8012 | 0·8044 | 0·8097 | 0·8172 | 0·8270 |
| 1·0 | 1·0325 | 1·0204 | 1·0113 | 1·0048 | 1·0011 | 1·0000 | 1·0016 | 1·0057 | 1·0124 | 1·0219 | 1·0342 |
| 1·2 | 1·2384 | 1·2241 | 1·2132 | 1·2056 | 1·2012 | 1·2000 | 1·2020 | 1·2071 | 1·2152 | 1·2268 | 1·2417 |
| 1·4 | 1·4440 | 1·4275 | 1·4149 | 1·4063 | 1·4013 | 1·4001 | 1·4025 | 1·4086 | 1·4183 | 1·4319 | 1·4495 |
| 1·6 | 1·6493 | 1·6306 | 1·6165 | 1·6068 | 1·6014 | 1·6002 | 1·6032 | 1·6103 | 1·6216 | 1·6374 | 1·6578 |
| 1·8 | 1·8542 | 1·8335 | 1·8179 | 1·8072 | 1·8014 | 1·8003 | 1·8039 | 1·8122 | 1·8252 | 1·8433 | 1·8665 |
| 2·0 | 2·0587 | 2·0360 | 2·0191 | 2·0076 | 2·0014 | 2·0005 | 2·0048 | 2·0143 | 2·0291 | 2·0496 | 2·0758 |
| 2·2 | 2·2628 | 2·2383 | 2·2201 | 2·2078 | 2·2014 | 2·2008 | 2·2059 | 2·2168 | 2·2335 | 2·2565 | 2·2858 |
| 2·4 | 2·4665 | 2·4403 | 2·4209 | 2·4080 | 2·4015 | 2·4012 | 2·4073 | 2·4196 | 2·4384 | 2·4640 | ⋮ |
| 2·6 | 2·6697 | 2·6420 | 2·6215 | 2·6081 | 2·6015 | 2·6018 | 2·6089 | 2·6228 | 2·6438 | 2·6722 | ⋮ |
| 2·8 | 2·8726 | 2·8434 | 2·8220 | 2·8081 | 2·8017 | 2·8026 | 2·8109 | 2·8265 | 2·8498 | 2·8811 | ⋮ |
| 3·0 | 3·0751 | 3·0445 | 3·0223 | 3·0082 | 3·0020 | 3·0037 | 3·0133 | 3·0308 | 3·0565 | 3·0910 | ⋮ |
| 3·2 | 3·2773 | 3·2455 | 3·2226 | 3·2083 | 3·2025 | 3·2051 | 3·2161 | 3·2357 | 3·2641 | 3·3018 | ⋮ |
| 3·4 | 3·4791 | 3·4462 | 3·4228 | 3·4085 | 3·4032 | 3·4069 | 3·4195 | 3·4413 | 3·4725 | 3·5138 | ⋮ |
| 3·6 | 3·6806 | 3·6468 | 3·6230 | 3·6089 | 3·6043 | 3·6092 | 3·6235 | 3·6477 | 3·6820 | 3·7270 | ⋮ |
| 3·8 | 3·8819 | 3·8473 | 3·8233 | 3·8094 | 3·8056 | 3·8120 | 3·8282 | 3·8550 | 3·8926 | 3·9416 | ⋮ |
| 4·0 | 4·0830 | 4·0478 | 4·0237 | 4·0103 | 4·0075 | 4·0154 | 4·0338 | 4·0633 | 4·1045 | 4·1578 | ⋮ |

Although the process is somewhat laborious, it is possible to sketch the streamlines step by step by means of eqn. (11) and the spacing can be checked† by the Mach numbers given by eqns. (3) and (10). The coordinates of the contours of constant Mach number are set out in Table 1. The points for which the flow is parallel to the $x$-axis

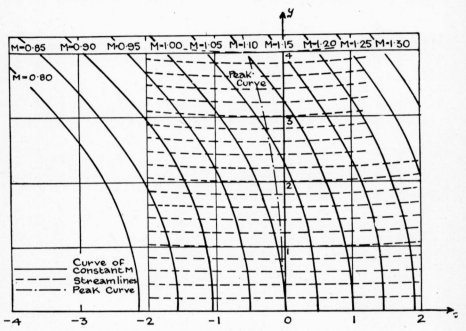

Fig. 131. Streamlines and lines of constant Mach number in a throat.

lie on a curve given by the equation $v = 0$. This is called the 'peak' curve and gives the position of the throat for each stream-tube. Table 1 includes also the direction of flow at each of the points $(x, y)$. The coordinates of the streamlines are given in Table 2, where the spacing has been so chosen that the fluid between consecutive lines would, if moving with sonic velocity, form a uniform stream of width 0·2 units. The lines of constant Mach number, the 'peak' curve, and the streamlines are drawn out in Fig. 131.

In Fig. 132 the calculated distribution of Mach number along the $x$-axis is compared with the distribution measured† in an experimental nozzle.

† Harrop, 'The design of supersonic nozzles', *Rep. Roy. Aircraft Estb.*, No. Aero. 2,293 (1948); *Rep. Memor. Aero. Res. Coun.*, No. 2,712 (1948).

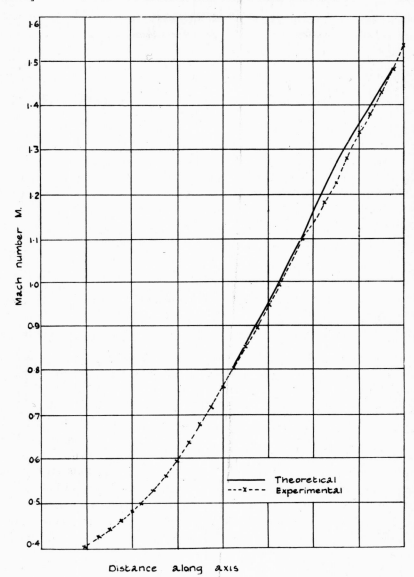

FIG. 132. Theoretical and experimental variations of Mach number along the axis of a nozzle in the vicinity of the throat.

In wind tunnels which operate over a wide range of supersonic speeds the change in throat size is so great that the walls cannot always be faired smoothly into the contraction cone. In such cases it is common to use an arrangement similar to that shown in Fig. 130 (c). Here the contraction ends in a parallel channel in which the nozzle is placed.

## § 5. Nozzle profiles

In cases where uniformity of velocity is not important, a crude supersonic nozzle can be designed on one-dimensional theory using eqn. (3) to relate the area of the throat to that of the working section and joining the two by a long smooth curve.

Where uniform flow at supersonic speeds is required, it is almost invariably the practice to design nozzles using the method of characteristics (see Chap. III, §§ 8, 10). This is often done graphically. The essential relation, which was obtained by Prandtl and Meyer, is that diversion of a sonic stream through an angle $\theta$ by a convex wall accelerates the stream to a Mach number given by

$$\theta = \sqrt{\left(\frac{\gamma+1}{\gamma-1}\right)} \tan^{-1} \sqrt{\left[\frac{\gamma-1}{\gamma+1}(M^2-1)\right]} - \tan^{-1}\sqrt{(M^2-1)}. \quad (12)$$

A stream at Mach number $M_1$ can be considered to have been turned through an angle $\theta_1$ related to $M_1$ by eqn. (12), so that deflexion through a further angle $\theta_2$ leads to a Mach number corresponding to

$$\theta = \theta_1 + \theta_2 \quad (13)$$

(see Fig. 133 (a), where $m$ denotes the Mach angle). Thus the final Mach number is dependent only on the total angular deflexion, and not on the sequence of $\theta_1$ and $\theta_2$ nor on the details of the wall profile.

In designing a nozzle, the first simplification is to replace the curved wall by a series of chords such that the deflexion is a small angle $\epsilon$ in passing from one to the next (see Fig. 133 (b)). In that case the changes of velocity take place within regions similar to $ROS$ contained between the Mach lines $OR$ at the end of one chord and $OS$ at the beginning of the succeeding chord.

The second simplification consists in imagining the acceleration and deflexion process to be concentrated along $OQ$ which is drawn to bisect $ROS$, i.e. making an angle·

$$m_m = \frac{m_1 + m_2 - \epsilon}{2}$$

with the approaching streamline.

This construction involves a lateral displacement of the downstream streamline from the correct position (drawn dotted) as shown

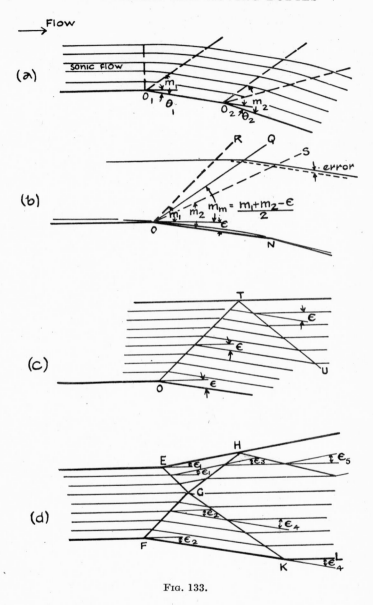

FIG. 133.

in Fig. 133 (*b*); but, in practice, the errors are usually comparable with the stretching and shrinking of good drawing-paper if the value of $\epsilon$ is taken to be 1°.

When an expansion wavelet reaches a solid surface as at $T$ in Fig. 133 (c), the flow is turned parallel to the wall by the formation of an expansion wavelet $TU$ which accelerates the stream by an amount corresponding to a further increment $\epsilon$. Conditions are assumed to be uniform within the area $OTU$.

If, now, two 'characteristics' meet at $G$, as in Fig. 133 (d), there are two conditions to be satisfied: streamlines which have passed through $EG$ and $GH$ are to be parallel to those which have passed through $FG$ and $GK$.

Therefore
$$\epsilon_1 - \epsilon_3 = \epsilon_4 - \epsilon_2, \qquad (14)$$

where the plus and minus signs correspond respectively to counterclockwise and clockwise deflexion. The static pressure (and therefore the Mach number) on streamlines which have passed through $EG$ and $GH$ is to be equal to that on those which have passed through $FG$ and $GK$.

Therefore
$$\epsilon_1 + \epsilon_3 = \epsilon_2 + \epsilon_4. \qquad (15)$$

In this case, a positive sign corresponds to an increase of $\theta$ in eqn. (12), i.e. it corresponds to an accelerating wavelet from a convex wall.

From eqns. (14) and (15)
$$\epsilon_1 = \epsilon_4,$$
$$\epsilon_2 = \epsilon_3.$$

The deflexion is the same in magnitude and direction across $EG$ as that across $GK$, which may be regarded as an extension of $EG$. By turning the wall at $K$ through an angle $\epsilon_4$ to the position $KL$, the reflection of the wavelet $GK$ is cancelled and the flow thereafter is parallel to the upstream direction. Thus a uniform, parallel, supersonic stream has been obtained from a similar stream moving with a lower Mach number.

In order to apply this method to the design of a nozzle it is necessary to determine the sonic or supersonic flow at the upstream end. The simplest scheme is to assume that the flow at the throat is one-dimensional so that the sonic line extends straight across the section of minimum area. Making this assumption, the nozzle can be designed either with a Prandtl–Meyer expansion centred at each wall of the throat (Fig. 134 (a)) or with a rounded throat as shown in Fig. 134 (b).

Nozzles which diverge rapidly are unsatisfactory because the longitudinal pressure gradient changes rapidly in the vicinity of the point of inflexion of the wall. This change causes the thickness of the boundary layer to alter suddenly with an effect which is equivalent to that of an irregularity in the wall.

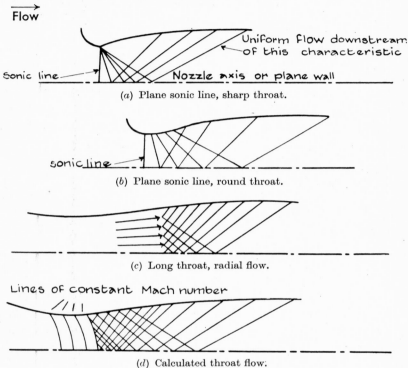

Flow

(a) Plane sonic line, sharp throat.

(b) Plane sonic line, round throat.

(c) Long throat, radial flow.

(d) Calculated throat flow.

Fig. 134. Alternative initial assumptions for graphical nozzle design.

The resultant distribution of Mach number for two W.V.A. nozzles designed in a manner similar to that sketched in Fig. 134 (b) is shown in Fig. 135. The coordinates of these nozzles are given in Table 3; these include an allowance for the growth of the boundary layer on all four walls of the tunnel.†

A more accurate alternative is to make the throat long and gradual and then to assume diverging flow initially‡ as shown in Fig. 134 (c).

† Owen, 'Note on the apparatus and work of W.V.A. Supersonic Institute at Köchel, S. Germany. Part II', *Tech. Notes Roy. Aircraft Estb.*, No. Aero. 1,712; *Rep. Aero. Res. Coun.*, No. 9,282 (1945).

‡ Puckett, 'Supersonic nozzle design', *J. Appl. Mech.* **13** (1946), 265.

Table 4 gives Puckett's ordinates for the final part of nozzles of this type. The throat sizes are to be found from eqn. (3) and faired in with a smooth curve. The coordinates do not include an allowance for boundary-layer growth.

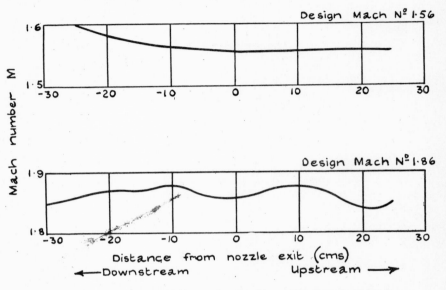

Fig. 135. Variation of Mach number for the nozzles given in Table 3.

A further method is to calculate the throat flow by, for example, Sauer's method described above, and with this information to proceed with the characteristic construction as shown in Fig. 134 (d). Table 5† gives the coordinates of nozzles designed in this way and subsequently corrected by experiment. The nozzles were intended for use in a tunnel in which one wall only was shaped, the opposite wall being flat and replacing the axis of a tunnel in which the nozzle is formed by shaping two opposite walls. The coordinates include an allowance for the growth of the boundary layer on all four tunnel walls. The distributions of Mach number measured along the flat wall are shown in Fig. 136.

At very high Mach numbers, due to the small angles of the characteristics in the major portion of the nozzle, the graphical method tends to become progressively less accurate. Analytical methods of

† Harrop, loc. cit. on p. 490.

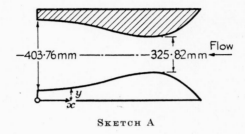

SKETCH A

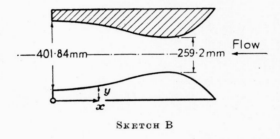

SKETCH B

## TABLE 3

### Coordinates of the W.V.A. Nozzles

(i) Nozzle for $M = 1.56$ (throat width 325·82 mm.; exit width 403·76 mm.) See sketch A facing

(ii) Nozzle for $M = 1.86$ (throat width 259·2 mm.; exit width 401·84 mm.) See sketch B facing

| | $x$ mm. | $y$ mm. | | | $x$ mm. | $y$ mm. |
|---|---|---|---|---|---|---|
| | 0 | 48·12 | | | 0 | 49·08 |
| | 11 | 48·23 | | | 20 | 49·38 |
| | 20 | 48·36 | | | 40 | 49·85 |
| | 40 | 48·72 | | | 60 | 50·47 |
| | 60 | 49·21 | | | 80 | 51·25 |
| | 80 | 49·83 | | | 100 | 52·20 |
| | 100 | 50·58 | | | 120 | 53·33 |
| | 120 | 51·47 | | | 140 | 54·61 |
| | 140 | 52·49 | | | 160 | 56·04 |
| | 160 | 53·64 | | | 180 | 57·04 |
| | 180 | 54·93 | | | 194 | 58·80 |
| | 200 | 56·36 | | | 229·2 | 62·2 |
| | 220 | 57·91 | | | 266·6 | 66·5 |
| | 240 | 59·61 | | | 304·3 | 71·4 |
| | 260 | 61·43 | | | 343·4 | 77·3 |
| | 280 | 63·40 | | | 384·1 | 84·1 |
| | 300 | 65·50 | | | 422·4 | 91·2 |
| | 320 | 67·74 | | | 457·0 | 97·9 |
| | 340 | 70·11 | | | 499·5 | 106·6 |
| | 360 | 72·57 | | | 542·0 | 115·2 |
| | 380 | 75·09 | Throat † | | 593·7 | 120·4 |
| | 390 | 76·36 | | | 812·6 | 0 |
| | 400 | 77·62 | | | | |
| | 410 | 78·88 | | | | |
| | 416·1 | 79·64 | | | | |
| Throat † | 495·8 | 87·09 | | | | |
| | 718 | 0 | | | | |

† Radius of curvature of throat 325·81 mm.

† Radius of curvature of throat 259·2 mm.

construction which are developed in detail in Chap. III should then be employed.

In practice, it is difficult to construct nozzles to coordinates or to allow for the effects of the boundary layer so accurately that the resulting flow is precisely uniform. The method of correcting errors is to follow the characteristics from an irregularity back to the walls and to alter the wall profile in a way which is clear from Fig. 133 (d). Examples of the improvement thus obtained are given in Fig. 136.

In addition to avoiding sharp changes in the boundary-layer pressure gradients with the resulting irregularities in the flow, it is necessary to enlarge the nozzle to allow for the boundary-layer

TABLE 4

*Coordinates for the Final Part of Nozzles with Radial Flow downstream of the Throat. (See Sketch C facing)*

| M = | | | | | | | | | | | |
|---|---|---|---|---|---|---|---|---|---|---|---|
| 1·99 | | 2·42 | | 2·82 | | 3·24 | | 3·62 | | 4·04 | |
| x | y | x | y | x | y | x | y | x | y | x | y |
| 0 | 7·50 | 0 | 7·50 | 0 | 7·50 | 0 | 7·50 | 0 | 7·50 | 0 | 7·50 |
| 4·38 | 7·42 | 4·52 | 7·42 | 5·62 | 7·40 | 4·94 | 7·41 | 5·52 | 7·40 | 5·94 | 7·40 |
| 8·36 | 7·28 | 8·69 | 7·28 | 9·70 | 7·26 | 9·43 | 7·26 | 10·39 | 7·23 | 11·20 | 7·21 |
| 11·97 | 7·09 | 12·47 | 7·08 | 13·38 | 7·07 | 13·47 | 7·05 | 14·89 | 7·00 | 16·10 | 6·96 |
| 15·19 | 6·88 | 15·91 | 6·84 | 16·64 | 6·84 | 17·15 | 6·79 | 18·75 | 6·73 | 20·22 | 6·67 |
| 18·06 | 6·62 | 19·04 | 6·56 | 19·67 | 6·57 | 20·41 | 6·50 | 22·24 | 6·42 | 23·94 | 6·34 |
| 20·65 | 6·35 | 21·80 | 6·27 | 22·35 | 6·29 | 23·41 | 6·19 | 25·39 | 6·09 | 27·17 | 6·00 |
| 21·84 | 6·60 | 24·34 | 5·96 | 24·80 | 5·99 | 26·03 | 5·87 | 28·08 | 5·76 | 30·11 | 5·64 |
| | | 26·57 | 5·65 | 26·95 | 5·69 | 28·42 | 5·53 | 30·56 | 5·41 | 32·69 | 5·28 |
| | | 27·58 | 5·49 | 28·90 | 5·37 | 30·46 | 5·21 | 32·73 | 5·07 | 34·95 | 4·92 |
| | | | | 30·70 | 5·07 | 32·35 | 4·87 | 34·66 | 4·73 | 36·96 | 4·57 |
| | | | | 32·20 | 4·77 | 33·99 | 4·56 | 36·35 | 4·40 | 38·69 | 4·23 |
| | | | | 32·90 | 4·62 | 35·44 | 4·25 | 37·87 | 4·08 | 40·26 | 3·90 |
| | | | | | | 36·13 | 4·09 | 39·20 | 3·77 | 41·62 | 3·58 |
| | | | | | | | | 39·80 | 3·62 | 42·79 | 3·29 |
| | | | | | | | | | | 43·32 | 3·15 |

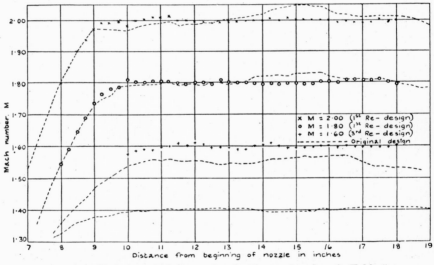

FIG. 136. Variation of Mach number for the nozzles given in Table 5.

growth. A comparatively rapid method† of doing this is to apply the momentum equation to obtain the boundary-layer thickness at the nozzle exit, assuming that the velocity profile is linear and that variation of stream Mach number along the nozzle contour is also

† Puckett, loc. cit. on p. 495.

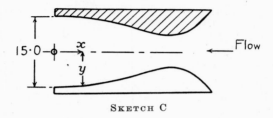

15·0 $x$ $y$ ← Flow

SKETCH C

Position of flat wall for one-sided or of axis for two-sided nozzle ← Flow

3·00″

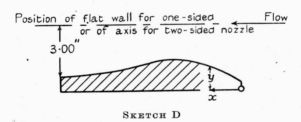

$y$
$x$

SKETCH D

## TABLE 5

*Coordinates of Nozzles designed with the Entry Flow shown in Fig. 131.*
*(See Sketch D facing p. 498)*

| Liner A | | Liner B | | Liner C | | Liner D | |
|---|---|---|---|---|---|---|---|
| *x* in. | *y* in. | *x* in. | *y* in. | *x* in. | *y* in. | *x* in. | *y* in. |
| 0·00 | 0·475 | 0·000 | 0·475 | 0·000 | 0·475 | 0·000 | 0·475 |
| 0·10 | 0·529 | 0·100 | 0·529 | 0·350 | 0·663 | 0·200 | 0·583 |
| 0·40 | 0·690 | 0·400 | 0·690 | 0·650 | 0·825 | 0·500 | 0·744 |
| 0·70 | 0·843 | 0·700 | 0·851 | 0·950 | 0·986 | 0·800 | 0·905 |
| 1·00 | 0·980 | 1·000 | 1·007 | 1·250 | 1·147 | 1·100 | 1·067 |
| 1·30 | 1·085 | 1·300 | 1·134 | 1·550 | 1·303 | 1·400 | 1·228 |
| 1·60 | 1·171 | 1·600 | 1·242 | 1·850 | 1·448 | 1·700 | 1·389 |
| 1·90 | 1·244 | 1·900 | 1·341 | 2·150 | 1·566 | 2·000 | 1·551 |
| 2·20 | 1·310 | 2·200 | 1·431 | 2·450 | 1·667 | 2·300 | 1·712 |
| 2·50 | 1·368 | 2·500 | 1·512 | 2·750 | 1·758 | 2·600 | 1·873 |
| 2·80 | 1·419 | 2·800 | 1·585 | 3·050 | 1·839 | 2·900 | 2·035 |
| 3·10 | 1·461 | 3·100 | 1·649 | 3·350 | 1·911 | 3·200 | 2·173 |
| 3·40 | 1·496 | 3·400 | 1·703 | 3·650 | 1·973 | 3·500 | 2·273 |
| 3·70 | 1·523 | 3·700 | 1·749 | 3·950 | 2·025 | 3·800 | 2·339 |
| 4·00 | 1·543 | 4·000 | 1·786 | 4·250 | 2·068 | 4·100 | 2·381 |
| 4·30 | 1·554 | 4·300 | 1·814 | 4·550 | 2·102 | 4·400 | 2·411 |
|  |  | 4·600 | 1·834 | 4·850 | 2·126 | 4·700 | 2·429 |
|  |  | 4·900 | 1·844 | 5·150 | 2·140 |  |  |
| 4·60 | 1·558 |  |  |  |  |  |  |
|  |  | 5·100 | 1·846 | 5·450 | 2·145 | 5·000 | 2·435 |
| 4·90 | 1·552 |  |  |  |  |  |  |
| 5·20 | 1·539 | 5·379 | 1·841 | 5·650 | 2·135 | 5·201 | 2·423 |
| 5·50 | 1·522 | 5·673 | 1·826 | 5·851 | 2·113 | 5·402 | 2·392 |
| 5·80 | 1·502 | 5·967 | 1·804 | 6·051 | 2·081 | 5·603 | 2·348 |
| 6·10 | 1·479 | 6·261 | 1·775 | 6·251 | 2·044 | 5·803 | 2·300 |
| 6·40 | 1·456 | 6·555 | 1·741 | 6·452 | 2·005 | 6·004 | 2·250 |
| 6·70 | 1·432 | 6·848 | 1·704 | 6·652 | 1·966 | 6·306 | 2·175 |
| 7·00 | 1·409 | 7·142 | 1·665 | 6·852 | 1·928 | 6·607 | 2·100 |
| 7·30 | 1·386 | 7·436 | 1·626 | 7·053 | 1·889 | 6·908 | 2·027 |
| 7·60 | 1·364 | 7·730 | 1·587 | 7·353 | 1·831 | 7·209 | 1·956 |
| 7·90 | 1·343 | 8·024 | 1·550 | 7·654 | 1·775 | 7·511 | 1·888 |
| 8·20 | 1·323 | 8·318 | 1·514 | 7·954 | 1·720 | 7·812 | 1·822 |
| 8·50 | 1·305 | 8·611 | 1·480 | 8·255 | 1·667 | 8·113 | 1·759 |
| 8·80 | 1·288 | 8·905 | 1·448 | 8·555 | 1·617 | 8·414 | 1·699 |
| 9·10 | 1·273 | 9·199 | 1·418 | 8·856 | 1·568 | 8·716 | 1·642 |
| 9·40 | 1·259 | 9·493 | 1·390 | 9·156 | 1·523 | 9·017 | 1·589 |
| 9·70 | 1·247 | 9·787 | 1·363 | 9·457 | 1·480 | 9·318 | 1·539 |
| 10·00 | 1·236 | 10·081 | 1·338 | 9·757 | 1·440 | 9·619 | 1·493 |
| 10·30 | 1·227 | 10·375 | 1·317 | 10·058 | 1·404 | 9·921 | 1·450 |
| 10·60 | 1·218 | 10·668 | 1·296 | 10·358 | 1·371 | 10·222 | 1·411 |
| 10·90 | 1·211 | 10·962 | 1·279 | 10·659 | 1·341 | 10·523 | 1·376 |
| 11·20 | 1·205 | 11·256 | 1·262 | 10·959 | 1·314 | 10·825 | 1·345 |
| 11·50 | 1·200 | 11·550 | 1·246 | 11·260 | 1·290 | 11·126 | 1·317 |
| 11·80 | 1·196 | 11·844 | 1·234 | 11·560 | 1·269 | 11·427 | 1·291 |
| 12·10 | 1·192 | 12·138 | 1·223 | 11·861 | 1·250 | 11·728 | 1·268 |
| 12·40 | 1·189 | 12·432 | 1·214 | 12·161 | 1·233 | 12·030 | 1·247 |
| 12·70 | 1·186 | 12·725 | 1·207 | 12·462 | 1·219 | 12·331 | 1·228 |
| 13·00 | 1·183 | 13·019 | 1·201 | 12·762 | 1·207 | 12·632 | 1·213 |
| 13·30 | 1·180 | 13·313 | 1·196 | 13·062 | 1·197 | 12·933 | 1·200 |
| 13·60 | 1·178 | 13·607 | 1·191 | 13·363 | 1·190 | 13·235 | 1·190 |
|  |  | 13·901 | 1·188 | 13·663 | 1·184 | 13·536 | 1·181 |
|  |  | 14·195 | 1·184 | 13·964 | 1·179 | 13·837 | 1·174 |
|  |  | 14·489 | 1·180 | 14·264 | 1·175 | 14·138 | 1·169 |
|  |  | 14·782 | 1·177 | 14·565 | 1·172 | 14·440 | 1·166 |
|  |  | 15·076 | 1·174 | 14·865 | 1·169 | 14·741 | 1·163 |
|  |  | 15·370 | 1·171 |  |  | 15·042 | 1·161 |
| STRAIGHT | | STRAIGHT | | STRAIGHT | | STRAIGHT | |
| 20·00 | 1·125 | 20·000 | 1·125 | 20·000 | 1·125 | 20·000 | 1·125 |

Liner *A*. Originally designed for *M* = 1·40. Original design given.
Liner *B*. Originally designed for *M* = 1·60. Third re-design given.
Liner *C*. Originally designed for *M* = 1·80. First re-design given.
Liner *D*. Originally designed for *M* = 2·00. First re-design given.

linear. The local skin friction is assumed to be independent of Reynolds number, and is calculated for the stream conditions at the nozzle exit. In addition, the boundary-layer thickness at the throat is taken to be zero.

Thus between Reynolds numbers of $5 \times 10^5$ and $5 \times 10^6$ based on test section height, and for Mach numbers of about 1·5 to 2·5, it is found that an allowance of 0·004 to 0·005 in. per in. of length per wall is satisfactory. Frequently the plane walls are made parallel, and double the above allowance put on each curved wall.

A more realistic method of estimating boundary-layer growth is given by Tucker.† Here the momentum theorem is again used, but the mean velocity in the boundary layer is approximated by a power-law profile, and low-speed skin-friction coefficients, depending on the Reynolds number, are extrapolated to high Mach number flows. Using this technique the calculated correction is found to agree to within 0·3 per cent. of the measured one at a Mach number of 2 for a 3·84 in. by 10 in. working section.

In order to simplify the problem of changing the liners of a tunnel when the Mach number is to be altered, multiple nozzles of either honeycomb or two-dimensional construction have been used to reduce the nozzle length. These are unsatisfactory,‡ however, because the wakes of the nozzle elements lead to irregularities in the flow, and because they lead to a substantial increase in the pressure ratio needed to drive the tunnel at a given Mach number.

## § 6. Test sections

For speeds far below the speed of sound, the shapes of wind-tunnel test sections are generally chosen with a view to minimizing the wall effects on the bound and trailing vortices. As the speed of sound is approached, the effect of 'blocking' the channel by any model and its wake becomes the main constraint effect (see p. 518), and the emphasis is mainly on cross-sectional area. At supersonic speeds the cross-sectional areas of models are restricted in a way discussed later (p. 532), but the main problem is to make sure that a model's own wave system is not reflected from the tunnel walls in such a way as

† 'Approximate turbulent boundary layer development in plane compressible flow along thermally insulated surfaces with application to supersonic tunnel contour correction', *Tech. Notes Nat. Adv. Comm. Aero.*, No. 2,045 (1950).

‡ Royle, Bowling, and Lukasiewicz, 'Calibration of two-dimensional and conical supersonic multi-nozzles', *Rep. Aero. Res. Coun.*, No. 11,039 (1947); *Rep. Roy. Aircraft Estb.*, No. Aero. 2,221 (1947).

to upset the measurements being made. It is not sufficient to ensure that the reflected waves do not strike the model itself; they must be kept clear of the wake until well downstream. This requirement means generally that supersonic tunnels should be square in cross-section if test bodies shaped roughly as solids of revolution are to be mounted in midstream. If half bodies are to be mounted on one wall it is sometimes assumed that the tunnel dimension normal to that wall may be reduced to half the width of that wall itself.

In order to compensate for the growth of the boundary layers on the walls of the working section, it is the usual practice to make the downstream end larger in cross-sectional area than the upstream end, the dimensions usually being determined by experience. Typical working sections are described in the papers cited below.†

## § 7. Diffusers

The flux of energy through a tunnel working section of cross-sectional area $A$ is given by

$$\tfrac{1}{2}\rho U^3 A = \tfrac{1}{2}\rho_0 a_0^3 A M^3 \left(1 + \frac{\gamma-1}{2} M^2\right)^{-(3\gamma-1)/2(\gamma-1)}, \qquad (16)$$

where $\rho$, $U$, and $M$ are the density, velocity, and Mach number in the working section, and $\rho_0$ and $a_0$ are the density and the velocity of sound at stagnation conditions. For air ($\gamma = 1\cdot 4$) the above equation gives, approximately, per unit working section area and for atmospheric stagnation conditions ($p_0 = 14\cdot 7$ lb./sq. in. abs., $T_0 = 288°$ K.),

$$\text{energy flux} = 3000 \frac{M^3}{(1+0\cdot 2M^2)^4} \text{ H.P./sq. ft.}$$

The energy flux is proportional to the first power of the stagnation pressure and to the square root of the absolute stagnation temperature, and it increases very rapidly with Mach number as shown in Table 6 and in Fig. 137. As compared with low-speed conditions ($M = 0\cdot 2$), a 50-fold increase takes place at high subsonic speeds and a 100-fold one at a Mach number of $1\cdot 6$.‡ It is thus apparent that at high Mach numbers efficient deceleration in a good diffuser will lead to large power economies. Since, in general, the diffuser

† Hutton, 'The development and work of the 2·8 metre subsonic high-speed wind tunnel at the L.F.A. Brunswick, Germany', *Tech. Notes Roy. Aircraft Estb.*, No. Aero. 1,811 (1946), *Rep. Aero. Res. Coun.*, No. 10,060 (1946); Thompson and Mair, loc. cit. on p. 482; Matt, 'The high-speed wind tunnel of the D.V.L.', A.V.A. Monogr. D1, *Rep. Aero. Res. Coun.*, No. 11,277 (1947).

‡ The energy flux attains a maximum at $M = \sqrt{3}$, irrespective of the value of $\gamma$.

efficiency decreases as the entry Mach number increases, the drop in the kinetic energy flux at Mach numbers larger than √3 has little significance in practice.

TABLE 6

*Relative Increase of Kinetic-energy Flux with Mach Number*

| $M$ | 0·2 | 0·5 | 0·8 | 1·0 | 1·5 | √3 | 2·0 | 4 |
|---|---|---|---|---|---|---|---|---|
| Relative K.E. flux H.P./sq. ft. | 1 | 13·3 | 40·7 | 62·5 | 98 | 103 | 97 | 26·5 |

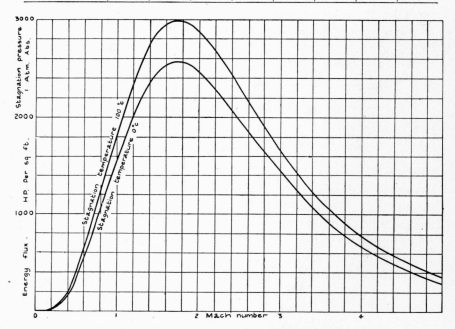

FIG. 137. Rate of energy flow through a wind tunnel H.P./sq. ft.

At low working-section Mach numbers, at which no serious compressibility effects are present in the flow about models (i.e. for, say, $M < 0·65$), a conical diffuser having a small divergence is suitable. Careful tests made by Squire† have shown that total vertex cone angles of from 4° to 10° are suitable, the efficiency increasing with Reynolds number (based on diffuser diameter at entry) in the lower angle range. With a 4 to 1 diffuser expansion ratio, the static pressure

† 'Experiments on conical diffusers', *Rep. Roy. Aircraft Estb.*, No. Aero. 2,216 (1947), *Rep. Aero. Res. Coun.*, No. 12,838.

rise in such diffusers amounts to about 90 per cent. of the theoretical value at Reynolds numbers of from $10^5$ to $10^6$ and is higher at larger Reynolds numbers. Since these results correspond to flow with no model in the tunnel working section, and with a particularly good velocity distribution at the diffuser entry, they must be regarded as the upper limits of the efficiencies attainable in actual wind-tunnel diffusers.

Owing to compressibility effects, the pressure gradients in a diffuser are increased at higher Mach numbers and, in order to avoid or reduce the effects of boundary-layer separation, a small angle of divergence is preferable. In small-scale experiments made by Simons[†] a two-dimensional diffuser with a total divergence of 6° gave a stagnation pressure recovery of 84 per cent. at a working-section Mach number of 1·06.

In a subsonic tunnel it is sometimes advantageous to accelerate the flow downstream of the working section to sonic velocity. In this way disturbances, which may originate in the diffuser or compressor, are not propagated upstream of the sonic choke[‡] and their effects on the flow in the working section are eliminated. The effects of such disturbances have been demonstrated[§],[‖] by taking photographs of two-dimensional aerofoils in transonic flow. Whereas appreciable oscillations of the shocks above the aerofoil surface were present in unchoked tunnels, the flow was remarkably steady when a sonic choke was provided downstream of the working section.

Since, following the sonic choke, an expansion to a slightly supersonic velocity must take place, the diffuser problem is similar in a high-speed subsonic wind tunnel fitted with a choke to that in a wind tunnel working at moderately high supersonic speeds.

At supersonic working-section velocities the problem of flow deceleration to subsonic speed is important. While it would seem that the flow through a supersonic nozzle could be reversed in such a way as to effect deceleration without loss, such an arrangement is in fact rendered irreversible by the boundary-layer motion and the tunnel

[†] 'Untersuchungen an Diffusoren für Überschallwindkanäle', *F.B.* 1738/1 (1943), *Rep. Aero. Res. Coun.*, No. 10,274 (1946).

[‡] Incidentally, the working-section Mach number control (at $M < 1$) is conveniently achieved by means of a variable-area sonic choke.

[§] Eggink, 'Fluctuation of flow in high-speed tunnels', *Rep. Aero. Res. Coun.*, No. 10,810 (1947), *Rep. Roy. Aircraft Estb.*, No. Aero. 2,204.

[‖] Liepmann and Ashkanas, 'Shock wave oscillations in wind tunnels', *J. Aero. Sci.* **14** (1947), 295.

starting requirements. If the process of development of the flow is considered† it is found that as the pressure ratio across the nozzle is increased, the length of supersonic flow downstream of the nozzle throat increases and a normal shock moves towards the nozzle exit or tunnel working section. It is thus immediately apparent that if a second nozzle (acting as a diffuser) were fitted downstream of the working section, its throat would have to be sufficiently large to pass the working section flow which has gained entropy in compression through the normal shock occurring at the working-section Mach number. On the assumption of one-dimensional flow, the minimum value of the ratio of 'second-throat' area to the nozzle-throat area at any working-section Mach number is equal to the ratio $(p_0/p_0')_w$ of the stagnation pressures upstream and downstream of the normal shock occurring at that Mach number. The corresponding contraction ratio $\Psi =$ area of working section/area of second throat is obtained as

$$\Psi = \left(\frac{\gamma+1}{\gamma-1}\right)^{(\gamma+1)/2(\gamma-1)}\left(\frac{\gamma-1}{2}\right)^{\frac{1}{2}}\left(\frac{2\gamma}{\gamma-1}-\frac{1}{M^2}\right)^{-1/(\gamma-1)}\left(\frac{\gamma-1}{2}+\frac{1}{M^2}\right)^{-\frac{1}{2}}. \quad (17)$$

The first two entries in Table 7 give values of $(p_0/p_0')_w$ and $\Psi$ for a range of Mach numbers. The contraction ratio increases with Mach number but cannot exceed 1·666 (for $\gamma = 1\cdot4$).

TABLE 7

Performance of Second Throats ($\gamma = 1\cdot40$)

| $\cdot M$ . . . | 1 | 1·5 | 2 | 3 | 4 | $\infty$ |
|---|---|---|---|---|---|---|
| $(p_0/p_0')_w$ . . . | 1 | 1·075 | 1·387 | 3·046 | 7·205 | $\infty$ |
| $\Psi$ . . . | 1 | 1·094 | 1·216 | 1·39 | 1·488 | 1·666 |
| $(p_0/p_0')_\Psi$ . . . | 1 | 1·024 | 1·20 | 2·27 | 4·96 | $\infty$ |

The above starting limitation, which has been confirmed experimentally,‡ imposes a theoretical limit on the minimum tunnel starting pressure ratio and diffuser contraction. With a continuously running tunnel and a constant geometry diffuser, the minimum operating tunnel pressure ratio $(p_0/p_0')_\Psi$ corresponds to a normal shock located in the second throat and occurring at a Mach number below the working-section value. Values of $(p_0/p_0')_\Psi$ are given in

† Lukasiewicz, 'Supersonic diffusers', *Rep. Memor. Aero. Res. Coun.*, No. 2,501 (1946).

‡ Simons, loc. cit. on p. 503.

Table 7 and some improvement in the tunnel pressure ratio, as compared with the starting value or, what is equivalent, with the value for a diffuser without contraction, is evident.

Theoretically the tunnel pressure ratio could be reduced by decreasing the diffuser throat area (and thus reducing the shock losses) after the supersonic flow is established.  In practice it is often found that, in continuously running tunnels, the resulting flow is unstable and the normal shock moves upstream into the first nozzle, the supersonic flow in the working section breaking down.  In vacuum-operated intermittent tunnels, in which very large pressure ratios are available initially, improvements have been reported using the above method, the tunnel running time being appreciably increased.

The theoretical tunnel pressure ratios $(p_0/p_0')_w$ and $(p_0/p_0')_\Psi$ which are given in Table 7 were computed on the assumption of isentropic subsonic compression downstream of the shock.  Actually part of the losses occurs in practice in the subsonic diffuser, but owing to the shock-boundary layer interaction effects it is not possible to separate the subsonic compression losses from the supersonic ones.  Crocco[†] proposed a curve for the tunnel pressure ratio based on normal shock compression at the working-section Mach number and a 75 per cent. efficient subsonic compression.  As seen in Fig. 138, Crocco's values are optimistic, particularly at the higher Mach numbers.

From supersonic wind-tunnel tests it is found[‡] in practice that in general the pressure recovery is increased when a diffuser contraction or a second throat is used.  It also appears favourable to provide a long parallel section at the diffuser throat (or at entry, for purely divergent diffusers), in which the shock system can be stabilized.  These favourable effects can be completely offset, however, if an open-jet working section, convenient from the point of view of balance installation, is used instead of a fully closed one. For an open jet the second throat is used primarily to equalize the static pressures inside and outside of the jet rather than to improve the pressure recovery.

Fig. 138 shows experimental values of the pressure ratios (i.e. the ratio of the total head upstream of working section to that downstream of the diffuser) required to maintain the flow through the working sections and diffusers of a number of supersonic tunnels.

† 'Gallerie aerodinamiche per alta velocità', *Aerotecnica*, **15** (1935), 237, 734.
‡ Lukasiewicz, loc. cit. on p. 504.

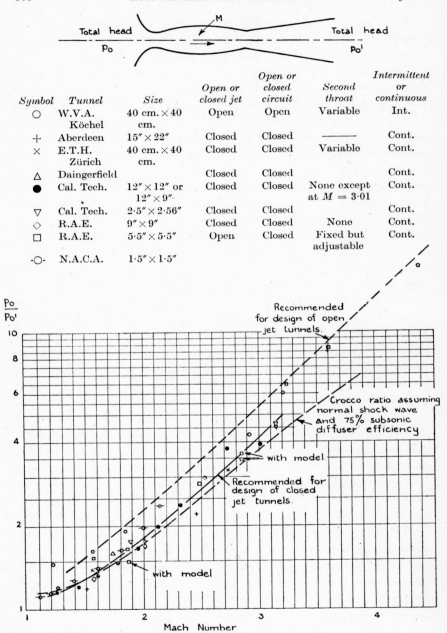

| Symbol | Tunnel | Size | Open or closed jet | Open or closed circuit | Second throat | Intermittent or continuous |
|---|---|---|---|---|---|---|
| ○ | W.V.A. Köchel | 40 cm. × 40 cm. | Open | Open | Variable | Int. |
| + | Aberdeen | 15″ × 22″ | Closed | Closed | —— | Cont. |
| × | E.T.H. Zürich | 40 cm. × 40 cm. | Closed | Closed | Variable | Cont. |
| △ | Daingerfield | | Closed | Closed | | Cont. |
| ● | Cal. Tech. | 12″ × 12″ or 12″ × 9″ | Closed | Closed | None except at $M = 3.01$ | Cont. |
| ▽ | Cal. Tech. | 2.5″ × 2.56″ | Closed | Closed | None | Cont. |
| ◇ | R.A.E. | 9″ × 9″ | Closed | Closed | Fixed but adjustable | Cont. |
| □ | R.A.E. | 5.5″ × 5.5″ | Open | Closed | Fixed but adjustable | Cont. |
| -○- | N.A.C.A. | 1.5″ × 1.5″ | | | | |

FIG. 138. Supersonic tunnel pressure ratios.
(Without allowance for turning vanes, driers, or coolers.)

For supersonic tunnels of medium size (1 sq. ft. working-section cross-sectional area), the pressure recovery of the E.T.H. closed-jet tunnel with variable second throat, and of the California Institute of Technology 1 ft. sq. tunnel can be regarded as representative of good practice. For open-jet tunnels, the W.V.A. (Köchel) points are typical. The recommended design curves are based on these values.

On the basis of the existing data it is not possible to assess the Reynolds number effects on diffuser efficiency at supersonic speeds. Although the magnitude of such effects may be small, they may be nevertheless important in view of the very high powers required to drive large supersonic tunnels.

## § 8. Methods for driving high-speed tunnels

In order to maintain steady motion through a high-speed tunnel some means must be provided for maintaining the pressure ratio shown in Fig. 138 across the intake and the end of the diffuser and, in addition, for overcoming the losses in the remainder of the circuit. Such additional losses arise from friction at the walls and at the turning vanes, and from the resistance of gauze screens, cooler tubes, and the model under test. They can be estimated by considering each item in turn in the manner described by Wattendorf† for low-speed tunnels. In practice most of the losses in a high-speed tunnel usually occur in the diffuser, and the additional losses may often be neglected in the preliminary design stages.

The main methods of driving high-speed wind tunnels are illustrated in Fig. 130. For some types of experiment, e.g. heat transfer and combustion experiments and engine tests, continuous rather than intermittent operation is nearly essential. The intermittent types of tunnel make much less severe power demands; but the volume of the necessary vacuum or pressure vessels may be inconveniently large. In practice, important advantages of the closed-circuit, continuously running, wind tunnel are the ease with which the stagnation pressure can be varied and the air dried. In this way the Reynolds number can be varied independently of the Mach number, and excessive loading of the models or supports can be avoided.

*Direct fan or compressor drive.* Wind tunnels can be driven very

† 'Factors influencing the energy ratios of return flow wind tunnels', *Proc. 5th Int. Congr. Appl. Mech.* (1935), *Tech. Memor. Nat. Adv. Comm. Aero.*, No. 808.

nearly to the speed of sound with single-stage axial-flow fans, but two or more stages may be needed if the blade-tip speed is limited to, say, 500 ft./sec. for quietness of running.† For supersonic operation a relatively large number of stages is required, and centrifugal or even reciprocating compressors may be used. The mass flow which the compressor must pass is given by eqn. (18) on p. 512. The matching of the compressor characteristics with the requirements of the wind tunnel over a wide range of speed usually necessitates controlling the compressor speed or the blade settings or by-passing the unwanted flow. All of these methods are used, sometimes more than one in a single installation. When the power is supplied as alternating current at fixed frequency, the provision of a wide range of precise speed control is a formidable problem. For powers less than about 5,000 h.p. it is a common practice to drive the fans with direct-current motors supplied at variable voltage by motor generators or by grid-controlled mercury-arc rectifiers. In cases where the powers exceed the capacity of a reasonable number of direct-current commutators, an alternating-current motor is used to turn the compressor, and the circuits are arranged to dissipate the slip energy in liquid resistances or to return it to the supply through a chain of auxiliary machines. At extreme powers and rotational speeds requiring very stiff rotating parts, the choice tends to be restricted to water, steam, or gas turbines, either coupled mechanically or through the intermediary of alternators and synchronous motors. Supersonic wind tunnels and subsonic tunnels fitted with sonic chokes are relatively insensitive to small changes in fan speed so that extreme precision of motor speed control is not usually required. In that case, and in small installations, the choice of possible drives is very wide.

*Induced drive.* The problems of matching the compressor and the wind tunnel may be avoided by using the flow from the compressor to induce that through the tunnel, and the independence of operation can be extended by storing air (or steam) in high-pressure receivers and blowing it off through an injector as needed. Knowler and Holder‡ find that an induced-flow tunnel can be operated at a given Mach number over a wide range of inducing-air pressures by

† Mair, 'Fans and guide vanes for high-speed wind tunnels', *Rep. Memor. Aero. Res. Coun.*, No. 2,435 (1944).

‡ 'The efficiency of high-speed wind tunnels of the induction type', ibid. No. 2,448 (1948).

altering the area of the injector slot. A typical family of pressure curves measured by Holder and North[†] on the tunnel shown in Fig. 130 (g) is given in Fig. 139. The rate of mass flow of inducing air increases as the area of the injector slot is increased and an account of the optimum conditions for both continuous and intermittent operation is given by Holder.[‡] Values of the mass ratio (i.e. the ratio of the rate of flow of induced to that of inducing air) measured on the tunnel shown in Fig. 130 (g) are given in Fig. 140. The use of steam instead of air as the inducing fluid is discussed by Poggi[§] and experiments on a model tunnel driven by low-pressure steam are reported by Lilley and Holder.[||] A steam-driven tunnel with a working section of 0·765 metre diameter is described by Ludwieg and Oltmann.[††]

## § 9. Intermittent tunnels

In some installations energy is stored gradually and is then released rapidly to provide the large power required to drive a high-speed tunnel. This is usually done either by evacuating a vessel and then allowing the air to flow in through the tunnel from the atmosphere, or by storing compressed air and releasing it directly through the tunnel or through an injector which induces the flow through the tunnel. The vacuum method has the advantages that it enables very high driving pressure ratios to be obtained, and that the conditions at the tunnel intake may be kept constant throughout the run. The main advantage of the pressure method is that it is usually more convenient to store potential energy in this way than as vacuum. When very high Mach numbers are required it is sometimes the practice to connect the tunnel between a compressed-air and a vacuum vessel.

When a compressed-air vessel is discharged, the temperature of the air falls so that the stagnation temperature in a tunnel through which the air is passed directly, or in an induced-flow tunnel fitted with a return duct (Fig. 130 (g)), will fall also. There is at present

† Loc. cit. on p. 482.

‡ 'The High-speed Laboratory of the Aerodynamics Division, N.P.L.', *Rep. Memor. Aero. Res. Coun.*, No. 2,560 (1946).

§ 'Study of a type of high-speed wind tunnel working by ejection with a steam jet as the impelling fluid', *Aerotecnica*, **19** (1939), 1038.

|| 'Experiments on an induction type high-speed wind tunnel driven by low-pressure steam', *Rep. Aero. Res. Coun.* No. 12,317 (1949).

†† 'High-speed Wind Tunnel of the A.V.A. with steam jet drive', A.V.A. Monogr. DI, Section II. 2. 3, *Rep. Aero. Res. Coun.*, No. 11,537 (1947).

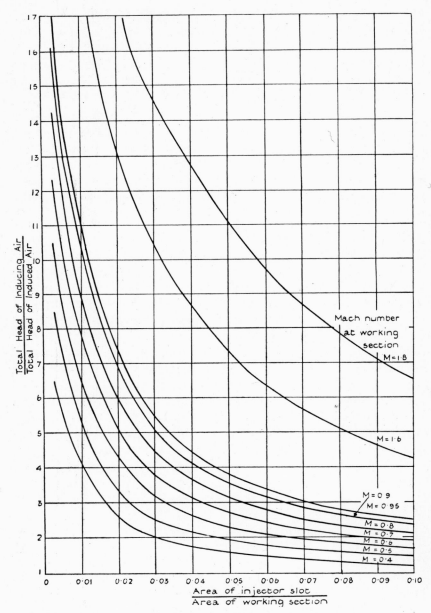

FIG. 139. Induced-flow tunnel pressure ratios.

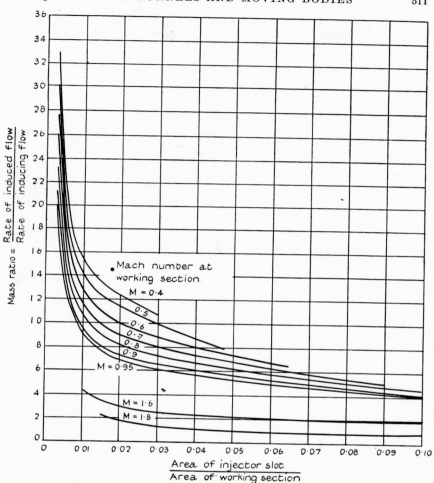

FIG. 140. Induced-flow tunnel mass ratios.

little information on the seriousness of the aerodynamic consequences of this effect, but in some cases, such as when temperature measurements are involved or when wire resistance strain gauges are used, it is likely to lead to difficulties with the instrumentation.

Since the pressure ratio across the tunnel changes as the run proceeds, it is necessary to fit a subsonic tunnel discharging into an evacuated vessel with a sonic choke downstream of the working section so that the Mach number can be controlled. For a supersonic tunnel the Mach number is determined by the shape of the nozzle (the pressure ratio being high enough to maintain the supersonic flow), but a second throat is sometimes used to increase the running time or to control the pressure round an open jet. These considerations apply also to a tunnel driven by connecting the intake directly to a compressed-air vessel, but in this case it is often the practice to fit a reducing valve ahead of the intake to keep the pressure there, and hence the pressure ratio across the tunnel, constant. A reducing valve is also used on most intermittent induced-flow tunnels to keep the pressure of the inducing air constant.

If the tunnel intake is directly open to the atmosphere, the air is usually dried by drawing it through beds of silica gel or alumina. For a tunnel driven from a compressed-air vessel it is, however, often preferable to dry the compressed air as it is stored and, in the case of an induced-flow tunnel, to use a return circuit as shown in Fig. 130 (g) to duct the dry air into the tunnel intake. Drying may also be done gradually in a vacuum tunnel by storing dry air in a gasometer or gas bag attached to the tunnel intake, and pumping this air back into the gasometer from the vacuum vessel after the tunnel run has ended.

*The running time of intermittent tunnels.* An intermittent tunnel may be run until the pressure in the storage vessel reaches a value corresponding to the minimum pressure ratio needed to drive the tunnel at the required Mach number. Typical values of the minimum pressure ratio for direct action tunnels are given in Fig. 138, and for the minimum pressure ratio of the inducing air of an induced-flow tunnel in Fig. 139. The running time may be calculated by dividing the change in the mass of air stored in the vessel between the initial and final conditions by the rate of flow into or from the vessel. The rate of mass flow $Q$ through the working section is

$$Q = \rho U A = \rho_0 a_0 A M \left(1 + \frac{\gamma-1}{2} M^2\right)^{-(\gamma+1)/2(\gamma-1)}, \qquad (18)$$

where $\rho$, $U$, $A$, and $M$ are the density, velocity, cross-sectional area, and Mach number at the working section, and $\rho_0$ and $a_0$ are the density and the speed of sound at the tunnel intake. For an induced flow tunnel the quantity given by eqn. (18) should be divided by the mass ratio (see, for example, Fig. 140) in order to determine the rate of discharge from the pressure vessel.

For a vacuum tunnel taking in air at the same temperature as the air in the vessel it is found that the temperature in the vessel remains substantially constant throughout the run. Making this assumption, the change in the mass of air stored in the vessel is given by

$$\rho_0 V\left(\frac{p_2}{p_0}-\frac{p_1}{p_0}\right), \tag{19}$$

where $V$ is the volume of the vessel and $p_1$ and $p_2$ are the pressures in the vessel at the beginning and end of the run respectively. The

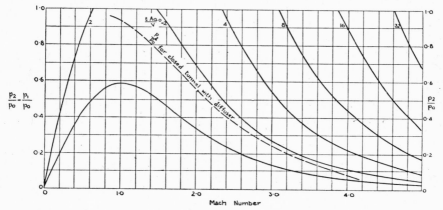

FIG. 141. Running times for wind tunnels blowing into evacuated vessels.

pressure at the tunnel intake is denoted by $p_0$ and $p_0/p_2$ is the minimum pressure ratio required to run the tunnel. The running time $t$ is then given by

$$t = \frac{V}{a_0 A M}\left(\frac{p_2}{p_0}-\frac{p_1}{p_0}\right)\left(1+\frac{\gamma-1}{2}M^2\right)^{(\gamma+1)/2(\gamma-1)}. \tag{20}$$

Values of $(p_2/p_0-p_1/p_0)$ are plotted against Mach number in Fig. 141 for different values of the quantity $tAa_0/V$. This figure also includes a curve (replotted from Fig. 138) showing the minimum pressure ratio required to drive a closed wind tunnel.

Similar curves may be plotted for the other types of intermittent tunnel discussed here. In calculating the change of mass contained in a compressed-air vessel, allowance must be made for the fall of temperature which accompanies the expansion. It is most conservative to arrive at the equivalent of eqn. (19) by assuming the expansion to be adiathermal. Allowance must sometimes also be made for the effect of the temperature fall on the rate of discharge (eqn. (18)), but this may often be neglected during the preliminary design stages.

## § 10. The wind-tunnel 'bump' technique

Not only does wall mounting of partial models in a wind tunnel often afford increased Reynolds number for a given tunnel cross-sectional area, and greater facility in leading out pressure and electrical leads, but suitable shaping of the wall itself permits sensitive local variation of the stream speed. Without choking the test section,

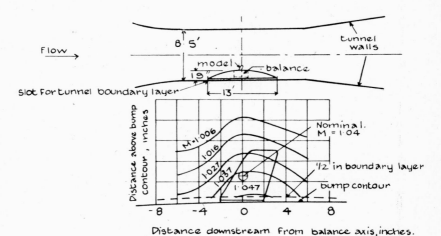

FIG. 142. Wind-tunnel 'bump' technique showing the Mach number distribution in the region occupied by the model.

the local Mach number may be varied continuously through unity. In such circumstances the flow is necessarily curved and non-uniform, but interesting results may nevertheless be obtained.† Fig. 142 illustrates the arrangement for by-passing the wind-tunnel boundary layer and also shows the Mach number distribution obtained.

## § 11. Shock tubes

A shock tube consists essentially of a long pipe closed at both ends and divided by a thin diaphragm into two compartments containing gases at different pressures. When the diaphragm is ruptured a normal shock wave advances into the gas initially at the lower pressure and is followed by a flow at constant velocity. The conditions remain steady for a very short time only.

† Weaver, 'A method of wind tunnel testing through the transonic range', *J. Aero. Sci.* **15** (1948), 28; Millikan, Smith, and Bell, 'High-speed testing in the Southern California Co-operative Wind Tunnel', ibid. 69.

A shock tube may be used to study problems of unsteady motion, or, alternatively, it may be used as a wind tunnel of very short running time to study the quasi-steady motion round a model placed in the tube.

Special observational techniques are required; these include measurements of the time taken for the shock to pass between different points along the tube, flow photography using short-duration exposures, and pressure measurements with piezo-electric pick-ups.

Details are given in a review by Lukasiewicz.†

## § 12. Moving-body tests

Although the wind tunnel undoubtedly provides the most convenient form of test for many purposes, its use at high speeds suffers from severe limitations. The attainable Reynolds number is limited at near-sonic speeds by the power required to run a large wind tunnel at reasonably high density. For these reasons a number of techniques have been developed in which the model is moved through still air.

In some cases the body is propelled steadily through the air, in others it 'coasts'. The high-speed propeller‡ is an example of the first kind. It is a compact form of test, but the interpretation of the results is complicated by the tendency of the boundary layer to flow radially. This difficulty can be avoided by carrying the test aerofoil or body on a carriage moving along a straight track. Several such carriages have been driven by rockets, and the measurements may either be recorded on the carriage or transmitted by telemeter methods to a stationary recorder.

The variety of methods for testing unconstrained bodies is very large. In some cases the body is essentially a model aeroplane driven by its own engine and fitted with working controls. Such models are well adapted for investigating the characteristics of complete aircraft, but their complication and cost make them unsuitable for uncertain or difficult experiments or for ones in which there is no desire to represent a whole aeroplane. In other cases the body may be dropped from an aircraft and allowed to fall freely, the motion being observed by ciné-theodolites or by radar or telemeter methods.

The ballistic range technique is described in Chap. XIII.

† 'Shock tubes', *Rep. Aero. Res. Coun.* No. 13,498 (1951).

‡ Perring, 'Wind tunnel tests with high tip speed airscrews', *Rep. Memor. Aero. Res. Coun.*, No. 1,134 (1928); Douglas and Perring, ibid. Nos. 1,086 (1927), 1,174 (1928), 1,198 (1928); Hilton, 'The photography of airscrew sound waves', *Proc. Roy. Soc.* A, **169** (1938), 174.

*The wing-flow method.* A method described† by Gilruth for use in flight is similar in principle to the wind-tunnel bump technique described above. The model under test is attached so as to project from the surface of a high-speed aircraft wing into the local region of high subsonic or supersonic flow close to the surface. The available Reynolds number depends on the size of the aircraft and on the altitude at which it can be flown at the required speed.

## Section II

## UNCERTAINTIES AND CORRECTIONS ARISING IN TUNNEL TESTS

### § 13. Introduction

The force $F$ on a body of area $S$ wholly submerged in a fluid may be written

$$F = \rho U^2 S f(R, M, \gamma, \sigma, \ldots),$$

where $\rho$ is the density and $U$ the velocity of the free stream, and $R$ is the Reynolds number, $M$ the Mach number, $\gamma$ the ratio of specific heats, and $\sigma$ the Prandtl number. Additional parameters must sometimes be considered, but the above are usually the most important. The force coefficients on geometrically similar bodies will, therefore, be the same if the values of the parameters given in the brackets are equal.

The requirement of equal $\gamma$ implies that, if the motion in air is to be simulated, the working fluid in the wind tunnel must be diatomic and, according to the dynamical theory of gases, it follows that if identity of $\gamma$ is achieved the values of $\sigma$ will be automatically equal. Thus, with a diatomic working fluid it is for most purposes necessary to reproduce the full-scale values of $R$ and $M$ alone. This is not normally possible in a high-speed wind tunnel unless special measures are taken to reduce the power requirements, and the usual practice is to achieve identity of Mach number and use a Reynolds number which is as close as possible to the full-scale value. The effects which arise from departures from the full-scale value of the Reynolds number are known as scale effects. The scale effect in transonic flow is discussed in Chap. X.

† 'Resumé and analysis of N.A.C.A. wing-flow tests', *Aero. Conf. Lond.* (1947), 363.

Even if the full-scale values of all of the parameters were reproduced in the wind tunnel, departures from the full-scale flow might still arise from differences between the levels of turbulence in the full-scale motion and in the tunnel. The effects of the walls of the wind tunnel and of the supports which are used to hold the model must also be considered. Finally it is necessary to ensure that the conditions of pressure and temperature in the wind tunnel do not differ so much from those in full-scale flight that appreciable differences arise between the laws governing the behaviour of the fluids in the two cases.

## § 14.  Interference from the boundaries of the working section

A body in an unbounded subsonic airstream will, in general, create a disturbance which extends for an unlimited distance in all directions, but when the same body is tested in a wind tunnel, which for practical reasons is limited in size, the disturbance cannot extend beyond the tunnel boundaries and the flow pattern is thereby altered. Due allowance must be made for this in wind-tunnel testing, and there are three ways of doing this. The first way is to calculate the effect of the tunnel boundaries on the effective stream velocity at the position of the model. For instance, the walls of a closed tunnel constrain the streamlines and thus produce an effect which is to a first approximation the same as increasing the velocity in an unbounded stream. The second way is to calculate the effect of the tunnel boundaries on the forces and pressures at the model. This is a less satisfactory method, because it requires a detailed knowledge of the flow at the model, but it has to be used in certain cases. The third way is to adjust the walls of a closed tunnel to conform to the calculated streamlines, a method which for practical reasons is limited in its application.

All three methods rely primarily on theory, and become unreliable at high subsonic speeds when the presence of mixed subsonic and supersonic flow makes the existing theory invalid. To minimize this uncertainty, the size of the model (and thus of the region of mixed flow) must be kept small in relation to the size of the tunnel for tests of this kind. The model must in any case be small for tests at high subsonic speeds to avoid the Mach number limitation imposed by tunnel choking. A closed tunnel is said to be choked when the Mach number (measured upstream of the model) cannot be further

increased by raising the fan speed or the pressure ratio across the
tunnel. This phenomenon is discussed in more detail below.

In supersonic flow, the disturbance produced by a body does not
extend in all directions, but is limited to within a finite region which
for certain simple bodies takes the form of a wedge or cone. The
presence of the tunnel boundaries thus does not necessarily affect
the flow at the model, and corrections are not usually required.

Since we are concerned here with the corrections applicable for
high-speed tunnel tests, it should be pointed out that although these
corrections are essentially the same as for low-speed tunnels, their
relative importance is very different. At low speeds the correction
to tunnel velocity is relatively insignificant, but at high speeds it
is the most important correction. This is partly because its magnitude
is considerably increased by compressibility, and partly because it
affects the Mach number of the stream, which is a most important
parameter at high speeds. For instance, in a test to investigate compressibility effects on drag, a change of 1 or 2 per cent. in Mach
number has far greater significance than a change in $C_D$ of the same
order. The correction to the lift, on the other hand, which is important for a large model in a low-speed tunnel, becomes less significant in a high-speed tunnel where the model is necessarily small.

## § 15. Linear theory of tunnel constraint

The effect of tunnel boundary constraint may be obtained by considering a model in an unbounded stream and supplying a system of
images to satisfy the boundary conditions appropriate to the tunnel.
The velocity induced at the position of the model by these images
will then give the interference effect of the tunnel boundaries. For
the simple case of a model near a single plane wall parallel to the
stream, the mirror image of the model in the wall suffices to satisfy
the boundary conditions, since there will be no flow across the plane
of symmetry of the model and its image. For a two-dimensional
tunnel with plane parallel walls an infinite row of images is needed,
and for a three-dimensional closed rectangular tunnel a doubly infinite array of images, spaced at distances equal to the height and
breadth of the tunnel, is needed.

A similar image system can be used for a free jet with plane
boundaries, but here the sign of alternate images must be reversed,
to satisfy the condition of constant pressure (i.e. zero increment of

longitudinal velocity) along the boundaries. For a circular or elliptical tunnel the image system is less simple, but an analogous method can be used which involves a series of Bessel functions.

In all cases the image system must be such that there is no induced velocity a long way upstream of the model, because this is where the tunnel velocity is effectively measured.

*Induced velocities.* Let $U$ be the velocity of the main stream, and $u$, $v$, $w$ the velocities induced by the images in the directions $x$, $y$, $z$, $x$ being measured along the stream and $y$ vertically upwards. In high-speed tests the most important effect of the images is the longitudinal induced velocity $u$, because this affects the Mach number $M$, and also the pressure and density of the free stream. The vertical induced velocity $v$ is also important, since it affects the direction of the stream or the attitude of the model. The velocity gradient $\partial u/\partial x$ represents a pressure gradient affecting the drag of the model, and $\partial v/\partial x$ a curvature of the flow affecting the lift and pitching moment. The other induced velocities and their derivatives are not important unless lateral or directional measurements are to be made.

We shall first discuss the calculation of these induced velocities, and then consider the method of applying corrections to the results of the tunnel tests.

*Method of calculation.* The induced velocities $u$, $v$, $w$ are assumed to be small enough to be calculated by linear theory, so that the effects of the various images can be obtained separately and then added together. For the purpose of calculation, the model is replaced by separate velocity potentials $\phi$ representing its size, its lift, and its wake, where $\phi$ in each case satisfies the linearized equation

$$(1 - M^2)\frac{\partial^2\phi}{\partial x^2} + \frac{\partial^2\phi}{\partial y^2} + \frac{\partial^2\phi}{\partial z^2} = 0 \tag{21}$$

and

$$u = \frac{\partial\phi}{\partial x}, \qquad v = \frac{\partial\phi}{\partial y}, \qquad w = \frac{\partial\phi}{\partial z}. \tag{22}$$

For brevity we will write $\beta^2 = 1 - M^2$, and $r^2 = x^2 + \beta^2 y^2 + \beta^2 z^2$, but it should be noted that $r$ is not a physical length. In two dimensions the terms in $z$ are omitted.

The method can best be illustrated by considering a small model at the origin; the effects of finite thickness, length, and span are discussed later.

*Small model, three dimensions.* (a) *Size.* The size of any model can be represented by a suitable arrangement of sources and sinks, which for a small model can be reduced to an equivalent doublet (i.e. a doublet producing the same velocity field far from the model) of strength $\mu$, defined by its velocity potential

$$\phi = \frac{\mu}{4\pi} \frac{x}{r^3}. \tag{23}$$

The doublet strength for a thin body of volume $V$ is given by

$$\mu = UV, \tag{24}$$

but, for a body of finite thickness, $V$ must be replaced by an effective volume $V'$ which may be calculated by considering the source strength distribution required to represent the body surface. For an ovoid or streamline solid of revolution of length $l$ and maximum diameter $d$, the empirical relation

$$V'/V = 1+0\cdot4d/l \tag{25}$$

is sufficiently accurate for practical purposes. (The factor $\lambda$ used by Lock[†] and Glauert[‡] is equal to $4V'/\pi d^3$.) For an aerofoil of finite span with thickness $t$ and chord $c$ the corresponding formula is

$$V'/V = 1+1\cdot2t/c. \tag{26}$$

(b) *Lift.* The lift of an aerofoil has associated with it an arrangement of trailing vortices, and for a model of small span the lift can be represented by an elementary horseshoe vortex, or doublet vortex trail, of strength $\kappa$, defined by

$$\phi = \frac{\kappa}{4\pi} \frac{\beta^2 y}{r(r-x)}, \tag{27}$$

where $\kappa$ is related to the lift $L$ by the equation

$$L = \kappa\rho_0 U, \tag{28}$$

where $\rho_0$ is the density of the undisturbed stream.

(c) *Wake.* The wake of a model is a region of reduced total head which cannot be accurately represented by a potential function. Its main effect, however, is to displace the surrounding air, and for

† 'The interference of a wind tunnel on a symmetrical body', *Rep. Memor. Aero. Res. Coun.*, No. 1,275 (1929).

‡ 'Wind tunnel interference on wings, bodies and airscrews', ibid. No. 1,566 (1933).

this purpose it can be replaced by the semi-infinite body given by a source $Q$, defined by

$$\phi = -\frac{Q}{4\pi}\frac{1}{r}. \tag{29}$$

The source strength $Q$ is related to the drag $D$ of this semi-infinite body, which is assumed equal to the profile drag of the model producing the wake,[†] by the equation

$$D = Q\rho_0 U. \tag{30}$$

*Small model, two dimensions.* A similar method is used in two dimensions, as follows:

(a) *Size.* A small model is represented by a doublet of strength $\mu$, defined by

$$\phi = \frac{1}{\beta}\frac{\mu}{2\pi}\frac{x}{r^2}. \tag{31}$$

The doublet strength for a thin model of cross-sectional area $A$ is given by

$$\mu = UA, \tag{32}$$

and for an aerofoil of thickness $t$ and chord $c$, an empirical formula for the effective area $A'$ to replace $A$ in the above equation is

$$A'/A = 1 + 1 \cdot 2t/c. \tag{33}$$

The factor $\lambda$ used by Lock[‡] and Glauert[§] in two dimensions is equal to $2A'/\pi t^2$.

(b) *Lift.* A vortex of strength $\kappa$ is used, defined by

$$\phi = -\frac{\kappa}{2\pi}\tan^{-1}\frac{\beta y}{x}, \tag{34}$$

where $\kappa$ is related to the lift per unit span, $L$, by

$$L = \kappa\rho_0 U. \tag{35}$$

(c) *Wake.* A source $Q$ is used, defined by

$$\phi = \frac{1}{\beta}\frac{Q}{2\pi}\log r, \tag{36}$$

where $Q$ is related to $D$, the drag per unit span, by

$$D = Q\rho_0 U. \tag{37}$$

[†] This assumption is preferred, on account of its simplicity, to an alternative assumption (Allen and Vincenti, 'Wall interference in a two-dimensional flow tunnel, with consideration of the effect of compressibility', *A.R. Rep. Nat. Adv. Comm. Aero.*, No. 4K03 (1944)) which postulates a semi-infinite body giving not the same drag as the model but the same pressure drop a long way downstream in a closed tunnel. The drag of this body is $[1+(\gamma-1)M^2]$ times the drag of the model, and $Q$ is increased in the same ratio. Neither assumption can be justified fundamentally.

[‡] Loc. cit. on p. 520.          [§] Loc. cit. on p. 520.

## § 16. Total induced velocity

These potential functions are used to represent the images of the model in the system representing the boundary conditions for a given tunnel, and for each image the velocity induced at the middle of the tunnel can thus be calculated. The total induced velocity is then obtained by summing a series. For instance, in the calculation of the longitudinal velocity induced by the images in a closed rectangular tunnel of height $h$ and breadth $b$, the series giving the total contribution $u_1$ from the effect of the model size is

$$u_1 = \frac{\mu}{4\pi\beta^3} \sum_{m=-\infty}^{m=+\infty}{}' \sum_{n=-\infty}^{n=+\infty}{}' \frac{1}{(m^2h^2+n^2b^2)^{\frac{3}{2}}} \qquad (38)$$

(omitting the term $m = n = 0$), which may be written

$$u_1 = A_1 \frac{\mu}{\beta^3} \frac{1}{(bh)^{\frac{3}{2}}}, \qquad (39)$$

where $A_1$ is a constant depending on the shape of the tunnel, i.e. the ratio $b/h$. Similar expressions can be obtained for each of the components of induced velocity, and their derivatives, for a tunnel of any shape.

When the image system produces a finite velocity at an infinite distance upstream, a further correction must be made. In order to satisfy the condition referred to above, that the image system must not affect the flow upstream at infinity, an equal and opposite velocity must be superimposed on the whole field. For instance, the image sources representing the wake of the model (eqn. (29)) in a closed rectangular tunnel produce at infinity upstream a uniform velocity

$$-\frac{1}{2}\frac{Q}{\beta^2 bh}.$$

To satisfy the boundary conditions it is therefore necessary to add a velocity

$$u_2 = \frac{1}{2}\frac{Q}{\beta^2 bh}. \qquad (40)$$

Table 8 gives a summary of the values of $u$, $v$, $\partial u/\partial x$, and $\partial v/\partial x$ produced by the model images in a two-dimensional tunnel of height $h$ and in a three-dimensional tunnel of cross-sectional area $A_0$, height $h$, and breadth $b$.

The numerical constants $A_1$, $A_2$, etc., which for a small model depend only on the shape of the tunnel and the nature of its boundaries, are given in Table 9 for some typical tunnel shapes. These have been collected from various sources: $A_1$ from Glauert† (whose $\tau = \pi A_1/2$ in two dimensions and $2A_1/\sqrt{\pi}$ in three dimensions) and Thom‡; $A_2$ from Thom‡; $A_3$ from Glauert†; $A_4$ from Glauert† for two dimensions, Sanders§ for a rectangular tunnel (his $\delta_1 = \frac{1}{2}A_4$, Glauert's $\delta' = A_4$), and Baranoff‖ for a circular tunnel (his $K_g/\xi \to \frac{1}{2}A_4/A_3$ as $\xi \to 0$).

TABLE 8

| Property of model | Effect | 2-dimensional tunnel | 3-dimensional tunnel |
|---|---|---|---|
| Size . . . | $u_1$ | $A_1\,\mu/\beta^3 h^2$ | $A_1\,\mu/\beta^3 A_0^{\frac{3}{2}}$ |
| Wake . . . | $u_2$ | $A_2\,Q/\beta^2 h$ | $A_2\,Q/\beta^2 A_0$ |
| Lift . . . | $v$ | $A_3\,\kappa/h$ | $A_3\,\kappa/A_0$ |
| Wake . . . | $\partial u/\partial x$ | $A_1\,Q/\beta^3 h^2$ | $A_1\,Q/\beta^3 A_0^{\frac{3}{2}}$ |
| Lift . . . | $\partial v/\partial x$ | $A_4\,\kappa/\beta h^2$ | $A_4\,\kappa/\beta h A_0$ |

TABLE 9

| | $A_1$ | $A_2$ | $A_3$ | $A_4$ |
|---|---|---|---|---|
| Closed tunnels: | | | | |
| 2-dimensional . . . | $\frac{1}{6}\pi$ | 0·5 | 0 | $\frac{1}{12}\pi$ |
| 3-dimensional | | | | |
|   Rectangular $0\cdot5 \times 1\cdot0$ . | 0·912 | 0·5 | 0·274 | 0·585 |
|   Rectangular $0\cdot7 \times 1\cdot0$ . | 0·766 | 0·5 | 0·240 | 0·473 |
|   Square . . . . | 0·716 | 0·5 | 0·274 | 0·480 |
|   Circular. . . . | 0·706 | 0·5 | 0·250 | 0·50 |
| | | | | |
| Open tunnels: | | | | |
| 2-dimensional . . . | $-\frac{1}{12}\pi$ | 0 | $-0\cdot5$ | $-\frac{1}{6}\pi$ |
| 3-dimensional | | | | |
|   Rectangular $0\cdot5 \times 1\cdot0$ . | .. | 0 | $-0\cdot524$ | .. |
|   Rectangular $0\cdot7 \times 1\cdot0$ . | .. | 0 | $-0\cdot375$ | .. |
|   Square . . . . | $-0\cdot211$ | 0 | $-0\cdot274$ | $-0\cdot407$ |
|   Circular. . . . | $-0\cdot183$ | 0 | $-0\cdot250$ | $-0\cdot40$ |

## § 17. Method of applying corrections

The induced velocities and derivatives obtained as described above may be used to apply corrections to values measured in wind-tunnel tests.

† Loc. cit. on p. 520.

‡ 'Blockage corrections in a closed high-speed tunnel', *Rep. Memor. Aero. Res. Coun.*, No. 2,033 (1943).

§ 'Wall interference in wind tunnels of closed rectangular section', *Rep. Nat. Res. Coun. Can.*, No. MA–180 (1946).

‖ 'On tunnel corrections for compressible subsonic flow' ('Zur Frage der Kanalkorrectur bei kompressibler Unterschallströmung'), *M.O.S.*, R. and T. No. 333 (F.B. 1272 (July 1940)) (1947).

The longitudinal induced velocity $u = (u_1+u_2)$ is added to the measured tunnel velocity $U$, giving an effective free stream velocity $(U+u)$. The total head of the stream is unaffected by the presence of the tunnel boundaries, but its pressure $p$, density $\rho$, and temperature $T$ are altered by the change in speed according to the usual homentropic laws. Writing $\epsilon = u/U$, and using the symbol $\Delta$ to denote the correction to be added to the measured values, we have

$$\left.\begin{array}{ll} \dfrac{\Delta p}{p} = -\gamma M^2\epsilon & \dfrac{\Delta M}{M} = \{1+\tfrac{1}{2}(\gamma-1)M^2\}\epsilon \\[2mm] \dfrac{\Delta\rho}{\rho} = -M^2\epsilon & \dfrac{\Delta\tfrac{1}{2}\rho U^2}{\tfrac{1}{2}\rho U^2} = (2-M^2)\epsilon \\[2mm] \dfrac{\Delta T}{T} = -(\gamma-1)M^2\epsilon & \dfrac{\Delta p}{\tfrac{1}{2}\rho U^2} = -2\epsilon \end{array}\right\}. \qquad (41)$$

This correction to the free stream is commonly called the blockage correction. It is of considerable importance in high-speed tests, partly because it affects the Mach number, which is a most important parameter, and partly because its magnitude increases rapidly at high values of $M$, chiefly on account of the $1/\beta^3$ term in the expression for $u_1$.

The vertical induced velocity $v$ affects the direction of the free stream, and may be allowed for by adding a correction $\Delta\alpha = v/U$ to the measured model incidence. When a conventional balance is used for measuring forces, a correction must also be applied to the measured drag $D$ to allow for the change in axes. The correction to be added is $\Delta D = L\Delta\alpha$, where $L$ is the measured lift force. The corresponding correction to lift, $\Delta L = -D\Delta\alpha$, is usually negligible.

These induced velocities $u$ and $v$ can thus be allowed for quite simply, since they merely alter the direction and velocity of the free stream without affecting its uniformity. The derivatives $\partial u/\partial x$ and $\partial v/\partial x$, however, introduce distortions in the stream which can be allowed for only by calculating their effect on the model and applying corrections to the forces or pressures measured. This method is limited in its application, because it requires some knowledge of the flow at the model.

The pressure gradient represented by $\partial u/\partial x$ gives a 'buoyancy' effect on the model which can be allowed for by adding to the measured drag a correction[†]

$$\Delta D = V'\rho U\, \partial u/\partial x, \qquad (42)$$

[†] Glauert, loc. cit. on p. 520.

where $V'$ is the effective volume referred to above (see eqns. (24), (25), (26)). In two dimensions the same equation applies to the drag per unit span if $V'$ is replaced by $A'$, the equivalent sectional area. This correction is usually insignificant except for large models tested at low speeds.

The curvature of the flow represented by $\partial v/\partial x$ is equivalent to a change in the effective camber of a model aerofoil in the tunnel. For a thin two-dimensional aerofoil of chord $c$, this camber change can be allowed for by adding to the observed lift and pitching moment coefficients (the latter referred to the quarter-chord point) corrections† given by

$$\Delta C_L = \frac{\pi}{2} \frac{1}{\beta} \frac{c}{U} \frac{\partial v}{\partial x}, \tag{43}$$

$$\Delta C_m = \frac{\pi}{8} \frac{1}{\beta} \frac{c}{U} \frac{\partial v}{\partial x}. \tag{44}$$

## § 18. Effect of location of vortex and source

In the foregoing analysis the doublet, vortex, and source representing the model have been regarded as located all at the same point. The lift vortex should, however, be located at the centre of pressure, and this involves a further correction,† to be added to the measured incidence, which for a two-dimensional aerofoil is given by

$$\Delta \alpha = \left( \frac{C_m}{C_L} + \frac{1}{4} \right) \frac{c}{U} \frac{\partial v}{\partial x}, \tag{45}$$

where $c$ is the aerofoil chord, $C_L$ the lift coefficient, and $C_m$ the pitching moment coefficient referred to the quarter-chord point.

For a three-dimensional model this effect is generally negligible, but for a model of a conventional aircraft a correction must be applied to the tail-setting angle. If the tail arm is $l_T$, measured between the quarter-chord points of wing and tailplane, the measured tail-setting $\eta_T$ must be corrected† by adding

$$\Delta \eta_T = \frac{l_T}{U} \frac{\partial v}{\partial x}. \tag{46}$$

When the source representing the drag is located at the trailing edge of the aerofoil instead of at its mid-chord, a similar correction

† Glauert, loc. cit. on p. 520.

is applicable to the free-stream velocity $U$. This is given by

$$\Delta U = -\tfrac{1}{2}c\frac{\partial u}{\partial x},\tag{47}$$

but is generally insignificant.

## § 19. Effects of span and length

So far we have considered a model so small in relation to the size of the tunnel that its images can be satisfactorily represented each by a single doublet, vortex, and source, and the velocity induced at the middle of the tunnel by these images can be taken as the effective mean value over the model (apart from the corrections due to velocity gradients). When the model is large, however, neither of these simplifications is permissible. The model must be represented by the appropriate spanwise and longitudinal distribution of vortices, doublets, and sources, and the velocities induced by their images must be calculated not only at the centre of the tunnel but over the whole of the model. Finally the effect of these induced velocities on the model forces and pressures must be calculated, and the necessary corrections applied to the values measured. This method, like that used for the corrections for velocity gradients described above, is limited in its application, because it requires some knowledge of the flow distribution over the model and of the effect of any local velocity or incidence changes.

In tests at high subsonic speeds such information is usually not available, particularly when there are local supersonic regions on the model, and reliable estimates of these tunnel boundary effects cannot be made unless the model is small. This condition is generally satisfied in practice, because the phenomenon of choking puts an upper limit to the size of model that can be tested in a given tunnel.

For low-speed tests, the interference effects produced by the lift on a model of finite span have been worked out in some detail by various authorities,[†] and the variation of the factors $A_3$ and $A_4$ is given for a few typical cases in Table 10. Very little work of this kind has been done on the influence of finite span on the size and drag effects, because these are relatively small at low speeds. For a model of 6-ft. span in a 7 ft. × 10 ft. closed rectangular tunnel, Thom[‡] has calculated the induced velocity $u_1$ at the middle of the

---

† Glauert, loc. cit. on p. 520; Sanders, loc. cit. on p. 523.
‡ Loc. cit. on p. 523.

tunnel (which for this case is within 1 per cent. of the value for a
model of zero span and the same volume) but does not give the
effective mean velocity over the span.

TABLE 10

| Model span / Tunnel breadth | 0 | 0·3 | 0·6 |
|---|---|---|---|
| Type of tunnel | Values of $A_3$ | | |
| Rectangular 0·5 × 1·0  . | 0·274 | 0·242 | 0·198 |
| Rectangular 0·7 × 1·0  . | 0·240 | 0·230 | 0·224 |
| Square  .    .    . | 0·274 | 0·268 | 0·284 |
| Circular  .    .    . | 0·250 | 0·250 | 0·256 |
| | Values of $A_4$ | | |
| Rectangular 0·5 × 1·0  . | 0·585 | 0·548 | 0·570 |
| Rectangular 0·7 × 1·0  . | 0·473 | 0·458 | 0·436 |
| Square  .    .    . | 0·480 | 0·486 | 0·502 |

## § 20.  Validity of linear theory

For tests at high subsonic speeds, the correction to the Mach
number of the stream is more important than any of the other tunnel
constraint corrections, and the validity of the linear theory must
be assessed mainly for the Mach number correction obtained from
$u_1 + u_2$. It has already been explained that no satisfactory allowance
can be made for the effects of flow distortion, and it is therefore
sufficient to consider the case of a small model, for which the corrections are given in Tables 8 and 9.

In determining $u_1$, the first stage is to obtain the strength of the
equivalent doublet $\mu$ in terms of the model volume $V$. This is
calculated from potential theory, which is not valid when shock
waves are present. When the shock waves near the model are limited
in extent, however, it is still legitimate to postulate the existence
of some equivalent doublet, which could replace the model plus its
associated shock wave system and produce the same flow pattern
at some distance away. This principle is used in alternative methods
of applying the corrections, where the effective doublet strength is
obtained experimentally by measurements at the tunnel wall.

The source strength $Q$, to represent the drag, is not subject to the
same uncertainty, because it is obtained from the model drag as
measured, not from the calculated flow at the model. There is, however, the more fundamental doubt as to whether the wake can be

adequately represented by a source, which takes no account of the loss of total head. The magnitude of this uncertainty can be roughly assessed by the fact that the alternative (and apparently no less valid) derivation of $Q$, given in a footnote above (page 521), increases $u_2$ by the factor $(1+0\cdot4M^2)$.

Given the doublet and source to represent the model, the method for calculating the induced velocity is valid as long as

(a) the shock waves from the model do not extend to the tunnel boundaries, and

(b) the induced velocities are small.

A convenient criterion for defining condition (b) is that the magnitude of the correction $u$ is sensibly the same whether the value of $\beta\,\{=\,\surd(1-M^2)\}$ used in the formulae is obtained from the corrected or uncorrected value of the tunnel Mach number $M$. When this difference is appreciable, there is some empirical justification for using the corrected value of $M$, which has to be obtained by successive approximations. Above some value of $M$ (generally near choking) the approximations do not converge, and the method breaks down altogether.

Thom†, ‡ has suggested modifying the linear theory, to allow for the exaggerated effects near the choking condition, by multiplying the calculated correction by a factor which is a function of the ratio of the tunnel Mach number to the choking Mach number. The theoretical derivation of this factor involves difficulties, however, even for the comparatively simple case of a two-dimensional aerofoil, and it seems better to use measurements of tunnel-wall velocities as described below.

## § 21. Alternative methods

*Adjustable walls.* An alternative method of allowing for tunnel constraint, based on the same linear theory, can be used in a two-dimensional closed tunnel provided with adjustable flexible walls. This method, which has certain advantages, is used in the N.P.L. 20 in. × 8 in. high-speed tunnel, and has been fully described by Lock and Beavan.§

† Thom, loc. cit. on p. 523.

‡ Thom and Jones, 'Tunnel blockage near the choking condition', *Rep. Roy. Aircraft Estb.*, No. Aero. 2,056 (1945), *Rep. Memor. Aero. Res. Coun.*, No. 2,385 (1945).

§ 'Tunnel interference at compressibility speeds using the flexible walls of the rectangular high-speed tunnel', ibid. No. 2,005 (1944).

The principle of the method is that the walls cause no interference if they are set to lie along two of the streamlines round the model in an unbounded stream. To obtain this wall setting it is assumed, as before, that the aerofoil can be represented by a doublet, vortex, and source. First the effect of the model is measured by adjusting the walls by trial till the *pressure* along them is uniform, then a certain fraction of this wall displacement is used for the streamline setting. The exact value of this fraction, calculated from potential theory, is not quite constant along the length, and also varies to some extent with the position of the upstream datum, but 0·6 can be used as a fair average value for a doublet or source. For a vortex this method is not conveniently applicable, because the constant pressure setting would require a bend in the tunnel axis, and with a lifting aerofoil the walls are therefore first set to give *different* uniform pressures on the two sides. The streamline setting for the doublet and source is then obtained from the mean displacement on the two walls, and to this is added the wall displacement for the vortex calculated from the equation

$$\delta = -\frac{\beta\kappa}{4\pi U}\log\left\{1+\left(\frac{2x}{\beta h}\right)^2\right\}, \tag{48}$$

in which $\delta$ is the upward wall displacement at a distance $x$ from the origin, $\kappa$ is the vortex strength given in terms of the lift by eqn. (35), and $h$ is the tunnel height.

This method of allowing for tunnel-wall constraint eliminates some of the uncertainties of the direct method of calculating corrections. The strength of the equivalent doublet, which cannot be calculated when local shock waves are present, is effectively obtained experimentally, and the difficulty of calculating the effect of the velocity gradients $\partial u/\partial x$ and $\partial v/\partial x$ is overcome by eliminating these. A further advantage, of a more empirical nature, is that when the disturbances are too large for linear theory to be strictly applicable, the flexible wall method makes some allowance for this, if it can be assumed that the effect of non-linearity on the calculated wall displacement is of the same order as on the calculated free streamlines. Since choking can be postponed indefinitely by sufficiently careful shaping, adjustable walls enable higher Mach numbers to be reached with a given model size. The speed, however, is still limited to that at which a shock wave from the model reaches the tunnel wall, because, apart from the difficulty of adjustment in this critical condition, it is mechanically impracticable to represent the necessary discontinuity in the slope of the streamline.

To offset these advantages, the method has the drawback of requiring a separate adjustment of the walls for each Mach number and incidence, a slow and tedious operation. Also, with the exceptions mentioned above, it is subject to the same limitations as the conventional method of applying corrections and does not, for example, allow for any secondary effects produced by the finite length of the model.

*Velocity increments at tunnel walls.* A simpler way of obtaining most of the advantages of the flexible wall technique is to measure the velocity increment produced at the tunnel wall by the presence of the model, and to take a certain fraction of this as the correction to be added to the tunnel velocity. This method, used for obtaining $u_1$, eliminates the uncertainty of the strength of the equivalent doublet and also to some extent the limitations of the linear theory.

A doublet produces a peak velocity increment at the walls which is $m$ times the increment $u_1$ produced at the middle of the tunnel by the images, where $m$ is a factor which can be calculated by potential theory. This factor depends only on the geometry of the tunnel, and on linear theory is independent of Mach number. The wake of the model gives a velocity increment $u_2$ which is uniform across the tunnel section. The total wall velocity increment (after eliminating the effect of lift by taking the mean of the top and bottom walls) is thus $mu_1+u_2$. Hence $u_1$ can be determined by calculating $u_2$ from the measured drag, as described above, subtracting this from the measured wall increment, and dividing by the factor $m$. Typical values† of $m$ are given in Table 11. The values shown in brackets for models of finite size must be used with reserve, because when the model is large enough to affect the value of $m$ it is probably not safe to assume that the velocity increment at the middle of the tunnel applies over the whole model.

This method is probably valid nearly up to the choking speed of

† Thom and Jones, 'Notes on tunnel blockage at high speeds', *Rep. Roy. Aircraft Estb.*, No. Aero. 2,020 (1945), *Rep. Aero. Res. Coun.*, No. 11,160; Göthert, 'Wall corrections for high subsonic velocities with special regard to closed tunnels of circular cross-sections' ('Windkanalkorrekturen bei hohen Unterschallgeschwindigkeiten unter besonderer Berücksichtigung des geschlossenen Kreiskanales'), *M.O.S.*, R. and T. No. 411 (May 1946), F.B. 1216 (May 1940); Millikan, Smith, and Bell, loc. cit. on p. 514.

the tunnel, although definite evidence of this is lacking. The doubt about the value of $\beta$ to be used for obtaining the correction $u_1$ is removed, as in the flexible wall method, but still remains in the calculation of $u_2$. For this Göthert has used the uncorrected tunnel Mach number, and Millikan the local Mach number measured at the tunnel wall, but it appears that the best value to use lies somewhere between these extremes.

## TABLE 11

| Type of tunnel | Size of model | | Values of m | |
|---|---|---|---|---|
| | | | Top and bottom (longer) walls | Side (shorter) walls |
| 2-dimensional | $c/h = 0$ | | 3·0 | .. |
| Rectangular $h/b = 0.7$ | $2s/b$ | $l/b$ | | |
| | 0 | 0 | 3·6 | 1·8 |
| | 0·3 | 0 | (3·2) | (2·0) |
| | 0·6 | 0 | (2·8) | (3·1) |
| | 0 | 0·3 | (2·9) | (1·7) |
| | 0 | 0·6 | (1·8) | (1·5) |
| $h/b = 1.0$ | 0 | 0 | 2·6 | 2·6 |
| Circular Radius $a$ | $2s/a$ | $l/a$ | | |
| | 0 | 0 | 2·2 | 2·2 |
| | 0·25 | 0 | 2·2 | .. |
| | 0·5 | 0 | (2·0) | .. |

*Special tunnels.* The boundary effects in closed and open tunnels are generally of opposite signs, which suggests the possibility of devising some intermediate type of tunnel for which the interference effects would be zero. One proposal is to make longitudinal slots in the tunnel walls, another is to provide an annular airstream of relatively low velocity between the boundary of a free jet and the surrounding wall. These devices, however, rest on the same theoretical basis as conventional methods and are subject to the same uncertainties, and it is not yet established whether there is any gain in accuracy to justify the extra complications in the construction and use of such a tunnel.

## § 22. Experimental verification

The only satisfactory way of checking experimentally the reliability of any method of allowing for tunnel blockage effects is to make measurements on similar models of different sizes in the same tunnel (or, alternatively, on the same model in similar tunnels of different sizes). The results can then be extrapolated to give values for a model of zero size for which there would be no interference. In practice, there are difficulties in eliminating such effects as differences of Reynolds number, tunnel turbulence, and model surface roughness, and very little systematic work seems to have been done.

Another method for a closed tunnel is to compare the measured velocity increments at the tunnel wall due to the presence of a model with those given by the theory: this gives an indirect check on the validity of some of the assumptions.

Unpublished results of R.A.E. tests (using both these methods) indicate that the theory gives reasonably good results as long as the corrected Mach number is used to define the compressibility factor $\beta$. This is subject to the limitations already mentioned, of which one of the most important is the axial length of the model. The ratio of this to the height of the tunnel is effectively multiplied by $1/\beta$ at high speeds, and when this ratio is not small the equivalent doublet $\mu$ must be replaced by a source-sink system. This has a .considerable effect on the wall velocity factor $m$ (Table 11).

## § 23. Supersonic tunnels

When a model is tested in a supersonic tunnel there are usually shock waves extending to the walls, and the method described above cannot be used to obtain the corrections for wall interference. However, interference effects can be avoided altogether by using a small enough model and this is generally done.

Fig. 143 shows a two-dimensional supersonic tunnel; $AB$ is a thin aerofoil at zero incidence with a sharp leading edge at $A$, and $A'B'$ is its image in one of the tunnel walls. At a Mach number $M$ $(> 1)$ a bow wave will extend from $A$ along the line $AP$ defined by

$$\sin \widehat{PAB} = 1/M, \tag{49}$$

and a reflected bow wave $PD$, originating at the leading edge of the image aerofoil $A'B'$, will meet the axis of the tunnel at a point $D$. The image aerofoil will produce no disturbance of the flow ahead of its bow wave $A'D$, and thus cannot affect the flow over the model $AB$ as long as $D$ is behind $B$ in the tunnel. The condition for this is clearly

$$(c/h)^2 < (M^2-1), \tag{50}$$

where $c$ is the aerofoil chord and $h$ the tunnel height, and when it is satisfied there will be no tunnel wall interference on the model.

This is a simplified argument which ignores the effects of finite leading-edge radius and aerofoil thickness and the possibility that disturbances may pass upstream in the subsonic regions of the wake and of the boundary layers of the tunnel walls. In practice it is,

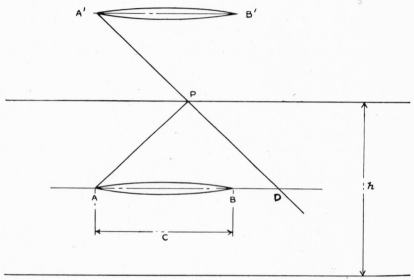

FIG. 143. Wall effect in a supersonic tunnel.

therefore, not advisable to use a value of $c/h$ greater than about one-half that given by eqn. (50).

In a three-dimensional tunnel, exactly the same reasoning applies, and a body of length $l$ will experience no wall interference if

$$(l/h)^2 < (M^2-1), \tag{51}$$

where $h$ is now twice the distance from the body to the nearest wall. In practice the length of the body should be two or three body diameters shorter than the value of $l$ given by this equation.

These criteria are based on the assumption that the flow is every-where supersonic, but the results are not affected by the presence of small subsonic regions behind the bow wave and elsewhere. If the subsonic region extends to the tunnel wall, or if a shock wave reflected from the wall strikes a region of subsonic flow extending from the model, the results must be treated with great caution.

## § 24. Tunnel choking and testing near $M = 1$

Tunnel choking, in its simplest form, is characterized by the formation of a sonic throat at the minimum cross-section of a closed tunnel, which fixes the upstream Mach number at a definite value. This minimum section, unless for some reason it is definitely located elsewhere, generally occurs at the model, and then imposes an upper limit on the (uncorrected) Mach number of a subsonic tunnel. This choking Mach number can be estimated by assuming uniform flow across the throat and using eqn. (3) which with $\gamma = 1\cdot 4$ may be written

$$\frac{A_0}{A_0 - F} = \frac{1}{M}\{\tfrac{5}{6}(1 + \tfrac{1}{5}M^2)\}^3, \tag{52}$$

where $A_0$ is the cross-sectional area of the tunnel and $F$ the net frontal area of the model.

In actual practice, conditions are more complicated than this, and choking may occur when the flow is supersonic near the model and subsonic near the wall, but eqn. (52) gives surprisingly good results for a variety of models tested in the R.A.E. 10 ft. × 7 ft. high-speed tunnel (Fig. 144).

A similar effect puts a lower limit on the speed at which a supersonic tunnel can be run, the value of $M$ being given by the supersonic solution of eqn. (52). In this case the formation of a throat at the model prevents the formation of the upstream sonic throat which is essential for supersonic operation.

There is thus a speed range round $M = 1$ in which testing in a conventional closed tunnel is impossible. The extent of this range depends on the size of the model: a frontal area of 1 per cent. of the tunnel cross-section gives limiting Mach numbers of about 0·9 and 1·1, $\frac{1}{4}$ per cent. gives 0·95 and 1·05. These are values of the uncorrected subsonic Mach number; in some cases the application of the appropriate blockage correction, within the range where it is reliable, may give a corrected Mach number higher than the measured choking speed.

This limitation on tunnel tests at speeds near $M = 1$ is fundamental. It arises in a subsonic tunnel when the local supersonic field round the model approaches the tunnel boundaries; this happens even in an open jet tunnel, or one with adjustable walls, where choking in the ordinary sense does not occur.

At speeds just above $M = 1$, testing is impossible when the reflected bow wave from the wall disturbs the flow at the model or in its wake as explained above, and this is usually a more severe limitation than choking, especially for three-dimensional models.

Even when the use of a very small model makes it theoretically possible to make tests near $M = 1$, there are practical difficulties in maintaining steady flow in the tunnel for this critical condition,

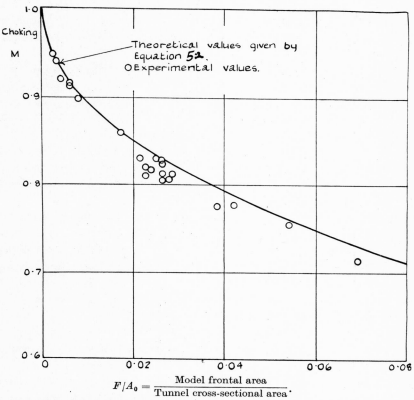

$$F/A_0 = \frac{\text{Model frontal area}}{\text{Tunnel cross-sectional area}}.$$

FIG. 144. Choking Mach numbers in the R.A.E. 10 ft. × 7 ft. high-speed tunnel.

where the speed is very sensitive to small changes in tunnel area such as variations in boundary-layer thickness. Weaver[†] has attempted to overcome this difficulty by making one wall of the tunnel convex, as shown in Fig. 142, in order to give a local sonic or slightly supersonic field in which very small models can be tested. There is,

† Weaver, loc. cit. on p. 514.

however, some doubt about the validity of the measurements, which are made in a region where there are appreciable velocity gradients.

## § 25. Effects of the model supports

The supports which are used to hold the model affect the measurements in three ways. There are first the aerodynamic loads on the supports which in the case of balance measurements must be subtracted from the measured overall forces. Secondly there is the blockage effect of the supports which may produce a change of Mach number at the model, and, thirdly, there are the interference effects of the supports on the flow round the model.

The aerodynamic load on the supports can be reduced by placing them inside shields, but the advantage thus gained may be offset by the increased blockage and interference introduced. For this reason shields were not used in the D.V.L. tunnel.† Shields were, however, at one time used in the R.A.E. high-speed tunnel‡ and the corrections which must be applied for blockage are discussed by Thom.§ The blockage effect may be reduced by sweeping the supports back so that only a relatively small part of each cross-section of the tunnel is obstructed.

The interference effects arising close to the points at which the supports meet the model may be very large at high speeds. Experiments by Matt‖ have shown that the interference may be reduced by moving the point of attachment towards the rear of the wing, but it is seldom possible to take advantage of this because considerations of strength usually require that the attachment shall be close to the position of maximum wing thickness. Methods for determining the corrections which are to be applied for the interference of the supports at high subsonic speeds have been described by Millikan†† and by Thompson and Mair.‡‡

For tests at transonic and supersonic speeds, the most satisfactory method of support is by a sting protruding from the rear of the model. A balance using this type of support is described on p. 575, where the procedures for determining the effect of the sting are also outlined. Experiments have been made at the W.V.A.‡‡ to determine

---

† Matt, loc. cit. on p. 501.

‡ Thompson and Mair, loc. cit. on p. 482.        § Loc. cit. on p. 523.

‖ 'Einfluß verschiedener Windkanalaufhängungen auf die aerodynamischen Beiwerte von Flügeln', *Lilienthal-Ges. Luftfahrtforsch.*, No. L.G.L. 156 (1942), 114.

†† Loc. cit. on p. 482.

‡‡ Owen, 'Note on the apparatus and work of the W.V.A. Supersonic Institute at Köchel, Part III.' *Rep. Aero. Res. Coun.* No. 9,361 (1945).

the interference effect of a sting. Tests on a family of spheres showed that for Mach numbers between 1·2 and 4·4 the sting had no effect on the drag if its frontal area was less than one-tenth of that of the sphere. This criterion was adopted at the W.V.A. for the determination of the permissible sting size for all model tests.

For two-dimensional tests in a closed tunnel the model may be held between the two side walls of the working section and the only support effects which then arise are due to the boundary layers on the side walls.

## § 26. Factors which may cause the behaviour of the working fluid to depart from that of a perfect gas

In theoretical work, and in the reduction of experimental observations, it is usual to assume that the working fluid behaves as a perfect gas with constant specific heats and obeying an equation of state

$$\frac{p}{\rho} = \mathscr{R}T, \tag{53}$$

where $\mathscr{R}$ is a constant for a particular gas. That is, it is assumed that the enthalpy $(c_p T)$ and the internal energy $(c_v T)$ are functions of temperature alone or, for example, that the enthalpy curves in the temperature-entropy diagram† for dry air shown in Fig. 145 are horizontal straight lines. This is so when the pressure is moderate and the degree of superheat high, but breaks down when the liquefaction-point curve is approached.

The behaviour of the atmosphere under the conditions of pressure and temperature encountered in flight at altitudes and Mach numbers which are not extreme is very close to that of a perfect gas. The pressure and temperature in a wind tunnel usually differ, however, from those in flight and it is necessary to ensure that the behaviour in the tunnel does not depart from that of a perfect gas or the observations may be of little value for full-scale application. There is little difficulty in satisfying this requirement in a wind tunnel if the Mach number is not too high and the air is dry. If, however, the air contains water vapour, this may condense at the pressure and temperature in the working section and cause a serious departure from perfect-gas behaviour. It is, therefore, necessary to control the humidity of the air entering the tunnel so that condensation is

† Ruhemann, *The Separation of Gases*, Oxf. Univ. Press (1940).

either avoided altogether, or, if this is impracticable, so that its effects are small.

Condensation of water vapour sometimes occurs in flight close to the surface of a wing, but the low water content of the atmosphere at high altitudes usually limits the effects to negligible proportions.

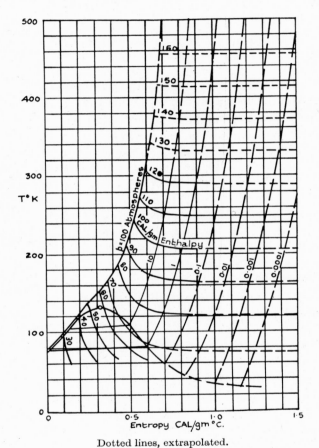

Dotted lines, extrapolated.

FIG. 145. Temperature-entropy data for dry air.

Moreover, since the temperature fall which accompanies the acceleration round a body in flight is usually small compared with that associated with the acceleration between the intake and working section of a wind tunnel, the tendency for condensation to occur is less severe.

*Relaxation-time effects.* It is also usual to assume that the energy content of the working fluid is capable of instantaneous changes following the external conditions so that the internal energy is always a uniquely defined function of the temperature, but this is not precisely true. The internal energy $E$ of unit mass of a gas may be written (see Chap. II, § 3 (vii))

$$E = E_t + E_r + E_i, \tag{54}$$

where $E_t$, $E_r$, and $E_i$ denote the energies due to translation, rotation, and vibration of the molecules respectively. At a particular temperature each of these quantities has an equilibrium value which may be calculated by statistical mechanics. If the temperature changes, the translational and rotational energies reach their new equilibrium values very rapidly, but the vibrational energy is relatively much less quickly adjusted. The relaxation time is a measure of the time constant representing the time taken for the vibrational energy to achieve equilibrium conditions. It has been shown[†] that for air the effects of relaxation time are negligible at the temperatures and Mach numbers usually encountered in flight or in a wind tunnel. The effects may, however, be more important for other gases some of which have been suggested[‡] for use in wind tunnels in order to reduce the power requirements for given Mach and Reynolds numbers.

*Possibility of liquefaction.* Goldstein[§] has examined theoretically the behaviour of dry air in a wind tunnel and concludes that, if the liquefaction point is not approached too closely, the departure of the behaviour from that of a perfect gas with $\gamma = 1{\cdot}40$ has a negligible effect on the results of calculations relating to the flow in the working section.

The logarithms of the vapour pressures of oxygen and nitrogen are plotted against the reciprocal of the absolute temperature in Fig. 146. This method of plotting is that suggested by Dodge and Davis,[||]

[†] Gunn, 'Relaxation time effects in gas dynamics', *Rep. Memor. Aero. Res. Coun.*, No. 2,338 (1946); Kantrowitz, 'Heat capacity lag in gas dynamics', *A.R. Rep. Nat. Adv. Comm. Aero.*, No. 4A22 (1944).

[‡] Smelt, 'Power economy in high-speed wind tunnels by choice of working fluid and temperature', *Rep. Aero. Res. Coun.*, No. 9,007 (1945), *Rep. Roy. Aircraft Estb.*, No. Aero. 2,081.

[§] 'The behaviour of dry air in a supersonic wind tunnel', *Rep. Memor. Aero. Res. Coun.*, No. 2,337 (1946). See also Chap. II, § 3 (viii).

[||] 'An investigation of the co-existing liquid and vapour phases of solutions of oxygen and nitrogen', *J. Amer. Chem. Soc.* **49** (1927), 610.

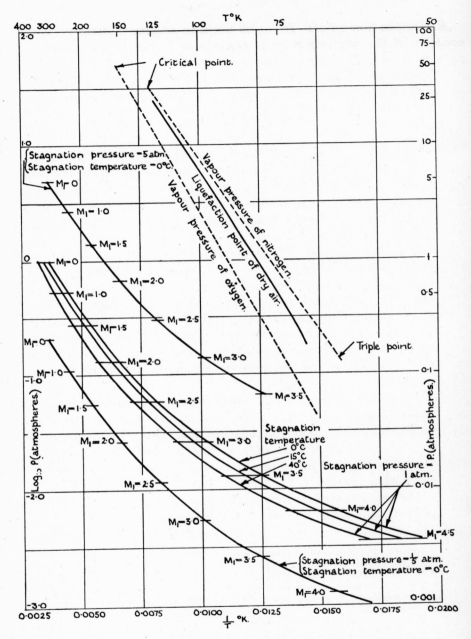

FIG. 146. Vapour pressure of oxygen and nitrogen and liquefaction point of dry air.

and the curves have been drawn from empirical equations given by these authors. The liquefaction-point curve for dry air is also included and has been drawn from data given by Dodge and Dunbar† and by Inglis‡ together with data from the International Critical Tables. Curves representing the conditions at the working section of a wind tunnel for a number of stagnation pressures and temperatures are also given in Fig. 146 and these show that the liquefaction point is not approached under the conditions prevailing in most wind tunnels. Thus for a stagnation pressure of 1 atmosphere or less, and stagnation temperature above 0° C., the liquefaction point is not approached at $M = 4$. The tendency for liquefaction to occur is most severe when the pressure is high and the temperature low and it is usually necessary to raise the stagnation temperature if very high Mach numbers are needed. As in the case of water vapour discussed below, there is evidence§ that a certain degree of supersaturation occurs in practice before liquefaction takes place.

## § 27. The effects of moisture and of condensation

It may be shown that the relative humidity at the working section of a wind tunnel is related with sufficient accuracy to that at the intake by the equation

$$\phi_1 = \phi_0 \frac{p_{s0}}{p_{s1}} \left(\frac{T_1}{T_0}\right)^{\gamma/(\gamma-1)}, \tag{55}$$

where $\phi$ is the relative humidity, $p_s$ the saturation vapour pressure, $T$ the static temperature, and suffixes 0 and 1 refer to the intake and working section respectively. The Mach number $M_1$ corresponding to the temperature $T_1$ may be obtained from the equation

$$M_1^2 = \frac{2}{\gamma-1}\left(\frac{T_0}{T_1} - 1\right) \tag{56}$$

and the absolute humidity $\Omega$, defined as the weight of water vapour present in unit weight of the mixture of air and water vapour, from the equation

$$\Omega = \frac{W_W}{W_A} \frac{p_s}{p} \phi, \tag{57}$$

† *J. Amer. Chem. Soc.* **49** (1927), 591.
‡ 'The isothermal distillation of nitrogen and oxygen and of argon and oxygen', *Phil. Mag.* **61** (1906), 640.
§ *Inter Avia*, No. 1,823 (1949).

where $W_W$ and $W_A$ are the molecular weights of water vapour and air respectively ($W_W/W_A = 0.622$).

The saturation vapour pressure is a function of temperature alone and is given in Table 12 which has been prepared from the International Critical Tables.

TABLE 12

*Saturation Vapour Pressures for Water and Ice*

| | Over water | | | | Over ice | | |
|---|---|---|---|---|---|---|---|
| $T°$ $C.$ | $p_s$ mm. Hg | $T°$ $C.$ | $p_s$ mm. Hg | $T°$ $C.$ | $p_s$ mm. Hg | $T°$ $C.$ | $p_s$ mm. Hg |
| −15 | 1·436 | 70 | 233·70 | −90 | 0·00007 | −40 | 0·0966 |
| −10 | 2·149 | 75 | 289·10 | −85 | 0·00017 | −35 | 0·1681 |
| −5 | 3·163 | 80 | 355·10 | −80 | 0·00040 | −30 | 0·2859 |
| 0 | 4·579 | 85 | 433·60 | −75 | 0·00090 | −25 | 0·476 |
| 5 | 6·543 | 90 | 525·76 | −70 | 0·00194 | −20 | 0·776 |
| 10 | 9·209 | 95 | 633·90 | −65 | 0·0040 | −15 | 1·241 |
| 15 | 12·788 | 100 | 760·00 | −60 | 0·0080 | −10 | 1·950 |
| 20 | 17·535 | 110 | 1,074·56 | −55 | 0·0157 | −5 | 3·013 |
| 25 | 23·756 | 120 | 1,489·14 | −50 | 0·0295 | 0 | 4·579 |
| 30 | 31·824 | 130 | 2,026·16 | −45 | 0·0541 | | |
| 35 | 42·175 | 140 | 2,710·92 | | | | |
| 40 | 55·324 | 150 | 3,570·48 | | | | |
| 45 | 71·88 | 160 | 4,636·00 | | | | |
| 50 | 92·51 | 170 | 5,940·92 | | | | |
| 55 | 118·04 | 180 | 7,520·20 | | | | |
| 60 | 149·38 | 190 | 9,413·36 | | | | |
| 65 | 187·54 | 200 | 11,659·16 | | | | |

Equations (55) and (56) together with Table 12 enable the relative humidity at the working section to be calculated in terms of the Mach number and the conditions at the intake. If the relative humidity $\phi_1$ exceeds unity, supersaturation occurs and it is then often termed the degree of supersaturation. The Mach numbers $M_1$ at which saturation and degrees of supersaturation of 4, 6, and 8 occur are plotted in Fig. 147 as functions of the relative humidity $\phi_0$ at the intake for an intake stagnation temperature $T_0$ of 20° C.

Condensation usually begins not when saturation is reached but only when there is a certain degree of supersaturation. Thus, referring to the section of the temperature-entropy diagram for water vapour shown in Fig. 148, the water vapour expands isentropically from the conditions 0 at the intake until saturation is reached at the point $S$. The isentropic expansion then proceeds to a point $K$ at which the vapour is supersaturated and at which condensation begins and the conditions begin to move over to the saturation line. The difference between the temperature at any point on the line $SK$ and the temperature at $S$ has been termed[†] the adiabatic super-cooling at that point and the magnitude of this quantity is found in some cases (see below) to have an important effect on whether

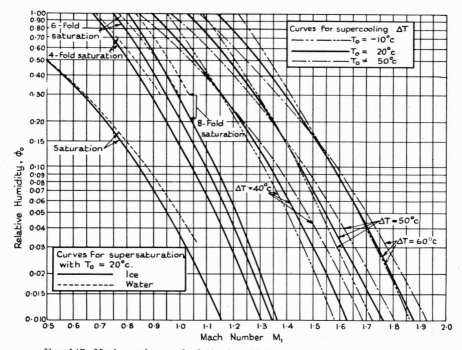

Fig. 147. Mach numbers and relative humidities for various degrees of super-saturation and adiabatic supercooling.

condensation occurs or not. Curves of the relative humidities $\phi_0$ at the tunnel intake against the Mach numbers $M_1$ are plotted in Fig. 147 for values of the adiabatic supercooling $\Delta T$ of 40° C., 50° C., and 60° C. for a range of stagnation temperatures $T_0$.

*The mechanism of condensation.*[‡] Wilson[§] found that when saturated air containing dust particles was expanded in an insulated

---

† Lukasiewicz, 'Humidity effects in supersonic flow of air', *Rep. Memor. Aero. Res. Coun.*, No. 2,563 (1947).

‡ See also Chap. VI, § 11.

§ 'Condensation of water vapour in the presence of dust-free air and other gases', *Philos. Trans.* A, **189** (1897), 265.

cylinder condensation began almost at once and continued as the
expansion proceeded so that virtually no supersaturation occurred.
When the air was free of dust, condensation did not begin until the
degree of supersaturation was between about 4 and 8. Experiments
by Stodola† using saturated steam show that the magnitude of the

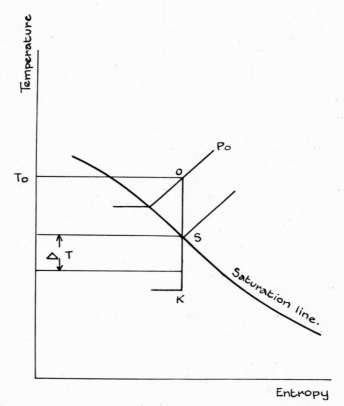

FIG. 148. Temperature-entropy diagram for water vapour.

effect of dust particles depends on the rate of expansion. He found
that when the steam was expanded slowly in a cylinder (the time
being of the order of 0·05 sec.) condensation began at once, but
that when it was expanded rapidly by passing it through a nozzle
(about $4 \times 10^{-4}$ sec.) condensation never occurred upstream of the
throat where the degree of supersaturation was about 5.

† *Steam and Gas Turbines*, McGraw-Hill (1927).

In a dust-free supersaturated stream condensation begins round nuclei consisting of a few molecules of water formed by chance grouping. The stability of such a drop has been investigated by Kelvin[†] and by von Helmholtz,[‡] who show that the curvature of the surface of separation determines the pressure for coexistence of the vapour and the drop at a given temperature. Thus, although molecular nuclei are formed continuously, in general they re-evaporate quickly and only those whose radii are sufficiently large persist and grow. The rate of formation of the nuclei which persist is discussed by Becker and Döring[§] who find that it depends mainly on the adiabatic supercooling (defined above) as shown in Table 13 which is due to Oswatitsch.

### TABLE 13

*Rate of Formation of Molecular Nuclei*

(Per cm. along the direction of flow per cu. cm.)

| Adiabatic super-cooling °C. . . | 30 | 40 | 50 | 60 | 70 |
|---|---|---|---|---|---|
| Rate of formation . | $< 1$ | $10^6$ to $10^7$ | $10^{11}$ | $10^{13}$ | $10^{14}$ to $10^{15}$ |

This table shows that the rate of formation begins to increase enormously when the adiabatic supercooling is between 30° C. and 40° C.

During expansion the temperature of the vapour falls with falling pressure, but that of the nuclei is reduced mainly by heat transfer to the vapour. Temperature equilibrium is not, therefore, achieved because the water drops are hotter than the surrounding vapour so that the rate of growth of the drops is difficult to calculate. Oswatitsch[||] has shown, however, that the rate of condensation due to the growth of the nuclei is negligible compared with that due to the formation of fresh nuclei when the adiabatic supercooling is of

---

† 'On the equilibrium of vapour at a curved surface of liquid', *Phil. Mag.* **42** (1871), 448.

‡ 'Dämpfe und Nebel', *Wied. Ann.* **17** (1886), 508.

§ 'Kinetic treatment of the formation of nuclei in supersaturated vapours', *Ann. Phys.* **24** (1935), 719.

|| 'Kondensationserscheinungen in Überschalldüsen', *Z. angew. Math. Mech.* **22** (1942), 1; 'Die Nebelbildung in Windkanälen und ihr Einfluß auf Modelversuche', *Jb. dtsch. Luftfahrtforsch.* **1** (1941), 692; 'Die Nebelbildung in Hochgeschwindigkeits- und Überschallkanälen', *Göttingen Monogr.* D$_1$-5.2 (1947).

the order of from 30° C. to 40° C. He has also shown that under these conditions condensation due to the presence of dust particles may be neglected.

*The effects of condensation.* If condensation does not take place, the presence of water vapour in the airstream in a wind tunnel is usually unimportant, but if condensation occurs important changes of the flow may follow. There will be a release of latent heat, a removal of the partial vapour pressure of the water vapour, and possibly also a small change in the values of the specific heats and their ratio $\gamma$. Also, the presence of water or ice particles in the airstream after condensation may make it difficult to interpret the readings of measuring instruments, cause deposits on the surfaces of models and exploring apparatus, and lead to uncertainty as to the significance of observations because of the possibility of re-evaporation.

Of these effects that due to the release of latent heat is in general the most important and depends on the amount of water vapour condensed, on the initial enthalpy of the stream, and on whether ice or water is formed after condensation. The overall effect may often be determined with sufficient accuracy from the equations for heat addition in one-dimensional flow given in Chap. VI and in the references cited below.[†] Calculations of this type are set out by Lukasiewicz,[‡] who assumes that all[§] the water vapour condenses apart from that required to saturate the air under the conditions prevailing after condensation has taken place, and obtains good agreement with observations made by Cope and Vincent[||] in a supersonic tunnel. The criteria which determine whether condensation will occur, and the effects of condensation are, in general, different in supersonic and subsonic tunnels.

[†] Hawthorne and Cohen, 'Pressure losses and velocity changes due to heat release and mixing in frictionless compressible flow', *Rep. Roy. Aircraft Estb.*, No. E. 3,997 (1944), *Rep. Aero. Res. Coun.*, No. 7,623; Hicks, 'Addition of heat to a compressible fluid in motion', *A.C. Rep. Nat. Adv. Comm. Aero.*, No. E. 5A29 (1945); Hermann, 'Condensation shock waves in supersonic wind tunnel nozzles', *Rep. Aero. Res. Coun.*, No. 6,185 (1942), *Luftfahrtforsch.* **19** (1942), 201; Chambré and Lin, 'On the steady flow of a gas through a tube with heat exchange or chemical reaction', *J. Aero. Sci.* **13** (1946), 537.

[‡] Loc. cit. on p. 543.

[§] The maximum quantity which can condense is that producing unit Mach number downstream. If more water vapour is present than is necessary to do this, part only can condense.

[||] 'Note on humidity effects in the N.P.L. 11 in. supersonic tunnel', *Rep. Aero. Res. Coun.*, No. 10,205 (1946).

*Condensation in supersonic tunnels.* The Mach numbers at which adiabatic supercoolings of 40°, 50°, and 60° C. occur can be seen from Fig. 147 for three different stagnation temperatures $T_0$ at the tunnel intake and for a range of intake relative humidity $\phi_0$. This diagram together with Table 13 shows that for normal atmospheric intake conditions the rate of formation of nuclei may be expected to increase rapidly at, or a little downstream of, the throat. Experiments by Oswatitsch,[†] by Hermann,[‡] and by Lukasiewicz[§] with air and by Stodola,[‖] by Binnie and Woods,[††] and by Yellot[‡‡] with steam suggest that in nozzles of moderate size (say up to about 1 ft. square at exit) the expansion in the region of subsonic flow upstream of the throat is so rapid that no appreciable condensation occurs here so that the air passes the throat in a supersaturated state. Condensation then begins with the rapid formation of nuclei and is usually complete within a comparatively small part of the nozzle length. Indeed, the condensation occurs so abruptly that the region in which it takes place is sometimes referred to as a condensation shock by analogy with ordinary shocks (see Chap. IV). A condensation shock in a nozzle is, in general, inclined to the stream and its reflection produces disturbances which are propagated downstream and may cause the pressure distribution in the working section to deteriorate. The heat release which accompanies the condensation reduces the Mach number at the end of the nozzle by an amount which can usually be predicted with sufficient accuracy by the equations of Chap. VI.

More precise investigations of the amount of adiabatic supercooling which may occur in a nozzle before condensation takes place have been made by Oswatitsch[§§] and by Lukasiewicz.[§] These authors conclude that in a nozzle of about 1 sq. ft. cross-section at exit, condensation begins when the supercooling first exceeds about 50° C. The effect of nozzle size has been investigated by Hermann,[‡] who finds that the supercooling for condensation decreases with an increase of size. In most tunnels, however, condensation may be avoided by adjusting the relative humidity and the temperature at the intake to values (see Fig. 147) for which the supercooling does

---

† 'Kondensationstöße in Lavaldüsen', *V.D.I.* **86** (1942), 702.
‡ Loc. cit. on p. 546.                                    § Loc. cit. on p. 543.
‖ Loc. cit. on p. 544.
†† 'The pressure distribution in a convergent-divergent steam nozzle', *Proc. Instn. Mech. Engrs.* **138** (1938), 229.
‡‡ 'Supersaturated steam', *Engineering*, **137** (1934), 303.
§§ Loc. cit on p. 545.

not reach 50° C. at any point in the flow. It is, however, not always possible to satisfy this criterion, particularly if the Mach number is high.

An alternative approach has been used by Hermann,† who suggests that if the absolute humidity is reduced to 0·0005 (i.e. 0·5 g. of water per kg. of air) the amount of heat release which can occur on condensation is so small that in most practical cases the effects will be negligible. This criterion was used in most of the German supersonic wind tunnels. The corresponding relative humidities at the tunnel intake are 5, $3\frac{1}{2}$, and 0·67 per cent. at temperatures of 15°, 20°, and 30° C. respectively.

*Condensation in subsonic tunnels.* The supercooling in a subsonic tunnel is usually such that the rate of formation of nuclei is small by comparison with that in a supersonic tunnel. In subsonic tunnels, therefore, condensation may occur gradually along the length of the working-section and also the rate of condensation may be influenced appreciably by the presence of dust particles in the airstream. The overall effect of the condensation may again be calculated with reasonable accuracy by the equations given in Chap. VI if the amount of water vapour which has condensed is known. The tendency is for the Mach number to increase and this may result in an apparent fall in the choking speed of the tunnel. In contrast to a supersonic tunnel where it is usually permissible to assume that condensation is complete well upstream of the model so that the Mach number at the model can be estimated, the stage which the condensation has reached at the model and, therefore, the Mach number there are usually unknown in a subsonic tunnel. Moreover, if the air remains supersaturated at the model, sudden condensation may occur in the regions of high local velocity close to the surface producing large and unpredictable effects.

The amount of water vapour which can be tolerated in the airstream entering the tunnel is more difficult to assess than for a supersonic tunnel since the effects depend on the size of the tunnel, the type of measurement which is being made and, as mentioned above, on the amount of dust which is present. The experience in the 20 in. × 8 in. tunnel at the N.P.L.‡ is that condensation effects are usually negligible if the degree of supersaturation in the free stream does not exceed 4 and that in some cases values up to 8 may be used

† Loc. cit on p. 546.          ‡ Holder, loc. cit. on p. 509.

without serious trouble. Further research is necessary before more precise values can be specified.

*The effects of condensation on the reading of a pitot tube.* If condensation takes place in a wind-tunnel the total head is reduced, but if a pitot tube is placed in the stream it is possible that the water or ice particles formed on condensation may re-evaporate† in the regions of high local temperature close to the mouth of the tube and thus produce an increase of total head. In a supersonic tunnel the reading is also affected by the reduction of the loss of total head in the bow-wave of the tube (see p. 555) which follows from the fall of Mach number after condensation. There is little evidence on the relative magnitude of these effects, but observations by Cope and Vincent‡ suggest that in the case that they examined the reading is almost independent of the humidity at the tunnel intake.

An additional uncertainty has been discussed by Taylor,§ who shows that the pitot pressure depends on whether the water or ice particles are deflected with the airstream round the mouth of the tube or pass into the tube and strike the back without contributing to the measured pressure.

In view of these possibilities it seems that until further data are available the reading of a pitot tube in an airstream containing water particles should be regarded with caution.

The magnitude of the error which can arise in a subsonic tunnel if condensation takes place is illustrated by Fig. 149, which compares the results of pitot-traverse drag measurements in the N.P.L. 20 in. × 8 in. tunnel when wet and dry air was used. Although part of the discrepancy may be due to errors in the reading of the pitot tube in the moist airstream, it is probable that most of it arises from an error in the determination of the free-stream Mach number.

*The prevention of condensation.* All possibility of condensation can be avoided by reducing the relative humidity at the tunnel intake by an amount which is sufficient to prevent saturation at any point in the flow. Whilst this is sometimes possible in closed-circuit tunnels in which it is necessary to dry only a relatively small quantity of air, it is not an economical process, because the preceding paragraphs

---

† Re-evaporation may also occur close to the surface of any body placed in the airstream, including the model under test. No information on the magnitude of this effect has, however, been published.

‡ Loc. cit. on p. 546.

§ 'Pitot pressures in moist air', *Rep. Memor. Aero. Res. Coun.*, No. 2,248 (1948).

show that a certain degree of supersaturation can, in general, be tolerated. In practice the air entering the tunnel is dried by an amount which is sufficient to satisfy one of the criteria given above.

The relative humidity at the intake can be reduced either by removing water or by increasing the stagnation temperature.† The former may be done either by the use of adsorbent beds of silica gel

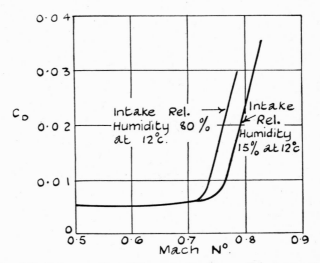

FIG. 149. Influence of humidity on profile drag coefficient measured by wake traverse method.

or activated alumina, or by a physical process involving either refrigeration and reheating or compression and expansion. The stagnation temperature may be raised by using a heater or, in the case of a closed tunnel, by reducing the amount of cooling which is applied.

An alternative method in which condensation is made to occur ahead of the nozzle of a supersonic tunnel by placing an auxiliary nozzle upstream has been examined experimentally by Royle.‡ If the tunnel nozzle is sufficiently close to the auxiliary nozzle for little re-evaporation to occur, the mixture of air and water drops can pass through the tunnel nozzle without further condensation. The pressure ratio required to drive the tunnel is increased, and, as mentioned

† Increase of stagnation temperature also reduces the effects of condensation because it increases the stagnation enthalpy (see Chap. VI).

‡ 'Control of condensation in supersonic tunnels by pre-expansion', *Rep. Aero. Res. Coun.*, No. 12,374 (1949).

above, the presence of water drops may lead to uncertainties in interpreting measurements made in the working section. In view of these disadvantages, further work is needed before it can be decided whether the method is a practicable one.

## § 28. The effects of turbulence and of disturbances from downstream of the working section

At free-stream Mach numbers below the critical value for the model under test the effects of the turbulence of the general stream are qualitatively similar to those at low speeds and are more or less confined to alterations of the positions on the surface of a body at which boundary-layer transition and separation occur. At transonic speeds where shock waves are present close to the surface, there is evidence (see Chap. X) that the state of the boundary layer ahead of the shock wave has an important effect on the flow, and for flows of this type it is known that the turbulence of the general stream is important. Few data are available on the effects of turbulence at supersonic speeds.

There is little precise information on the factors which determine the intensity of turbulence at the working section of a high-speed tunnel mainly because no satisfactory method has yet been developed for measuring turbulence at high speeds. Evidence obtained by measuring the drag of aerofoils and by observing the position of transition on the surface by one of the techniques described on p. 601 suggests, however, that the features required to give low turbulence are qualitatively the same as in low-speed tunnels.

No data are available on the effects of noise on the flow in high-speed tunnels, but there is evidence† that if the flow is subsonic, disturbances arising in the diffuser may pass upstream and develop into disturbances of quite large amplitude moving upstream in the working section. This may be prevented by placing a throat, behind which a small region of supersonic speed is formed, at the downstream end of the working section. Such a throat may be used also to regulate the rate of mass flow through the tunnel and hence the Mach number at the working section.

---

† Eggink, loc. cit. on p. 503; Liepmann and Ashkanas, loc. cit. on p. 503; Hutton, 'The use of interferometers in aerodynamics at the L.F.A. Brunswick, Germany', *Rep. Memor. Aero. Res. Coun.*, No. 2,366 (1946).

SECTION III

MEASUREMENTS

## § 29. Introduction

In some experiments detailed measurements of the local conditions may be necessary at the surface of the model under test, in
the neighbouring stream, or, for calibration purposes, in the empty
tunnel. In such explorations the quantities which can be measured
most easily are usually the static pressure, the total head, the total
temperature, and the direction of the flow. Optical techniques are
sometimes used to measure the density, or a derivative of the density,
but involve rather complicated apparatus and are at present limited
in their application and not highly accurate. If measurements of
the local conditions mentioned above are made, most of the other
quantities which are of interest can be derived from them by using
the theory.

Apart from the optical methods and the measurement of the static
pressure at the surface of the model, the observations involve the introduction into the flow of a suitably designed instrument. This is not
always possible, particularly if the scale of the experiment is small,
because it is sometimes difficult to use and support such an instrument without causing intolerable disturbances. Detailed measurements are, moreover, laborious if a large field has to be covered,
so that although it is possible to obtain most of the information
which is required by this means, it is often impracticable to do so
and more direct methods are necessary. For example, unless the
model is of simple shape (e.g. two-dimensional or axially-symmetrical),
balances are generally used to measure the overall aerodynamic
loads. Direct methods of this type give little information about
details of the flow, and in research work they are often supplemented
by a few detailed measurements.

In many tests it is of value to use methods for visualizing the flow
so that a picture may be obtained of the physical phenomena which
are involved. The optical methods mentioned above are often used
for this purpose, no attempt being made to obtain the density
quantitatively from the results. When used in this fashion the
methods are, however, quantitative in the sense that they indicate
the position and shape of shock waves and other regions in which
the density changes rapidly, and thus give results from which the

Mach number and other quantities can be derived in simple cases by using the theory.

Other methods, similar to those employed in low-speed tunnels, are used to determine the position of the region in which transition takes place from laminar to turbulent flow in the boundary layer on the model and for observing the flow close to the surface.

## § 30. Pressure measurements

Most of the local conditions can be determined in terms of their stagnation values (suffix 0) by measuring the local values of the static pressure $p$ and the total head $p_0$. Thus the Mach number $M$, the density $\rho$, the temperature $T$, the speed of sound $a$, the velocity $U$, and the quantity $\frac{1}{2}\rho U^2$ are given by the equations (see Chap. VI)

$$M^2 = \frac{2}{\gamma - 1}\left[\left(\frac{p_0}{p}\right)^{(\gamma-1)/\gamma} - 1\right], \tag{58}$$

$$\frac{\rho}{\rho_0} = \left(\frac{p}{p_0}\right)^{1/\gamma}, \tag{59}$$

$$\frac{T}{T_0} = \left(\frac{p}{p_0}\right)^{(\gamma-1)/\gamma}, \tag{60}$$

$$\frac{a}{a_0} = \left(\frac{T}{T_0}\right)^{\frac{1}{2}}, \tag{61}$$

$$U = Ma, \tag{62}$$

$$\tfrac{1}{2}\rho U^2 = \tfrac{1}{2}\gamma p M^2. \tag{63}$$

The loads on the model due to normal pressures may be found by measuring the distribution of static pressure over the surface, and in some cases the profile drag may be determined by measuring the distribution of static pressure and total head across the wake.

Although the conditions are never quite constant across the intake of a wind tunnel, the tunnel design must be such that the irregularities are small, and for most purposes it is permissible to take a mean value so that, once a calibration has been made, the intake conditions can be found by making measurements at one point only. Since the speed at the intake is low, these measurements can be made with instruments of the type described in Vol. I (1938), chap. vi. It is usual to assume that if dry air is used the flow between the intake and the working section is homentropic so that, except in boundary layers, wakes, and behind shock waves, the total head in the working section is constant and equal to that at the intake. If the value of the total head at the intake is known, therefore, the Mach number and the other quantities given by eqns. (58) to (63) can be found over a large part of the working section from static pressure measurements only. Values of $M$ given by eqn. (58) are tabulated against $p/p_0$ for $\gamma = 1.40$ in Table 14.[†]

## TABLE 14

### *Mach Number as a Function of Total Head and Static Pressure*

| $M$ | $p/p_0$ | $M$ | $p/p_0$ | $M$ | $p/p_0$ |
|-----|---------|-----|---------|-----|---------|
| 0·0 | 1·000 | 1·1 | 0·468 | 2·1 | 0·109 |
| 0·1 | 0·993 | 1·2 | 0·412 | 2·2 | 0·094 |
| 0·2 | 0·973 | 1·3 | 0·361 | 2·3 | 0·080 |
| 0·3 | 0·939 | 1·4 | 0·314 | 2·4 | 0·068 |
| 0·4 | 0·896 | 1·5 | 0·272 | 2·5 | 0·058 |
| 0·5 | 0·843 | 1·6 | 0·235 | 2·6 | 0·050 |
| 0·6 | 0·784 | 1·7 | 0·203 | 2·7 | 0·043 |
| 0·7 | 0·721 | 1·8 | 0·174 | 2·8 | 0·037 |
| 0·8 | 0·656 | 1·9 | 0·149 | 2·9 | 0·032 |
| 0·9 | 0·591 | 2·0 | 0·128 | 3·0 | 0·027 |
| 1·0 | 0·528 | | | | |

In order to determine the Mach number of the undisturbed stream in the working section of a wind tunnel, the static pressure is usually measured at a pressure hole in the wall sufficiently far upstream to be uninfluenced by the presence of the model under test. A preliminary calibration is made to enable corrections to be applied for small differences between the pressure measured at the wall and the static pressure in the empty tunnel at the position of the model. Instruments giving a direct indication of the ratio $p/p_0$ and hence of the Mach number are described on p. 568.

In many cases the assumption of homentropic flow from the intake cannot be made, and the local value of the total head is then found by placing a pitot tube at the appropriate position in the flow.

*The measurements of total head.* There is considerable evidence[‡] that, for Mach numbers less than unity, the pressure measured by a

[†] The symbol $p_0$ which is clearly appropriate in (58)–(63) is, for convenience, replaced in Chap. XII by the single symbol $H$.

[‡] Walchner, 'On the effect of compressibility on the pressure readings of a Prandtl tube situated in flows at subsonic velocity', *Jb. dtsch. Luftfahrtforsch.* **1** (1938), 518, also *Rep. Aero. Res. Coun.*, No. 4,181 (1939); Bäuerle, 'Measuring instruments for pressure velocity and direction measurements', *A.V.A. Mongr.* $D_2$; *Rep. Aero. Res. Coun.*, No. 11,222 (1947); Lock and Hilton, 'Calibration of standard pitot-static heads in the high-speed tunnel', *Rep. Memor. Aero. Res. Coun.*, No. 1,752 (1936).

PLATE 10

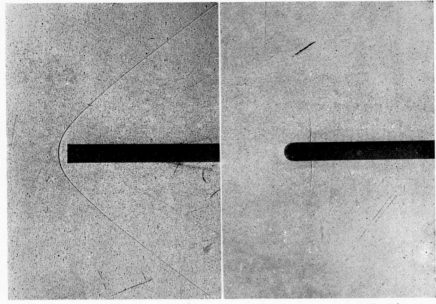

(a) Shock wave ahead of a pitot tube at
$M = 1.8$

(b) Shock wave on a static tube at
$M = 0.95$

(c) Density contour photograph at
$M = 2.0$

(d) Fringe displacement photograph at
$M = 1.4$

(c) and (d). Interferometer photographs of the flow round a 20° wedge

pitot tube (see Vol. I (1938), chap. vi) set up along the stream is to a high order of accuracy equal to the total head. This is illustrated by Fig. 150, which is due to Walchner,[†] and which also indicates that, for the tube shown, inclination of the axis of the tube to the stream has little effect if it does not exceed about 10 degrees. The

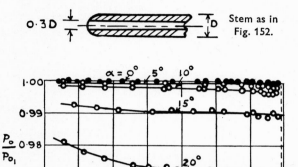

FIG. 150. Effect of Mach number and yaw on the reading of a pitot tube.

$p_0$ = Measured pressure.
$p_{01}$ = Total head of undisturbed stream.
$p_1$ = True static pressure.

sensitivity to yaw is, however, known[‡] to depend at low speeds on the shape of the nose of the tube and on the distance of the supporting stem downstream.

At supersonic speeds a shock wave is formed ahead of the tube as shown in Plate 10 (a) and the total head at the mouth of the tube is then less than that of the undisturbed stream. If the total head of the undisturbed stream is required, a correction for this effect is usually applied on the assumption[§] that the shock is normal to the

---

† Loc. cit. on p. 554.                           ‡ Bäuerle, loc. cit. on p. 554.

§ This assumption has been checked experimentally at Mach numbers of 1·6 and 1·8 by Holder and North ('Experiments with pitot tubes in supersonic airstreams', *Rep. Aero. Res. Coun.*, No. 13,268 (1950)). They find that the pressure reading of a square-nosed tube is independent of the ratio of the external diameter to the bore within the limits of at least 2 and 16. The Mach number calculated from this pressure on the assumption of a normal shock is found to be in fair agreement with that obtained from static pressure measurements.

flow across the stream-tube leading to the pressure hole. Making this assumption, the Mach number of the undisturbed stream may be determined from the ratio of the static pressure to the pitot pressure or from the ratio of the free-stream total head to the pitot pressure if the former is known from measurements at the tunnel intake. Thus if $p_{02}$ is the pitot pressure (i.e. the total head downstream of the shock wave) and $p_1$ is the static pressure of the undisturbed stream as measured by a static tube, the equations for a normal shock given in Chap. IV may be written:

$$\frac{p_1}{p_{02}} = \left(\frac{2}{(\gamma+1)M_1^2}\right)^{\gamma/(\gamma-1)}\left(\frac{2\gamma}{\gamma+1}M_1^2 - \frac{\gamma-1}{\gamma+1}\right)^{1/(\gamma-1)} \tag{64}$$

and

$$\frac{p_{01}}{p_{02}} = \left(\frac{(\gamma-1)M_1^2+2}{(\gamma+1)M_1^2}\right)^{\gamma/(\gamma-1)}\left(\frac{2\gamma}{\gamma+1}M_1^2 - \frac{\gamma-1}{\gamma+1}\right)^{1/(\gamma-1)}, \tag{65}$$

where $M_1$ is the Mach number and $p_{01}$ the total head of the undisturbed stream. Values calculated from these equations are given in Table 15 for $\gamma = 1.40$.

### TABLE 15

*Mach Number and Total Head as Functions of Pitot and Static Pressure in Supersonic Flow*

| $M_1$ | $p_1/p_{02}$ | $p_{02}/p_{01}$ | $M_1$ | $p_1/p_{02}$ | $p_{02}/p_{01}$ |
|---|---|---|---|---|---|
| 1·0 | 0·528 | 1·000 | 2·1 | 0·162 | 0·674 |
| 1·1 | 0·469 | 0·999 | 2·2 | 0·149 | 0·628 |
| 1·2 | 0·415 | 0·993 | 2·3 | 0·137 | 0·583 |
| 1·3 | 0·369 | 0·979 | 2·4 | 0·127 | 0·540 |
| 1·4 | 0·328 | 0·958 | 2·5 | 0·117 | 0·499 |
| 1·5 | 0·293 | 0·930 | 2·6 | 0·109 | 0·460 |
| 1·6 | 0·263 | 0·895 | 2·7 | 0·101 | 0·424 |
| 1·7 | 0·234 | 0·856 | 2·8 | 0·095 | 0·389 |
| 1·8 | 0·214 | 0·813 | 2·9 | 0·088 | 0·358 |
| 1·9 | 0·194 | 0·767 | 3·0 | 0·083 | 0·328 |
| 2·0 | 0·177 | 0·721 | | | |

Surface tubes for exploring close to a surface have been described in Vol. I (1938), chap. vi, and are sometimes used for measurements in high-speed flows, an example being described by Fage and Sargent.†

*The measurement of static pressure.* The technique of measuring the pressures at a surface does not differ from that at low speeds and involves the use of small pressure holes drilled normal to the

† 'Shock-wave and boundary-layer phenomena near a flat surface', *Proc. Roy. Soc.* A, **190** (1947), 1.

surface and connected to leads communicating with the manometer. Close to the pressure holes the surface must be free from burrs or hollows, and the hole itself should be of constant cross-section for a depth of at least one diameter below the surface.

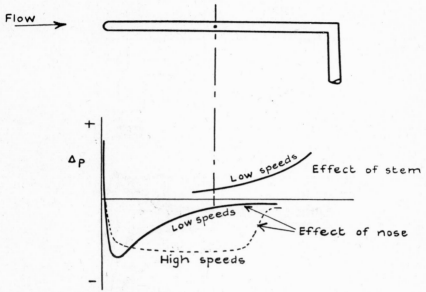

Fig. 151. Pressure round a static tube (diagrammatic).

The design of static tubes for the measurement of the pressure in a low-speed flow usually involves a choice of the position of the nose and of the supporting stem so that their effects cancel at the position of the pressure holes. Thus, referring to Fig. 151, the position of the holes is chosen so that the decrease of pressure associated with the flow round the nose balances the increment due to the stem. As the Mach number is raised the effects of the nose and stem are at first qualitatively the same as at low speeds, but the critical Mach number is ultimately reached and a region of supersonic flow then appears a little behind the nose and, in general, terminates in a shock-wave as shown in Plate 10 (*b*). Under these conditions the effect of the nose on the measured pressure becomes different from that at low speeds, and moreover the effect of the stem is reduced when the shock passes back over the pressure holes. When this happens the measured pressure might be expected to fall below the true static

pressure. This is illustrated by Fig. 152 (due to Walchner†) in which
the ratio of the measured pressure to the true static pressure‡ is
plotted as a function of free-stream Mach number for a range of

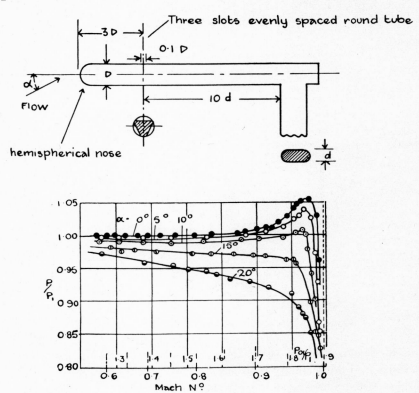

FIG. 152. Effects of Mach number and yaw on the reading of a static tube.

$p$ = Measured pressure.
$p_1$ = True static pressure.
$p_{01}$ = Total head of undisturbed stream.

values of the inclination of the axis of the tube to the stream. The
initial rise of static pressure for values of the yaw below 10° occurs
when the shock wave is ahead of the pressure holes and is due to the
pressure rise in the shock-wave. Pressure changes which are qualitatively similar to those shown in Fig. 152 occur with most static tubes

† Loc. cit. on p. 554.
‡ The true static pressure was here taken as the pressure measured in the chamber
surrounding the jet of the tunnel. The assumption that the pressure is uniform
across the jet is, however, questionable at the higher Mach numbers.

as the Mach number is raised, the speed at which they begin depending mainly on the distances of the nose and the stem from the holes. Lock, Knowler, and Pearcey† find that the effects may be postponed to a higher Mach number by increasing these distances but that the shape of the nose itself is relatively unimportant if the holes are far enough downstream.

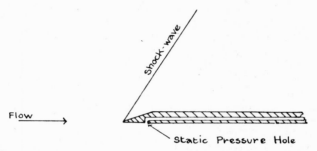

Fig. 153. A wedge for measuring static pressure.

There is little information on the design of static tubes for the exploration of supersonic flows. Such tubes are usually made with conical noses (ogival noses have sometimes been used) of whole angle about 10° and with the static holes about ten diameters behind the shoulder of the cone. With the holes so far back, the measured pressure is not sensitive to the nose shape.‡ An alternative instrument has been described by Schaefer§ and consists of a wedge, as shown in Fig. 153, with one face placed along the stream and fitted with a static hole outside the Mach cones of the tips of the leading edge of the wedge. It is probable, however, that with this arrangement the measured pressure is sensitive to the inclination of the stream to the wedge, and for this reason a tube is usually to be preferred.

For low-speed work the static holes are usually spread along a small length of the tube, but because the pressure may vary more rapidly in high-speed flow it is usual in this case to place the holes in a common plane. Even if this is done, however, the presence of the boundary-layer on the surface of the tube may prevent the accurate measurement of sudden pressure gradients such as those

† 'The effect of compressibility on static heads', *Rep. Memor. Aero. Res. Coun.*, No. 2,386 (1943).
‡ Holder, North, and Chinneck, 'Experiments with static tubes in a supersonic airstream', *Rep. Aero. Res. Coun.*, No. 13,269 (1950).
§ 'Machmeters for high-speed flight research', *J. Aero. Sci.* **15** (1948), 351.

occurring in shock waves (see Chap. X, § 18). The interaction of a strong shock wave with the boundary layer on an exploring tube may in some cases lead to an extensive region of separated flow of the type observed by Lukasiewicz.†

*Pitot-static tubes.* It is usually permissible to assume that the separate effects discussed above for pitot and static tubes are independent in the case of pitot-static tubes. Although very small pitot-static tubes have been made,† they tend to be more bulky than individual pitot and static tubes and are therefore less frequently used in high-speed than in low-speed tunnels. With a pitot-static tube, the two pressures are measured at different points in the flow so that a tube of this type is not very suitable for observations in flows where there are large pressure gradients.

## § 31. Forces due to normal pressures

The method described in Vol. I (1938), chap. vi for obtaining the lift, pitching moment, and form drag from measurements of the distribution of normal pressure over the surface of a body may be used at any Mach number. Typical methods for constructing pressure-plotting models for use in high-speed tunnels are described by Thompson and Mair‡ and by Holder.§

Two alternative coefficients (see also Chap. XII) have been used for expressing the pressure measurements. The first is defined by

$$C_p = \frac{p - p_1}{\frac{1}{2}\rho_1 U_1^2},$$

where $p$ is the local static pressure and suffix 1 refers to the conditions of the free stream. This coefficient has the advantages that it enables the effects of change of pressure distribution on the overall force coefficients to be seen easily, and that it gives a pressure distribution which is sensibly independent of Mach number at low speeds. The second coefficient is $p/p_{01}$, where $p_{01}$ is the total head of the undisturbed stream, and has the advantage that a scale of local Mach number (which is exact only upstream of shock waves and regions of boundary-layer separation) may be appended.

*Lift from pressure measurements at the tunnel walls.* If it is assumed

---

† 'Conical flow as a result of shock and boundary layer interaction on a probe', *Rep. Memor. Aero. Res. Coun.*, No. 2,669 (1948); *Tech. Notes Roy. Aircraft Estb.*, No. Aero. 1,968.

‡ Loc. cit. on p. 482.                                   § Loc. cit. on p. 509.

that any force on the model in a wind tunnel normal to the stream is transmitted by pressure to the tunnel walls, it should be possible to obtain the lift by integrating the wall pressures. This method has been used by Lock and Beavan† and by others to obtain the lift of an aerofoil completely spanning a closed rectangular working section with straight walls. The technique was to measure the pressures along the centre lines of the top and bottom walls (the aerofoil being in a horizontal plane) and to assume that the pressure was constant across the walls. It was found that an accurate estimate of the lift was possible provided that the working section was sufficiently long for the differential pressure on the two walls to be negligible at the ends, or that a correction was applied for the effects of any residual pressure difference that was present. This was done by representing the model by a simple vortex.

## § 32. The determination of profile drag by wake traverses

It is known that at low Mach number the profile drag may be determined with sufficient accuracy from measurements of the total head and static pressure across a section of the wake. At high Mach number the measurement of a third quantity such as the density is theoretically necessary but this is, of course, inconvenient in practice. On certain assumptions it has been possible, however, to devise methods which require measurements of the total head and static pressure alone and these methods are now generally used. The first method of this type was developed by Lock and Hilton,‡ but contained a theoretical mistake which was subsequently corrected by Young,§ whose method was then simplified by Lock, Hilton, and Goldstein.‖ Although the method given by Lock, Hilton, and Goldstein is probably more convenient than any other of comparable accuracy, it is nevertheless laborious and it is usual to employ a simpler approximate technique, returning to the more accurate one only in special cases.

Taking the $x$-axis along the undisturbed stream, and denoting the velocity component in this direction by $U$, it follows from the

† Loc. cit. on p. 528.
‡ 'Measurement of profile drag in the high-speed wind tunnel by the pitot traverse method', *Rep. Aero. Res. Coun.*, No. 2,826 (1937).
§ 'Note on momentum methods of measuring profile drags at high speeds', *Rep. Memor. Aero. Res. Coun.*, No. 1,963 (1940).
‖ 'Determination of profile drag at high speeds by a pitot traverse method', ibid. No. 1,971 (1940).

momentum theorem that the drag $D$ of a two-dimensional body is given by

$$D = \int (p_1 - p)\, dy + \int \rho U (U_1 - U)\, dy, \qquad (66)$$

where $p$ and $\rho$ are the local static pressure and density, and suffix 1 refers to the undisturbed stream. Similarly, the drag of any three-dimensional body is given by

$$D = \int (p_1 - p)\, dS + \int \rho U (U_1 - U)\, dS. \qquad (67)$$

In both cases the integrals are taken right across the wake in a plane at right angles to the undisturbed stream.

Equations (66) and (67) are true generally, and are identical to those given in Vol. I (1938), chap. vi for the particular case of an incompressible flow. If it is assumed that the plane in which the wake is traversed is sufficiently far downstream for the static pressure across it to be uniform and equal to that in the undisturbed stream eqn. (66) becomes, as in Jones's method† for low-speed flow,

$$D = \int \rho U (U_1 - U)\, dy. \qquad (68)$$

Referring now to Fig. 154, let $AA$ be a plane far enough upstream for the conditions across it to be constant and again let these be denoted by suffix 1. Let $BB$ be a plane far enough downstream for the static pressure to have returned to the free stream pressure $p_1$ and let $T$, $T'$ be the boundaries of the wake‡ at $BB$. The lines $PQST$ and $P'Q'S'T'$ are streamlines of the steady flow past the aerofoil and, since the wake widens downstream, these lie entirely outside the wake and the boundary layer of the aerofoil upstream of $BB$. Outside these streamlines the motion is, therefore, practically irrotational and the influence of viscosity and conductivity is negligible so that the total energy and the entropy are constant. Thus the density is equal to $\rho_1$ and the velocity to $U_1$ across $BB$ except in the wake where the conditions are denoted by suffix 3. Let $CC$ be the section across which the wake is to be explored and let conditions here be denoted by suffix 2. If any inclination of the stream at $CC$ to the normal to this section may be ignored, the continuity equation gives

$$\rho_2 U_2\, dy_2 = \rho_3 U_3\, dy_3, \qquad (69)$$

† Camb. Univ. Aero. Lab., 'The measurement of profile drag by the pitot traverse method', *Rep. Memor. Aero. Res. Coun.*, No. 1,688 (1936).

‡ Defined as the region in which the total head differs from that of the undisturbed stream.

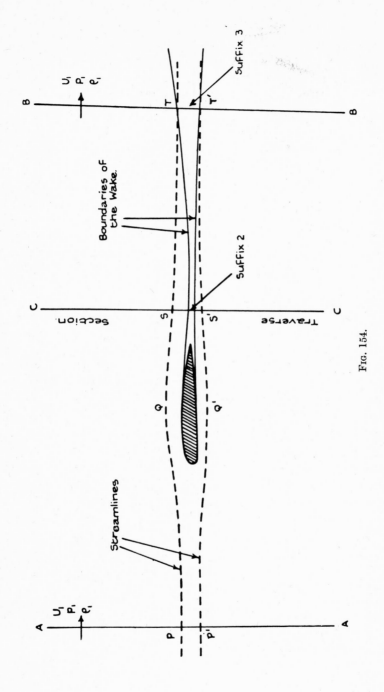

FIG. 154.

where $dy_2$ is the breadth of a stream tube at $CC$ and $dy_3$ its breadth at $BB$. It follows from eqn. (68) that the drag per unit length of the aerofoil is given by

$$D = \int \rho_2\, U_2 (U_1 - U_3)\, dy_2 \qquad (70)$$

and, if $c$ is the chord of the aerofoil, it is convenient to write the drag coefficient $C_D$ in the form

$$C_D = \frac{D}{\frac{1}{2}\rho_1 U_1^2 c} = \int C_D' \frac{dy_2}{c}, \qquad (71)$$

where

$$C_D' = 2\,\frac{\rho_2}{\rho_1}\frac{U_2}{U_1}\left(1 - \frac{U_3}{U_1}\right) \qquad (72)$$

and represents the drag contribution from any point in the wake traverse. The integral in eqn. (71) is taken between the points where $C_D' = 0$. In eqns. (70) and (71) the integrals are taken over the wake at the section $CC$, and $U_3$ is the velocity at the section $BB$ on the streamline passing through the point at the section $CC$ at which the velocity is $U_2$.

It is now required to express $C_D'$ in terms of the observable quantities, namely the static pressure $p_2$ and the total head $p_{02}$ at the section $CC$. To do this the following assumptions have been made by Young[†] and by Lock, Hilton, and Goldstein.[‡]

   (i) That the total energy is constant everywhere, including the wake, and is equal to the value far ahead of the aerofoil.

  (ii) That mean streamlines may be drawn in the wake along which the total head may be assumed to be constant between $SS'$ and $TT'$. When the total energy is constant this is equivalent to the assumption that the entropy is constant along each streamline.

Since the energy equation (Chap. II) may be written

$$\text{total energy} = c_p\, T + \tfrac{1}{2}q^2 = c_p\, T_0, \qquad (73)$$

where $T_0$ is the total temperature, $T$ the static temperature, and $q$ the resultant velocity, the first assumption is satisfied if the stagnation temperature is constant everywhere. This has been checked to a certain approximation by Lock, Hilton, and Goldstein,[‡] who made measurements with a pitot-thermocouple (see p. 571) in the wake of an aerofoil.

† Loc. cit. on p. 561.                                        ‡ Loc. cit. on p. 561.

The second assumption is analogous to that made by B. M. Jones[†]
for an incompressible fluid, and has been checked by comparing the
drags obtained from wake traverses at different distances behind the
trailing edge. The results of one series of traverses of this type are
shown in Fig. 155, which is due to Lock, Hilton, and Goldstein.[‡]

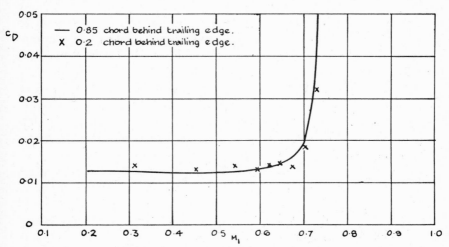

FIG. 155. Comparison of drags deduced from traverses at different distances behind
an aerofoil.

The validity of both assumptions is supported by the agreement
between the drags obtained from wake measurements and by direct
balance measurements. Additional support is given by agreement
with the drags obtained by an alternative method due to Young,[§]
who related the conditions at the sections $BB$ and $CC$ (Fig. 154)
by means of the momentum equation of the wake.

If assumptions (i) and (ii) are made it is easy to show[‡] that eqn.
(72) may be written

$$C'_D = 2\left(\frac{p_2}{p_1}\right)^{1/\gamma}\left(\frac{p_{02}}{p_{01}}\right)^{(\gamma-1)/\gamma}\left\{\frac{1-\left(\frac{p_2}{p_{02}}\right)^{(\gamma-1)/\gamma}}{1-\left(\frac{p_1}{p_{01}}\right)^{(\gamma-1)/\gamma}}\right\}^{\frac{1}{2}}\left\{1-\left[\frac{1-\left(\frac{p_1}{p_{02}}\right)^{(\gamma-1)/\gamma}}{1-\left(\frac{p_1}{p_{01}}\right)^{(\gamma-1)/\gamma}}\right]^{\frac{1}{2}}\right\}$$

(74)

which is the required equation in $p_1$, $p_{01}$ and $p_2$, $p_{02}$ alone. Although

† Camb. Univ. Aero. Lab., loc. cit. on p. 562.
‡ Loc. cit. on p. 561.                    § Loc. cit. on p. 561.

the evaluation of this equation is helped by the use of the tables given by Lock, Hilton, and Goldstein[†] and by a chart given by Thompson[‡] it is, nevertheless, laborious and approximate methods are often employed when the wake-traverse method is used for routine drag measurements. One such method has been described by Beavan and Manwell[§] and depends on the observed fact that in many cases $C_D'$ is at a given speed approximately proportional to $(p_{01}-p_{02})$. Simpler approximations have been suggested by Thompson[‡] and by Beavan[||] who use integrating factors to relate the integrated total-head loss directly to $C_D$. Analogous methods have been used in the U.S.A. and have been compared with the British methods by Beavan.[||]

Examples of the distribution of total-head loss in a plane one chord behind the trailing edge of an aerofoil are shown in Fig. 156. These show the increase in the width of the wake which is produced at high speeds by the growth of shock waves close to the surface of the aerofoil. When integrating such curves, allowance must be made for the fact that, when there is a gradient of total head across the mouth of a pitot tube, the effective centre of the tube is displaced from the geometrical centre towards the region of higher velocity so that the area under the curve is less than it should be. The magnitude of this effect at low speeds has been investigated by Young and Maas,[††] who find that for tubes of the dimensions usually employed for wake traverses it is sufficiently accurate to take the displacement as 0·18 times the external diameter of the tube. The arithmetical value of the abscissa should, therefore, be increased by this value at every point and, as far as the integration is concerned, it is, therefore, sufficient to add a quantity equal to twice the product of the maximum ordinate and the displacement (expressed nondimensionally if the abscissa is plotted in this manner) to the area under the curve.

There is little doubt that eqn. (74) remains valid when the free-

† Loc. cit. on p. 561.

‡ 'A simple method of computing $C_D$ from wake traverses at high speeds', *Rep. Aero. Res. Coun.*, No. 8,462, *Rep. Roy. Aircraft Estb.*, No. Aero. 2,005 (1944).

§ 'Tables for use in the determination of profile drag at high speeds by the pitot traverse method', *Rep. Memor. Aero. Res. Coun.*, No. 2,233 (1941).

|| 'Note on methods at the N.P.L. and in the U.S.A. for calculating the profile drag at high speeds from pitot traverse measurements', ibid. No. 2,102 (1943).

†† 'The behaviour of a pitot-tube in a transverse total pressure gradient', ibid. No. 1,770 (1936).

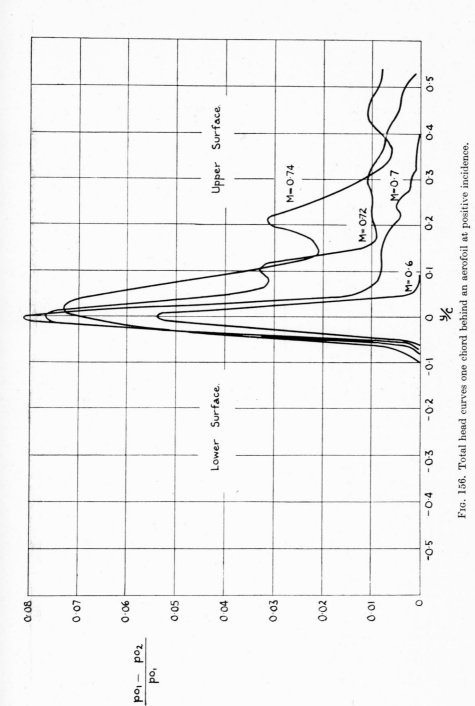

Fig. 156. Total head curves one chord behind an aerofoil at positive incidence.

stream Mach number becomes greater than unity. Since, however, in this case the wake becomes very wide the method is laborious, and since over much of the wake the total head is nearly equal to that of the undisturbed stream only poor accuracy is obtained.

## § 33. Manometers

Pressures in high-speed flow are usually required as absolute measurements, but to simplify the manometers and to reduce the pressure differences to be measured an intermediate datum is generally used—for example, the total head or static pressure of the undisturbed stream. Vertical-tube manometers with mercury, water, or alcohol as the gauging liquid are most common. Mercury is difficult to keep clean, but water and alcohol are not satisfactory at very low absolute pressure because they tend to boil or to liberate dissolved air. Other liquids with densities up to about 3 have been used, but they usually have some disadvantages such as chemical instability or high viscosity. A typical multi-tube manometer† containing mercury is shown in Fig. 157, with arrangements for adjusting the reservoir zero and for 'freezing' the readings by means of a clamp on the pressure connexions at the top.

Various special types of liquid manometer have been used to enable readings to be recorded automatically, such as a manometric balance in which the displacement of mercury in a U-tube is weighed on a self-balancing steelyard,‡ or manometers in which a photo-electric follower is used to indicate the level.§ Photographic recording has been used to give aerofoil pressure distribution curves which can be integrated directly to give lift and pitching moment.‖

Capsules or diaphragms in which the force or displacement is measured mechanically or electrically are sometimes used instead of liquid manometers. These are compact and can be designed to measure rapidly fluctuating pressures. An application is described below.

## § 34. Mach meters

In a subsonic wind tunnel it is convenient to use an instrument which gives a direct reading of Mach number instead of calculating

† Holder, loc. cit. on p. 509.

‡ Thompson and Mair, loc. cit. on p. 482.

§ Klein, 'Micromanometers', *A.V.A. Monogr.* D.2, *Rep. Aero. Res. Coun.*, No. 11,391 (1947).

‖ Göthert and Matt, loc. cit. on p. 479.

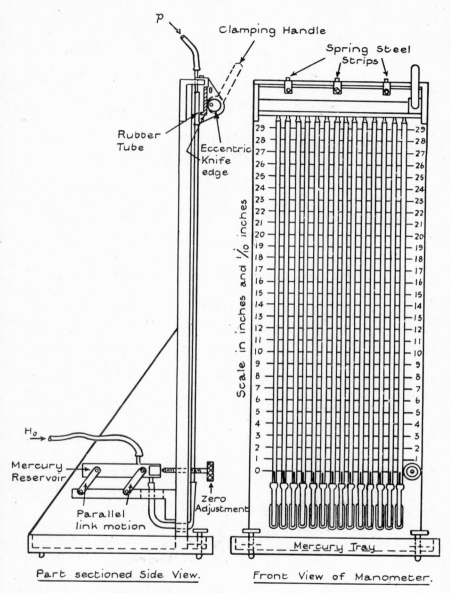

P

Clamping Handle

Spring steel
Strips

Rubber
Tube

Eccentric
Knife
edge

Scale in inches and ¹/₁₀ inches

$H_o$

Mercury
Reservoir

Zero
Adjustment

Parallel
link motion

Mercury Tray

Part sectioned Side View.

Front View of Manometer.

FIG. 157. A multi-tube mercury manometer.

this quantity from separate measurements of total head and static pressure. Instruments called Mach meters or Mach-number gauges are sometimes used for this purpose. They are seldom used in supersonic tunnels because the Mach number is then determined by the shape of the nozzle and cannot usually be adjusted except by replacing the nozzle by one of different design.

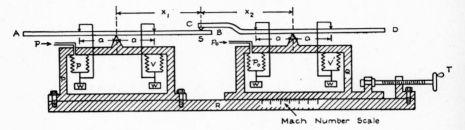

FIG. 158. A Mach-number gauge.

Equation (58) shows that the Mach number is an explicit function of the ratio of the static pressure $p$ to the total head $p_0$ and the purpose of a Mach meter is, therefore, to indicate this ratio. Suitable instruments are described by Thompson and Mair,[†] by Liepmann,[‡] by Schaefer,[§] and by Giles.[||]

The apparatus shown in Fig. 158 has been used at the N.P.L.[††] It consists of two balance arms $AB$ and $CD$ pivoted on the frames $P$ and $Q$ and connected by a knife edge at $S$. The distance $x_1$ may be adjusted by sliding the frame $Q$ along the bed plate $R$ by turning the hand wheel $T$. Four bellows $p$, $p_0$, $V$, and $V'$ are connected to the arms by stirrups and the weights $W$ are used to ensure that the loads on the stirrups are always in a downwards direction. The interior of the bellows $p$ is connected to the static pressure $p$ of the undisturbed stream in the working section and that of the bellows $p_0$ to the total head $p_0$. The bellows $V$ and $V'$ are evacuated and the whole gauge is subject externally to atmospheric pressure. It is easily shown by equating forces at $S$ that under balanced conditions $x_1/x_2 = p/p_0$ and, since $x_2$ is constant, a scale of Mach number may

† Loc. cit. on p. 482.

‡ Liepmann and Ashkanas, loc. cit. on p. 503;

§ Loc. cit. on p. 559.

|| 'The N.P.L. Mach number gauge', *Rep. Memor. Aero. Res. Coun.*, No. 2,131 (1945).

†† Beavan and Holder, 'Recent developments in high-speed research in the Aerodynamics Division of the N.P.L.', *J. Roy. Aero. Soc.* **54** (1950), 545.

be appended to a scale measuring the shift of $Q$ along $R$ for balance. In practice the position of $Q$ relative to $R$ is adjusted to correspond to the required Mach number and the tunnel speed is regulated to keep the arms in balance. Balance is indicated by an electrical device.

## § 35. The measurement of temperature

It is difficult to make a direct measurement of the static temperature because, since reheating to a temperature only a little below the stagnation value takes place in the boundary layer of a body placed in the flow, the thermometer would have to move with the stream. The static temperature could be found by measuring two other properties of the state of the fluid (e.g. the pressure and density), but this is difficult in practice, and the static temperature is best estimated by measuring the static pressure, total head, and stagnation temperature, and using eqn. (60).

Instruments for the measurement of stagnation temperature have been described by Eckert,[†] Wimmer,[‡] Franz,[§] and others, the most successful arrangements consisting of thermojunctions placed in the mouths of pitot tubes. To obtain accurate readings it is necessary to ensure that the rate of heat transfer to the thermojunction is large compared with the heat lost by the thermojunction by conduction, convection and radiation. The heat transfer to the thermojunction may be raised by placing it in a slow airstream (the speed being so low that the stagnation and static temperatures are sensibly equal) rather than in a region of stagnant air, and the response of the thermojunction to heat addition may be increased by making it of small thermal capacity. The heat losses from the junction may be reduced by shielding it against radiation, by making it of small surface area, and of metals of low thermal conductivity (an iron-constantan junction being preferable, for example, to a copper-constantan junction).

An instrument[§] incorporating these features is shown in Fig. 159 and consists of a thermojunction placed at the downstream end of a diffuser which is made of a thermal insulating material and pointed

---

† 'Temperature recording in high-speed gases', *Tech. Memor. Nat. Adv. Comm. Aero.*, No. 983 (1941).

‡ 'Temperature recording', ibid. No. 967 (1941).

§ 'Pressure and temperature measurements in supercharger investigations', ibid. No. 953 (1941).

into the wind. A small flow takes place past the thermojunction and out through a number of exit holes in the walls of the instrument.

In most wind tunnels it is necessary to arrange the design so that the stagnation temperature is roughly uniform across the intake. It is then usual, for most tests, to take a mean value and to assume that this remains unchanged in the working section. It is not usually

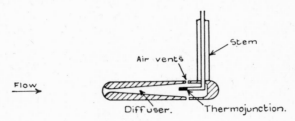

FIG. 159. A pitot-thermojunction.

necessary to know the stagnation temperature in order to determine the Mach number, the loads on the model, or the quantity $\frac{1}{2}\rho U^2$ as these can be found (see eqns. (58) to (63)) from pressure measurements. A knowledge of the stagnation temperature is, however, required in the determination of Reynolds number and in certain special tests.

When the temperatures at the surface of a body are to be measured it is usual to bury thermojunctions in the surface as described by Hilton and Wingham† and by Cope and Thurston.‡ For measurements of this type the material from which the body is made must be a good thermal insulator, and the scale of the model should be as large as possible so that the temperature gradients are small.

## § 36. Yawmeters

Several different instruments are available for the determination of wind direction, and the choice depends mainly on the nature and on the Mach number of the experiment which is to be made.

*Aerofoil yawmeter.* When the size of the instrument is unimportant, a symmetrical aerofoil may be used as a yawmeter. Two surface pressure holes are provided opposite each other, one in the upper and one in the lower surface. The incidence is adjusted until the

† 'Surface temperatures on an aerofoil at subsonic speeds', *Rep. Memor. Aero. Res. Coun.*, No. 2,230 (1946).
‡ Unpublished.

pressures at these two holes are equal, and the chord line is then taken to be along the wind direction. The position of the pressure holes along the chord is chosen so that, at the Mach number used, the pressures are sensitive to incidence. For an aerofoil of E.C. 1250 section (the front half being a semi-ellipse whose minor axis is 12 per cent. of the major axis) which has been used at high subsonic

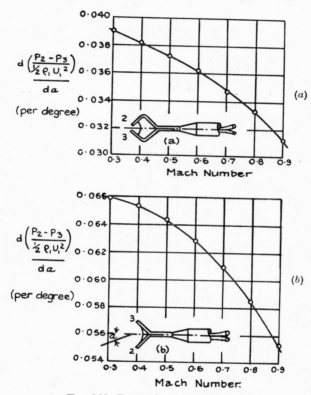

Fig. 160. Bent-tube yawmeters.

speeds at the N.P.L.[†] it was found that the most suitable position for the pressure holes was 0·15 of the chord from the leading edge. A wedge with one pressure hole in each surface has been used[‡] when the flow is supersonic.

*Bent-tube yawmeters.* Two different bent-tube yawmeters are shown in Fig. 160, which also shows the effect of Mach number on the

† Holder, loc. cit. on p 509.
‡ Ferri, *Elements of Aerodynamics of Supersonic Flows*, Macmillan (1949), p. 97.

sensitivity.† The incidence of the instrument is adjusted until the pressures at the two tubes become equal, and the axis of symmetry is then taken to be along the flow. The yaw head shown in Fig. 160 (a) is usually to be preferred to that shown in Fig. 160 (b) because the distance between the mouths of the two tubes is smaller and a reading is therefore attained at what is more closely a point in the

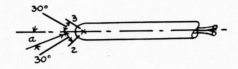

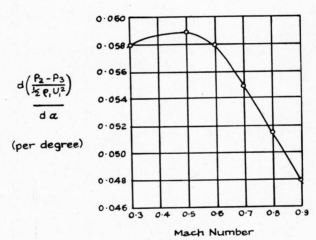

$$d\left(\dfrac{p_2 - p_3}{\frac{1}{2}\rho_1 U_1^2}\right)$$

$$\overline{d\,a}$$

(per degree)

FIG. 161. A hemispherical yawmeter.

flow. The sensitivity of the instrument shown in Fig. 160 (b) is, however, nearly twice that of the other yaw head.

*Hemispherical and cylindrical yawmeters.* A hemispherical yaw head and a typical calibration curve‡ are shown in Fig. 161. The method of operation is the same as for the instruments described above, and the sensitivity is comparable with that of the bent-tube instrument shown in Fig. 160 (b). The hemisphere has the advantages of being robust and capable of manufacture on a small scale so that the disturbance which is introduced into the flow is minimized.

† Holder, loc. cit. on p. 509; Bäuerle, loc. cit. on p. 554.
‡ Bäuerle, loc. cit. on p. 554.

A circular cylinder mounted with its axis perpendicular to the stream has sometimes been used instead of a hemisphere.[†]

Other types of yawmeter are described by Todd.[‡]

## § 37. Direct force measurements

*Balances.* The differences of design between the balances of low-speed and of high-speed wind tunnels arise mainly from the facts that in a high-speed tunnel the loads on the model under test and the interference effects of the model supports are usually greater than in a low-speed tunnel. Since the pressure in the working section is seldom atmospheric, either the balance of a high-speed tunnel (if external) must be enclosed in an airtight chamber in which the pressure is equal to that at the working section or special seals must be fitted where the model supports enter the tunnel.

In subsonic tunnels the model is sometimes held on struts and the arrangement of the external balance[§] is then often similar to that of a low-speed tunnel. For tests on complete models at high subsonic and supersonic speeds it is, however, more usual to support the model on a sting at the rear since this reduces the interference of the support on the flow round the model.

A sting balance which is arranged[||] so that the loads are measured outside the airstream is shown diagrammatically in Fig. 162. The sting $A$ is mounted on the strut $B$ which is exposed to the airstream and is in the form of a circular arc centred at the point on the model about which the incidence is to be changed and the pitching moment measured. The strut, $B$, is connected to a frame outside the airstream, and supported freely by three steel leaf springs, two of which, $C$ and $D$, are mounted vertically and the third, $E$, mounted horizontally. The loads on the model are transmitted to these springs and cause them to deflect slightly, the deflexions being measured by the change of inductance of the pairs of coils $F$, $G$, and $H$. The lift on the model is measured by the horizontal spring, and the drag and moment by the sum and difference of the deflexions of the vertical springs.

In order to determine the contribution of the loads on the strut, and the interference effect on the flow round the model, the sting $A$ is split into two halves one of which is normally attached to the

† Holder, loc. cit. on p. 509; Bäuerle, loc. cit. on p. 554.
‡ Loc. cit. on p. 482.
§ Thompson and Mair, loc. cit. on p. 482.
|| Owen, loc. cit. on p. 481.

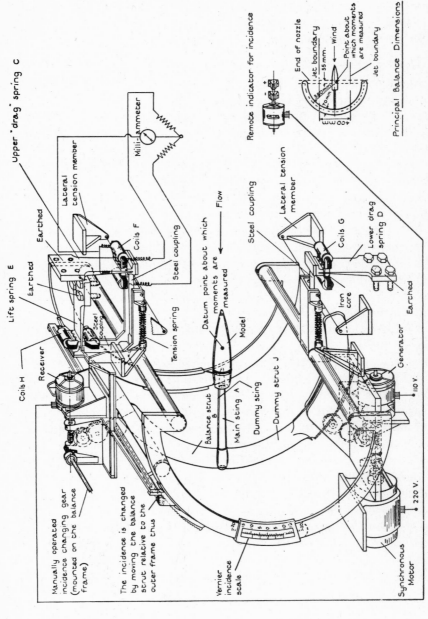

FIG. 162. Principle of the lift, drag, and pitching moment balance of the 40 cm. × 40 cm. W.V.A. supersonic tunnel.

model and to the strut $B$ and the other to a dummy strut $J$ only. This dummy strut is not connected to the main strut or to the balance frame. The true forces on the model are obtained by taking the difference between the forces measured with the model on the main sting and the balance strut $B$, and those measured with the dummy sting attached to the balance strut and with the model and the main sting attached to the dummy strut.

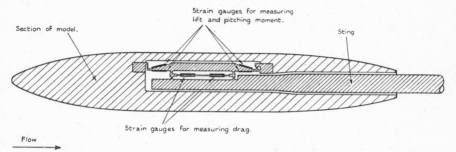

FIG. 163. Internal 3-component strain gauge unit for a sting-mounted model.

The incidence is changed manually by moving the main strut $B$ relative to the outer frame, and the dummy strut is simultaneously moved by means of a Selsyn coupling so that the gap between the two struts is kept constant.

The balance was used on the 40 cm. × 40 cm. intermittent tunnel at the W.V.A. It had the advantage that the recordings could be taken more quickly than if a null method had been used, and that by the use of springs the balance was made sufficiently robust to withstand the loads which occurred when the quick-acting valve connecting the tunnel to the vacuum reservoir was opened.

Fig. 163 shows a 3-component strain-gauge unit fitted inside a sting-mounted model. The loads on the model are transmitted to the sting through this unit, which is fitted with strain gauges by which the strain in the steel members can be measured as a change in electrical resistance. Suitable circuits connected to measuring instruments outside the tunnel give direct readings of lift, pitching moment, and drag.

The sting is mounted on an incidence-changing gear of the same general type as that shown in Fig. 162, but the fact that the balance is inside the model makes the readings independent of airloads on the supporting strut.

*Oscillation tests.* Measurements of the aerodynamic damping of a model performing pitching oscillations in a supersonic airstream have been made on a two-dimensional aerofoil at the N.P.L.† and a model projectile at the W.V.A.‡ The technique has been to mount the model so that it can oscillate in pitch either freely or under the constraint of torsion rods, and to observe the rate at which a displacement of the model from its equilibrium position decays or grows. A high-speed camera was used to determine the attitude of the model in the W.V.A. experiments, and a photo-electric device was employed at the N.P.L. Results obtained in the N.P.L. experiments are mentioned in Chap. IX.

## SECTION IV

## VISUALIZATION AND PHOTOGRAPHY OF FLUID MOTION

### § 38. Wool tufts

The use of wool tufts at low speeds is discussed in Vol. I (1938), chap. vi. The technique has been used at high subsonic speeds in the R.A.E. high-speed tunnel, an example of the type of photograph obtained being given in Plate 11. This shows the flow close to the surface of a swept-back wing at Mach numbers of 0·88 and 0·92. The tufts reveal the curvature of the streamlines close to the surface of the wing, and the disturbances created by the shock waves which are present. Since wool is too thick, it is frequently the practice to use nylon tufts for high-speed work.

### § 39. Methods depending on changes of refractive index

The refractive index $n$ of a particular gas is a function of the density $\rho$ and is given by the equation of L. Lorenz and H. A. Lorentz.§ For refractive indices close to unity this equation may be

---

† Bratt and Chinneck, 'Measurements of mid-chord pitching moment derivatives at high speeds', *Rep. Memor. Aero. Res. Coun.*, No. 2,680 (1947).

‡ Owen, loc. cit. on p. 536.

§ L. Lorenz, 'Über die Refractionsconstante', *Wied. Ann.* **11** (1880), 70; H. A. Lorentz, 'Über die Beziehung zwischen der Fortpflanzungsgeschwindigkeit des Lichtes und der Körperdichte', ibid. **9** (1880), 641.

PLATE 11

$M = 0.88$     $M = 0.92$

Surface-tuft photographs of a swept-back wing. R.A.E. 101, 10 per cent. thick section. $\alpha = 4°$. $C_L \approx 0.35$

written with sufficient accuracy in the form suggested by Gladstone and Dale:†

$$\frac{n-1}{\rho} = K, \tag{75}$$

where $K$ is a constant for a particular gas.

Thus the density changes which occur in the motion of a compressible fluid round a body are accompanied by changes of refractive index which may be observed by an optical technique. If this technique is such that the refractive index can be measured quantitatively either absolutely or in relation to some datum value (e.g. that of the undisturbed stream), the corresponding absolute or relative density can be calculated. Knowing the local density it is then possible in many cases to deduce the other local conditions either from a knowledge of the conditions at the intake of the wind-tunnel and that the flow is substantially homentropic, or by making supplementary local pressure measurements, or by allowing for the changes which take place through shock waves upstream of the measuring station.

Although the principal use of the methods is for the visualization of flows at high Mach numbers where there are comparatively large density changes, some of them have been used with success to observe the small density changes which are present in the flow in atmospheric tunnels working at speeds as low as 100 ft./sec. The methods have also been used to observe artificial refractive-index changes produced by introducing into the flow filaments or puffs of a gas whose refractive index differs from that of the general stream. This may be done by introducing a gas such as carbon dioxide into the wind tunnel or by heating a filament or a small volume of the airstream (see Vol. I (1938), chap. vi) or, in the case of a high-speed tunnel, by observing‡ the wake of a wire placed across the flow ahead of the working section. It must, however, be remembered that although filament lines or particle paths may be observed by the use of artificial changes of refractive index, this is not the case when the method depends on the natural changes of refractive index.

If an optical disturbance is placed in a ray of light falling on to a screen, the time of arrival at the screen of a point on a light wave'

---

† 'Researches on the refraction, dispersion, and sensitiveness of liquids', *Philos. Trans.* **153** (1863), 317.

‡ Valensi and Pruden, 'Observations on sharp-nosed profiles at supersonic speed' *Rep. Memor. Aero. Res. Coun.*, No. 2,482 (1947).

will be changed because the velocity of light $c$ is related to the refractive index $n$ by the equation

$$c = \frac{1}{n}c^*, \tag{76}$$

where $c^*$ is the velocity *in vacuo*. In the interferometer technique due to Mach[†] the refractive index in the disturbance is obtained by measuring this change in relation to the time of arrival of a point on a second wave which does not pass through the disturbance.

If in the disturbance there is a gradient of refractive index normal to the light ray, the ray will be bent and the deflexion is a measure of the first derivative of the density with respect to distance (i.e. of the density gradient) and may be observed by one of a number of so-called schlieren techniques. The most popular is that due to Toepler.[‡]

Should the refractive index gradient normal to the ray vary, the deviations of adjacent rays will differ so that they will converge or diverge giving increased or decreased illumination on the screen. These changes of illumination are observed in a particularly simple schlieren system termed the direct-shadow or shadowgraph and usually attributed to Dvořák.[§] On certain assumptions it may be shown that the observations obtained with a direct-shadow apparatus are a function of the second derivative of the density, but except in special cases it is difficult to measure the density quantitatively by the method.

Since the interferometer, the Toepler-schlieren, and the direct-shadow methods give observations which depend on the density and on different derivatives of the density, the three methods are complementary rather than alternative, each showing up features of the flow which may escape detection by the others. Of the three methods, the only one which has been used extensively for quantitative density measurements is the interferometer, and the main use of the Toepler-schlieren and direct-shadow methods is at present to show the positions and forms of major density changes such as those occurring in shock waves and wakes. Used in this fashion these two methods

[†] 'Über ein Interferenzrefraktometer', *S. B. Wien. Akad.* **98** (1889), 1318.

[‡] 'Optische Studien nach der Methode der Schlierenbeobachtung', *Poggendorf's Ann. Phys. Chem.* **131** (1867), 33.

[§] 'Über eine neue einfache Art der Schlierenbeobachtung', *Wiedemann's Ann. Phys. Chem.* **9** (1880), 502.

require only comparatively simple apparatus and have contributed largely to the knowledge of the physical nature of many phenomena of high-speed flow.

Optical methods have the inherent advantages that observations may be made without producing spurious disturbances by the introduction of exploring apparatus into the flow, and that because of the speed of photographic materials the inertia is extremely low, thus enabling unsteady flows to be examined. The methods have the additional advantage that they enable a relatively large area of the flow to be explored rapidly.

Because of the difficulties of interpreting the results, the methods are usually confined to the examination of two-dimensional and axially-symmetrical flows. This is often a severe limitation since at high Mach number the effects of aspect ratio and planform are very important in aerodynamics.

## § 40. The interferometer methods

It is well known that interference can occur if the light from two sources emitting waves of equal amplitude and of constant phase difference† is combined under suitable conditions. Thus if in a medium of constant refractive index the difference between the distances of two point-sources $S'$ and $S''$ (Fig. 164) from a point $P$ on the screen at which the waves are combined is a whole number of wave-lengths, the waves at $P$ will be in phase and produce a region of reinforced illumination. Conversely, if the path difference is an odd number of half wave-lengths the waves at $P$ will be out of phase and darkness will result. With the notation of Fig. 164, if $s$ and $y$ are small compared with $d$, the path difference may be written with sufficient accuracy as $ys/d$, and since the distance $b$ between successive regions of reinforcement or of darkness corresponds to a path difference of one wave-length $\lambda$,

$$b = \frac{\lambda d}{s}. \tag{77}$$

Since this equation does not contain $y$ it shows that the regions of reinforcement or of darkness are uniformly spaced along $OP$ and, moreover, since the path difference is approximately constant along lines on the screen perpendicular to $OP$, a number of uniformly

† This requirement of coherent light sources can only be met in practice by splitting the light from a single source into two beams.

spaced light and dark bands (interference bands or fringes) are formed
running perpendicular to $OP$. In practice the dark fringes appear
narrower and are used for measurements.

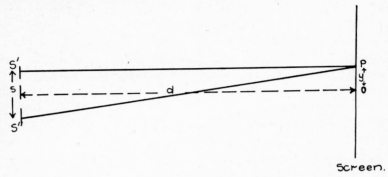

FIG. 164. Double-slit interferometer.

The formation of interference fringes by this process may be understood by a diagram (Fig. 165) due to Schardin.[†] Here the light rays
coming from $S'$ and $S''$ and converging towards $P$ are shown at the
sides. The waves reinforce at the projections (shown dotted) of the
full lines drawn through the wave crests perpendicular to the rays.
Similarly the projections of the intersections of the lines drawn
through the troughs of one wave train with the lines through the
crests of the other represent regions of darkness. If the length of
the path of one ray is increased (e.g. by moving $S''$ away from $P$)
by an amount $\delta q$, then the positions of the crests of this wave train
will shift by an equal amount (Fig. 166) and the corresponding shift
$\delta p$ of the interference fringes is given by

$$\frac{\delta q}{\lambda} = \frac{\delta p}{b}. \tag{78}$$

The same effect could, however, be produced by placing in the
original ray from $S''$ a length $\delta z$ of a medium of refractive index $n$
since by eqn. (76) this is equivalent to an increase of the light path
of $\dfrac{n-n_0}{n_0}\,\delta z$ in the original medium of refractive index $n_0$. Thus from
eqn. (78)

$$\frac{\delta p}{b} = \frac{1}{\lambda_0}\frac{n-n_0}{n_0}\,\delta z, \tag{79}$$

† 'Theorie und Anwendung des Mach–Zehnderschen Interferenz-Refraktometer',
*Z. Instrumentenkunde*, **53** (1933), 396; *Transl. Roy. Aircraft Estb.*, No. 79 (1946).

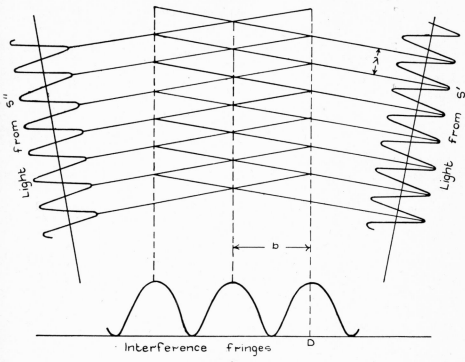

Interference fringes

FIG. 165. Formation of interference fringes.

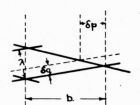

FIG. 166. Effect of change
of optical path.

and since $\dfrac{\lambda}{c} = \dfrac{\lambda^*}{c^*}$ where $\lambda^*$ is the wave-length *in vacuo*

$$\frac{\delta p}{b} = \frac{1}{\lambda^*}(n-n_0)\,\delta z$$

or

$$\frac{p}{b} = \frac{1}{\lambda^*}\int (n-n_0)\,dz, \qquad (80)$$

where the integral is taken along the length of the optical disturbance. Thus the local refractive-index change may be derived
from a measurement of the fringe shift if the relationship between
$n$ and $z$ is known. This requirement usually restricts the method to
two-dimensional or to axially-symmetrical flow, and even in these
cases it is necessary to assume as in the other methods discussed
below that the departure of the light ray in the disturbance from its
original rectilinear path is infinitesimal.

A double-slit interferometer of the type described above has been
used by Oswatitsch[†] to measure the density in a Laval nozzle giving
a Mach number of about 1·6. The technique was to pass one ray
through the nozzle and the other through a space behind the nozzle
wall in which the density could be given a suitable known value;
the interference fringes were then observed with a microscope.
Oswatitsch suggests that for explorations close to the surface of an
aerofoil a space inside the model could be used to pass the ray.
Since the dimensions of the exploring ray may be very small, the
method seems to be particularly suitable for detailed explorations
in a small area of flow such as in a boundary-layer.

The double-slit interferometer is, however, unsuitable for the
examination of a large field since the light beam is necessarily of
small cross-section and because the two beams need to be close
together. The interferometer which has been used most widely for
wind-tunnel measurements is, therefore, of different design. It is
the Mach–Zehnder instrument[‡] sketched in Fig. 167.

Here light from a monochromatic source[§] $S$ is converted into a
parallel beam by a lens and is then split into two mutually perpendicular beams by the semi-reflecting plate $P_1$. These two beams
are then reflected by the two plane mirrors $P_2$ and $P_3$ before being

---

† 'The measurement of the density in an airstream by means of a double-slit
interferometer', F.B. 1285; L.F.A. Volkenrode Transl. No. 35; German documentary
centre G.D.C. 10/1165T.

‡ Schardin, loc. cit. on p. 582; Zobel, 'Advances in optical methods of determining
air flow', Publ. BIOS/Gp2/AEC No. 2; Pack; 'Investigations of the flow past finite
wedges of 20° and 40° apex angle at subsonic and supersonic speeds using a Mach–
Zehnder interferometer', *Rep. Memor. Aero. Res. Coun.*, No. 2,321 (1946); Ladenburg,
Van Voorhis, and Winckler, 'Study of shock waves by interferometry', *Progr. Rep.* I.
*Princetown Univ. Station Div.* 2 (1944) and *Progr. Rep.* II (1944); Hutton, loc. cit. on
p. 551; Groth, 'On the evaluation of the density field at high subsonic speeds
measured with an interferometer', W.M. 2059; Weyl, 'Analytical methods in optical
examination of supersonic flow', *Rep. NAVORD* 211–45 (1945).

§ The conditions which arise when the source is not monochromatic are discussed
by Schardin, loc. cit. on p. 582.

reunited at a second semi-reflecting plate $P_4$ and passing on to a screen or a photographic plate $A$. If the instrument is set up with the

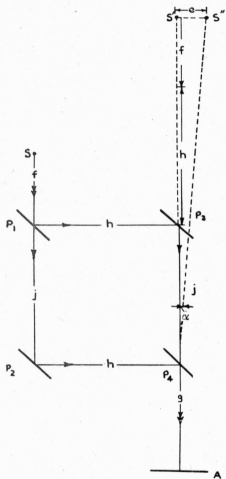

FIG. 167. The Mach–Zehnder interferometer.

plates and mirrors at 45° to the light paths and with $P_1 P_3$ equal to $P_2 P_4$ and $P_1 P_2$ equal to $P_3 P_4$, the image of the source will be at $S'$ whether it is due to light which has come via $P_2$ or via $P_3$. If the plate $P_4$ is then tilted through an angle $\alpha$, a new image of the source will be formed at $S''$ by the light coming via $P_2$ and interference can

I

occur between this image and $S'$. The fringe spacing $b$ on the screen is given by

$$b = \frac{\lambda(f+h+j+g)}{e} = \frac{\lambda(f+h+j+g)}{\alpha(f+h+j)},\qquad(81)$$

and if an optical disturbance is placed in one light path a fringe shift will be produced in accordance with eqn. (80) from which the refractive index may be determined.

An alternative method of setting up is possible. Here the apparatus is arranged so that, in the absence of the disturbance, the two beams are in phase and the illumination on the screen is uniform. The fringes which are formed when the disturbance is put into the beam are then such that the distance between successive fringes corresponds to a refractive-index change giving a fringe shift $p/b$ of unity. The fringes are, therefore, under these conditions curves of constant refractive index (eqn. (80)). In general, however, this method is less accurate than the fringe-displacement method described above.

In general, it is possible to identify a particular fringe only if the distorted fringes follow each other in monotonic sequence along lines perpendicular to the undisturbed fringes. Thus it is necessary to ensure that the combination of interferometer and wind tunnel is such that the fringes are not so numerous as to become crowded or to cross each other because of the refraction effect which is present if the density is not uniform (see p. 587). The number of fringes which are present must not, however, be too small or the accuracy will be low. Thus it is desirable to design the tunnel and interferometer as a single piece of apparatus; even if this is done it may still be difficult to interpret the fringe pattern in some regions of intense density change. In order to allow for the change of optical path due to the change of free-stream density when the tunnel is run up to speed, it is sometimes the practice to include a compensating chamber in the arm of the instrument opposite to that passing through the tunnel. This chamber has glass ends exactly similar to the side plates of the working section and its width is equal to that of the working section; the density inside is adjusted to approximate to that in the working section either by connecting the two with a pressure lead or by varying the pressure independently with a vacuum pump.

In practice difficulties arise from vibration and from the effects of temperature changes. These may be minimized by suitably designing

PLATE 12

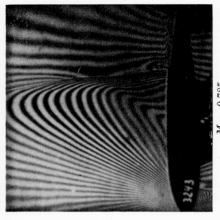

$M = 0.785$

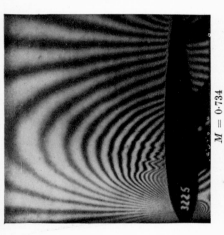

$M = 0.734$

(a) Density contour photographs

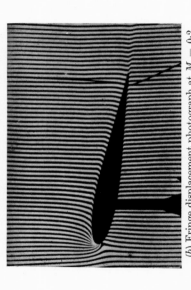

(b) Fringe displacement photograph at $M = 0.2$

$M = 0.665$

Interferometer photographs of the flow round an aerofoil

the structure of the instrument, by lagging it from the effects of temperature and sound, and by supporting it very rigidly or on vibration absorbers. The optical components must be manufactured to a very high order of accuracy, the departure of the optical surfaces from the plane being small compared with the wave-length of light.

Examples of the type of photograph obtained with the density-contour method of setting up the interferometer are shown in Plate 12 (a), where the flow is that round an aerofoil at high subsonic free-stream Mach number. The pressure distributions calculated[†] from these photographs are compared with those measured directly by surface pressure plotting in Fig. 168.

An example of a fringe-displacement photograph is given in Plate 12 (b), where the flow is that round an aerofoil at low Mach number.

Further examples[‡] of interferometer photographs are shown in Plate 10 (c) and Plate 10 (d) (p. 555) and of the derived pressure distribution in Fig. 169.

Details of the procedure which is used to obtain the pressure distribution from interferometer records are given by Groth,[†] by Hutton,[§] by Schardin,[||] by Weyl,[††] and by Ladenburg[‡‡]; details of the construction of the apparatus are given by Hutton,[§] and the use of the method in the observation of unsteady flows is described by Zobel.[§§]

## § 41. The schlieren methods

The schlieren methods depend on the deflexion of a ray of light from its undisturbed path when it passes through a medium in which there is a component of the gradient of refractive index normal to the ray. The curvature of the ray is proportional to the refractive index gradient in the direction normal to the ray, and if the $z$-axis is taken in the direction of the undisturbed ray, the curvatures in the $xz$ and $yz$ planes respectively are given by

$$\frac{\partial^2 x}{\partial z^2} = \frac{1}{n}\frac{\partial n}{\partial x}, \qquad (82)$$

$$\frac{\partial^2 y}{\partial z^2} = \frac{1}{n}\frac{\partial n}{\partial y}, \qquad (83)$$

† Groth, loc. cit. on p. 584.
§ Loc. cit. on p. 551.
†† Loc. cit. on p. 584.
§§ Loc. cit. on p. 584.

‡ Pack, loc. cit. on p. 584.
|| Loc. cit. on p. 582.
‡‡ Loc. cit. on p. 584.

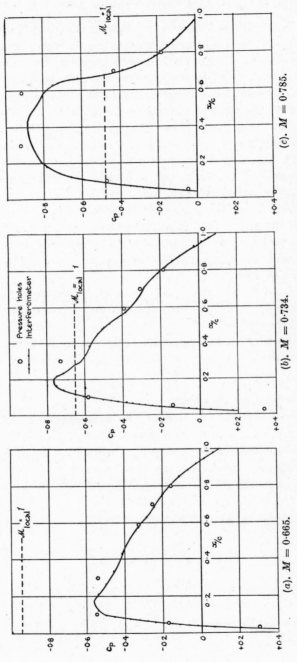

(a). $M = 0.665$.

(b). $M = 0.734$.

(c). $M = 0.785$.

Fig. 168. Comparison of pressures obtained from interferometer and measured directly.

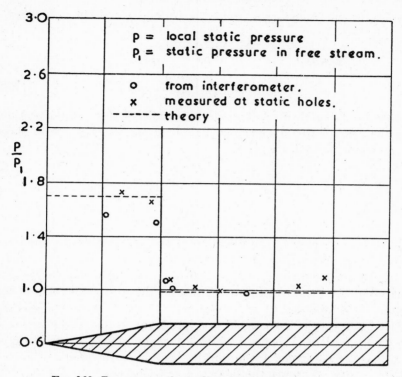

FIG. 169. Pressures on the surface of the wedge at $M = 2 \cdot 0$.

and if the total angular deflexions in the $xz$ and $yz$ planes are denoted by $\epsilon'_x$ and $\epsilon'_y$ respectively

$$\epsilon'_x = \int \frac{1}{n} \frac{\partial n}{\partial x} \, dz, \tag{84}$$

$$\epsilon'_y = \int \frac{1}{n} \frac{\partial n}{\partial y} \, dz. \tag{85}$$

If the optical disturbance is in the working section of a wind tunnel the ray of light will be deflected on leaving the tunnel so that

$$n \sin \epsilon' = n_0 \sin \epsilon, \tag{86}$$

where $n_0$ is the refractive index of the air surrounding the tunnel and $n$ that in the working section. Thus, for small angles, the final values for the deflexions $\epsilon_x$ and $\epsilon_y$ measured beyond the tunnel are

$$\epsilon_x = \frac{1}{n_0} \int \frac{\partial n}{\partial x}\, dz, \qquad (87)$$

$$\epsilon_y = \frac{1}{n_0} \int \frac{\partial n}{\partial y}\, dz, \qquad (88)$$

where the integrals are taken over the width of the working section. In the case of two-dimensional flow in a tunnel of width $L$ these expressions become simply

$$\epsilon_x = \frac{L}{n_0} \frac{\partial n}{\partial x}, \qquad (89)$$

$$\epsilon_y = \frac{L}{n_0} \frac{\partial n}{\partial y}, \qquad (90)$$

the deflexion being in the direction of the refractive-index gradient (i.e. towards the region of highest density).

A typical apparatus is sketched in Fig. 170. Here the source $S$ is placed at the focus of the lens $L_1$ so that the working section of the tunnel is illuminated by a parallel beam of light. A second lens $L_2$, placed beyond the working section, produces an image of the source in its focal plane $K$ beyond which a camera lens $L_3$ is used to give an image of the model in the working section on the screen or photographic plate $Q$. Since the light is parallel between $L_1$ and $L_2$, that from each point in the $(x, y)$-plane may be considered to give a separate image of the source in the focal plane of $L_2$. If there is no gradient of refractive index (or if the gradient is uniform) over the working section, the individual images of the source will coincide, but if the gradient in a small area differs from that in the rest of the field the deflexion of the light $\epsilon$ will cause the corresponding image in the plane $K$ to be moved by an amount given with sufficient accuracy by $f_2\epsilon$, where $f_2$ is the focal length of $L_2$. Several methods may then be used to measure the displacement of the image of the source.

*The Toepler method.* In the Toepler[†] method the displacement of the image of the source corresponding to the deflexion of the light passing through a particular point in the field is converted into a change of illumination of the image of this point on the screen $Q$. A rectangular source is used and a knife-edge (often termed the 'cut-off') is placed at the focal plane $K$. The edge is adjusted so

† Toepler, loc. cit. on p. 580.

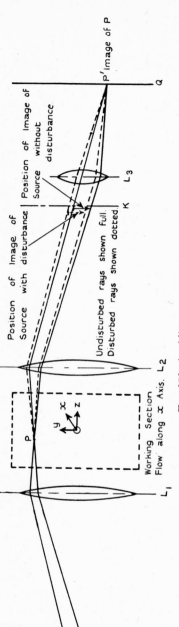

FIG. 170. A schlieren apparatus.

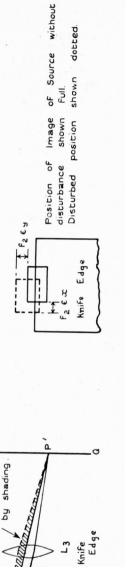

FIG. 171. The Toepler method.

that, in the absence of the optical disturbance, part of the light from the image of the source is cut off from the camera lens $L_3$ so that the illumination on the screen is reduced uniformly. If when the optical disturbance is introduced part of the image of the source is displaced as shown in Fig. 171, the illumination of the corresponding part of the image on the screen $Q$ will decrease or increase by an amount proportional to $\epsilon_y f_2$ according to whether the deflexion is towards or away from the opaque part of the knife-edge. Displacement of the image of the source parallel to the knife edge produces no effect on the screen so that the edge must be set up perpendicular to the direction in which density gradients are to be observed. Thus for shock-wave observations the edge is usually placed in a direction roughly parallel to the shock front and for boundary-layer observations it is placed parallel to the surface of the body.

In order to obtain quantitative information from the Toepler apparatus a photometric analysis of the image on the screen is necessary. This presents considerable difficulties, particularly if the flow is unsteady and photography is necessary, because the sensitivity of the photographic material is then involved. Also, the effects of diffraction at the knife edge may lead to difficulties, particularly if high sensitivity is required.

Plates 13 (a) and (b) are photographs of the flow round a $12\frac{1}{2}$ per cent. thick double-wedge aerofoil at a Mach number of 1·6. In the first photograph the knife-edge was perpendicular to the chord so that the components of the density gradient parallel to the chord of the aerofoil are observed. The positive directions of these components are sketched in the diagram and, the deflexion of the light being in this direction (eqn. (90)), the shock waves appear as regions of decreased illumination and the expansions as highlights. In the second photograph the knife-edge was parallel to the chord and the positive directions of the components of the density gradients perpendicular to the chord are shown. In this case the images of the shock waves above the model are regions of increased illumination and those of the shock waves below the model regions of decreased illumination; the converse is true for the images of the expansions. The density gradient changes sign in the middle of the wake, and one half of its image is of high and the other of low illumination. Further examples of photographs taken with the Toepler apparatus are shown in Plates 14 (a) and (b) taken with the knife-edge parallel

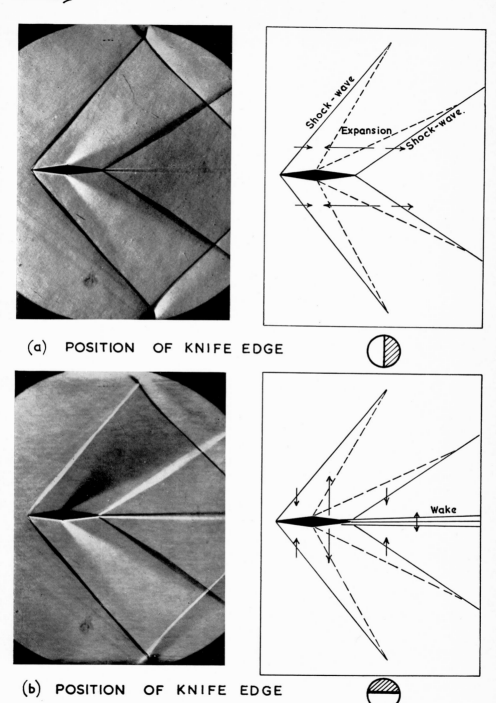

(a) POSITION OF KNIFE EDGE

(b) POSITION OF KNIFE EDGE

The arrows show the positive directions of the components of the density gradient normal to the knife edge

Schlieren photographs of a $12\frac{1}{2}$ per cent. double-wedge aerofoil at $M = 1\cdot6$

PLATE 14

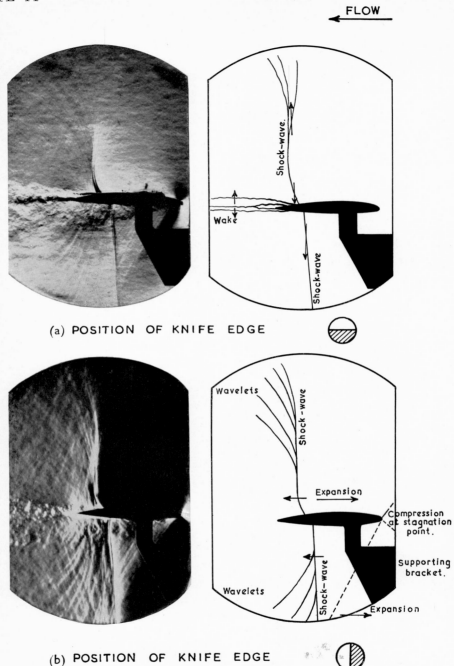

FLOW

(a) POSITION OF KNIFE EDGE

(b) POSITION OF KNIFE EDGE

The arrows show the positive directions of the components of the density gradient normal to the knife edge

Schlieren photographs of a 10 per cent. aerofoil at $M = 0.82$

PLATE 15

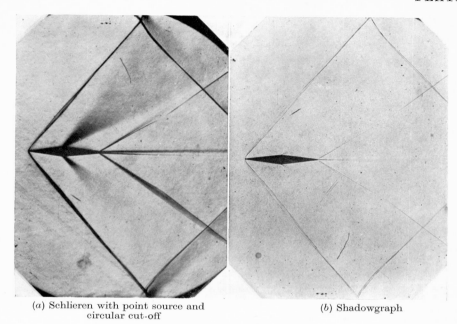

(a) Schlieren with point source and
circular cut-off

(b) Shadowgraph

(a) and (b). Schlieren and shadow photographs of a $12\frac{1}{2}$ per cent. double
wedge aerofoil at $M = 1\cdot6$

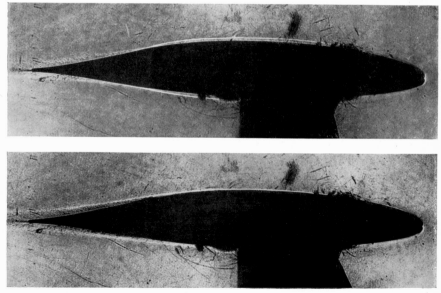

(c) and (d). Direct shadow photographs of the flow round an aerofoil at
$M = 0\cdot57$

to and normal to the chord respectively. The flow shown is that round a 10 per cent. thick cambered aerofoil at a Mach number of 0·82. Plate 14 (a) shows details of the flow in the boundary layer and the wake, and Plate 14 (b) shows details of the shock-wave pattern including a number of wavelets moving upstream from the wake. In both cases the exposure was of the order of one microsecond.

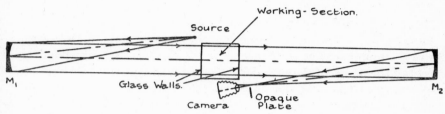

FIG. 172. Schlieren apparatus using mirrors.

Uniform sensitivity to density gradients in all directions can be obtained by using a point source and an opaque plate drilled with a central hole so that a deflexion of the image of the source in any direction reduces the illumination on the screen. An example is shown in Plate 15 (a), where the flow is again that round the double-wedge aerofoil discussed above. Since in the absence of an optical disturbance none of the light is cut off, the method has the advantage that the general level of illumination on the screen is high.

Since in practice it is easier to manufacture a mirror than a lens, it is common to use concave mirrors as shown in Fig. 172 instead of the lenses of Fig. 170. In general, it is necessary to use the mirrors with the source and its image off the axis as shown in order that the parallel light beam shall not be interrupted. In this case the mirrors should strictly be paraboloids figured off the axis, but if the aperture is not too large it is usually permissible to use spherical mirrors. Methods for setting up the apparatus to minimize the aberrations thus introduced are discussed by Barnes and Bellinger,† by Speak and Walters,‡ and by Schaefer.§ The quantities which determine the

† 'Schlieren and shadowgraph equipment for air flow analysis', *J. Opt. Soc. Amer.* **35** (1945), 497.

‡ 'Optical considerations and limitations of the schlieren method', *Tech. Notes Roy. Aircraft Estb.*, No. I.A.P. 908, *Rep. Aero. Res. Coun.*, No. 13,066 (1950).

§ 'Physical optic analysis of image quality in schlieren photography', *J. Soc. Mot. Pict. Engrs.* **53** (1949), 524.

sensitivity of the apparatus are discussed by Schardin,† by Weyl,‡ and by Holder and North.§

*The Ronchi method.* In the method which is usually attributed to Ronchi,‖ the source is bounded by straight lines on both sides and the knife-edge is replaced by a grating with opaque lines parallel to the edge of the source and of width and spacing equal to the width of the image of the source. The grating is adjusted so that, in the absence of the disturbance, the image of the source falls between two of the opaque lines and the screen is therefore uniformly illuminated. After the disturbance is introduced a point on the screen will be illuminated or not, depending on whether the corresponding part of the image of the source is deflected by an even or odd number of image widths, and the image on the screen is therefore one of alternate bright and dark fringes from measurements of which it is sometimes possible to determine the displacement of the image of the source. Difficulties may arise in the identification of a particular fringe and these are more severe than with the interferometer because the deflexions are larger. If the deflexions of the image of the source are small, it may be necessary to use a large number of lines on the grid in order to obtain sufficient accuracy, and diffraction effects may then become serious. An example of the use of the method has been given by Darby.††

An analogous method has been described by Stenger and Oswatitsch.‡‡ In this a grid is placed close to the light source, and a slit is placed in the focal plane of the second lens or mirror.

*Coloured schlieren pictures.* Coloured schlieren pictures can be obtained if a source of white light is used and a prism is placed in front of it so that a spectrum is produced in the focal plane of the second lens or mirror (Fig. 170). A slit parallel to the bands of the spectrum is then used instead of the knife-edge, and the colour of the light passing through on to the screen may be adjusted by

---

† 'Das Toeplersche Schlierenverfahren', *Forschungsh.* 5, No. 367 (1934), 1–31, *Rep. Aero. Res. Coun.*, No. 1,830; 'Die Schlierenverfahren und ihre Anwendungen', *Ergebn. exakt. Naturw.* **20** (1942), 303–439, *Rep. Aero. Res. Coun.*, No. 10,724.

‡ Loc. cit. on p. 584.

§ 'The Toepler schlieren apparatus', *Rep. Aero. Res. Coun.*, No. 13,068 (1950).

‖ *La prova dei sistemi ottichi*, Bologna (1925).

†† 'The Ronchi method of evaluating schlieren photographs', *Rep. NAVORD* 74–46 (1946), 31.

‡‡ 'Optical methods of flow measurement', *Rep. Aero. Res. Coun.*, No. 11,551 (1947).

moving the slit across the spectrum. If the light is deflected by a local gradient of refractive index in the working section, the corresponding spectrum moves across the slit and the image of the optical disturbance changes colour. The method is valuable for visual observations because the eye is more sensitive to changes of hue than of illumination but, although successful photographs have been taken, it is not particularly suitable for this purpose. The method may be used quantitatively by measuring the· displacement of the image of the source by traversing the slit until the image on the screen regains its original colour. One method of arranging the apparatus is described by Holder and North.†

## § 42. The direct-shadow methods

If the refractive-index gradient is non-uniform, the curvatures of adjacent rays will differ and they will converge or diverge on leaving the disturbance. Thus, referring to Fig. 173 and, as usual, assuming that the displacement within the disturbance of a ray from its undisturbed path may be neglected, the light which originally illuminated an area $dx dy$ now illuminates an area increased by an amount given approximately by $l\, dx dy \left( \dfrac{\partial \epsilon_x}{\partial x} + \dfrac{\partial \epsilon_y}{\partial y} \right)$, so that the change of illumination on the screen in terms of the initial illumination is

$$\frac{\Delta I}{I} = -l \left( \frac{\partial \epsilon_x}{\partial x} + \frac{\partial \epsilon_y}{\partial y} \right), \qquad (91)$$

where $l$ is the distance of the screen from the disturbance. Thus, by eqns. (87) and (88),

$$\frac{\Delta I}{I} = -\frac{l}{n_0} \int \left( \frac{\partial^2 n}{\partial x^2} + \frac{\partial^2 n}{\partial y^2} \right) dz, \qquad (92)$$

so that the change of illumination is proportional to the second derivative of the refractive index.

The conditions in practice are, however, usually more complicated‡ than the analysis given above suggests. For example, the deflexion of the light may cause the light from several points in the disturbance to fall on a common point on the screen. Thus it is only possible to obtain quantitative results from the shadowgraph method under particular conditions or if certain simplifying assumptions are justifiable. For example, eqn. (92) may be used if it is assumed that the

---

† 'A colour schlieren apparatus', *Rep. Aero. Res. Coun.*, No. 12,856 (1950).
‡ Weyl, loc. cit. on p. 584.

hypothesis of the infinitesimal deviation of a ray from its original path holds not only in the disturbance but also between the disturbance and the screen. This additional assumption is, however, seldom valid and the difficulties of the exact analysis are such that it has been attempted only in very few cases.

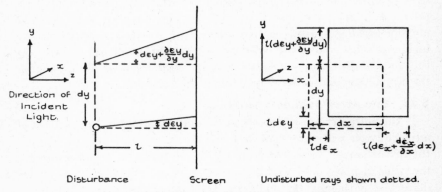

FIG. 173. A shadowgraph apparatus (simplified).

The formation of the image of a shock wave is sketched in Fig. 174, where it is assumed that the shock extends right across the tunnel. The variation of refractive index is sketched in Fig. 174 (i) and that of the first derivative of the refractive index in Fig. 174 (ii). The parallel rays of light entering the tunnel are bent in the manner shown in Fig. 174 (iii) (see eqn. (92)) and the illumination on the screen varies as sketched in Fig. 174 (iv) the image consisting of a region of low illumination on the low-pressure side of the shock followed by one of high illumination. The exact nature of the illumination of the image clearly depends, however, on the distance of the screen from the disturbance.

A simple solution is possible in the particular case of a spherical disturbance examined by Hilton† and by Lewy.‡ Suppose that a sphere with centre $O$ (Fig. 175) and having inside a uniform refractive index $n$, in excess of that $n_0$ of the surrounding air, is placed between a light source $S$ and the screen $Q$. A light ray which just misses the sphere passes on directly to the screen at $X$, whilst a ray striking the sphere at $A$ will be refracted downwards and will strike the

† Loc. cit. on p. 515.
‡ 'On the relation between the velocity of a shock wave and the width of the light gap it leaves on the photographic plate', *APG. BRL. Rep.*, No. 373 (1943).

screen at $Y$. As $A$ moves downwards, the distance $XY$ first decreases to a minimum value $XY_{min}$ and then increases again. Thus the illumination of the screen will be zero between $X$ and $Y_{min}$ and near $Y_{min}$ there will be a bright strip where the rays are crowded

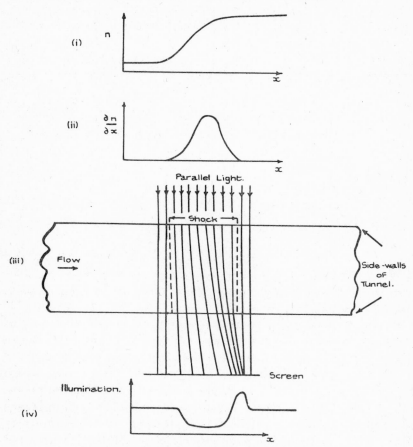

FIG. 174. Shadowgraph image of a shock wave.

together. An equation relating the indices of refraction to the width $d$ of the dark band, to the radius of the sphere, and to the geometry of the optical system has been given by Hilton and by Lewy. This may be written with sufficient accuracy as

$$d = 2 \cdot 381 \left( \frac{n - n_0}{n} \right)^{\frac{2}{3}} D^{\frac{2}{3}} R^{\frac{1}{3}}, \tag{93}$$

where $D$ is the distance between the screen and the point of contact $T$ of the sphere and the glancing ray, and where $R$ is the radius of curvature of the sphere as measured from the shadowgraph. It has been shown by Lewy† that the same formula can be used for a conical wave provided that $R$ is taken as the apparent distance measured perpendicular to the surface of the cone from the given point on the

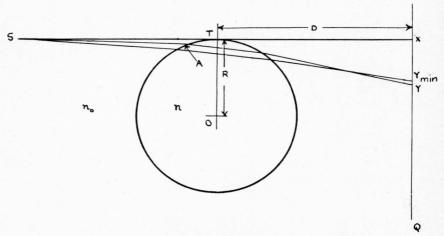

Fig. 175. Deflexion of light rays by a spherical disturbance.

cone to the axis. An example of the application of the method is given by Keenan.‡

For wind-tunnel observations it is usual to employ parallel incident light for shadowgraph photography. A typical apparatus is shown in Fig. 176, and an example of the results obtained is given in Plate 15 (b). This shows the flow round a $12\frac{1}{2}$ per cent. thick double-wedge aerofoil at $M = 1\cdot6$ and may be compared with the schlieren photographs reproduced in Plates 13 (a) and (b) and 15 (a). Photographs of the flow round an aerofoil at high subsonic speeds are given in Chap. XII, and it may be seen that although the shock waves and the wake are shown up clearly, little may be seen of the remainder of the flow.

Although the most usual application of the shadowgraph method is for the photography of two-dimensional flows, it is also possible§

† Loc. cit. on p. 596.

‡ 'Shadowgraph determination of the shock wave strength', *Bu. Ord. Explos. Res. Rep.*, No. 11 (1943).

§ Lamplough, 'Three-dimensional shock wave recorder', *Tech. Notes Roy. Aircraft Estb.*, No. I.A.P. 978, *Rep. Aero. Res. Coun.*, No. 11,659 (1948).

to obtain the contour of a shock wave in a plane just above the surface of a three-dimensional wing by the following method, which has been successfully used in a tunnel and on an aircraft in flight. The contour is recorded by moving chordwise a lamp or small source from which the light rays, after traversing the test section (which may be the full semi-wing span in flight tests), pass in turn through

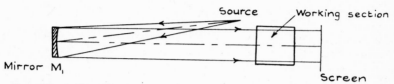

FIG. 176. A direct-shadow apparatus using a mirror to give parallel light.

two narrow horizontal slits on to a photographic film moving continuously behind the second slit. In this way a record is obtained of the shadow pattern produced by the shadow-forming elements of the shock wave during the movement of the lamp. The location of the element can then be graphically reconstructed.

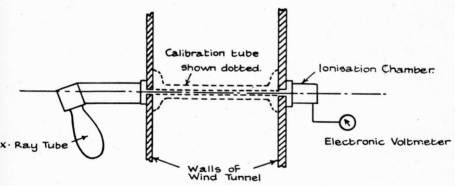

FIG. 177. Apparatus for measuring density with X-rays.

## § 43. Density measurements with X-rays

A technique for determining the density in the working section. of a wind tunnel by measuring the absorption of X-rays was tried at the W.V.A. in Germany† and has since been developed in the U.S.A. The German apparatus is sketched in Fig. 177 and consists of an X-ray tube from which the rays pass across the working

† Owen, loc. cit. on p. 536.

section and into an ionization chamber. The degree of absorption suffered by the rays during their passage across the tunnel was observed by measuring the potential difference across the ionization chamber, and since the absorption depends on the density of the air in the tunnel, this could be found from a preliminary calibration. The calibration was made by inserting an airtight cylinder round the beam of X-rays in the working section and varying the density inside by means of a pump.

## § 44. Determination of the Mach number from observations on wedges and cones placed in supersonic airstreams

If a wedge of semi-angle $\theta$ is placed at zero incidence in a supersonic airstream, the Mach number $M$ can be determined by observing the inclination $\beta$ of the (attached) bow wave to the direction of the undisturbed stream and using the result (see Chap. IV, eqn. (16))

$$\frac{1}{M^2} = \sin^2\beta - \frac{\gamma+1}{2}\frac{\sin\beta\sin\theta}{\cos(\beta-\theta)}. \tag{94}$$

Values calculated from this expression with $\gamma = 1\cdot40$ are set out in Table 16.

### TABLE 16
*Mach Numbers and Shock Angles for a Wedge*

| M | $\beta°$ for $\theta°$ = | | | | | |
|---|---|---|---|---|---|---|
|   | 0 | 2 | 5 | 10 | 15 | 20 |
| 1·0 | 90·00 | | | | | |
| 1·1 | 65·38 | | Detached bow-wave | | | |
| 1·2 | 56·32 | 61·05 | | | | |
| 1·3 | 50·28 | 53·50 | 59·97 | | | |
| 1·4 | 45·58 | 48·15 | 52·77 | | | |
| 1·5 | 41·82 | 44·08 | 47·90 | 56·70 | | |
| 1·6 | 38·68 | 40·88 | 44·32 | 51·10 | | |
| 1·7 | 36·03 | 37·93 | 41·03 | 47·17 | 56·00 | |
| 1·8 | 33·75 | 35·57 | 38·15 | 44·03 | 51·33 | |
| 1·9 | 31·75 | 33·47 | 36·22 | 41·48 | 48·00 | 57·87 |
| 2·0 | 30·00 | 31·67 | 34·32 | 39·32 | 45·33 | 53·33 |
| 2·1 | 28·43 | 30·03 | 32·62 | 37·43 | 43·17 | 50·37 |
| 2·2 | 27·03 | 28·58 | 31·08 | 35·80 | 41·23 | 47·97 |
| 2·3 | 25·77 | 27·27 | 29·73 | 34·32 | 39·63 | 46·00 |
| 2·4 | 24·62 | 26·12 | 28·53 | 33·00 | 38·22 | 44·33 |
| 2·5 | 23·58 | 25·08 | 27·43 | 31·87 | 36·93 | 42·90 |
| 2·6 | 22·62 | 24·10 | 26·43 | 30·78 | 35·80 | 41·63 |
| 2·7 | 21·73 | 23·17 | 25·50 | 29·83 | 34·78 | 40·50 |
| 2·8 | 20·93 | 22·37 | 24·63 | 28·93 | 33·83 | 39·50 |
| 2·9 | 20·17 | 21·58 | 23·83 | 28·12 | 33·00 | 38·55 |
| 3·0 | 19·47 | 20·88 | 23·13 | 27·35 | 32·22 | 37·72 |

The bow wave may be photographed by one of the optical techniques described above.

A cone is sometimes used instead of a wedge, the relationship between the Mach number $M$ and bow-wave angle $\beta$ for a cone of given semi-angle $\theta$ being that given in Table 17 (see Chap. V, § 11).

### TABLE 17
*Mach Numbers and Shock Angles for a Cone*

| M | $\beta°$ for $\theta°$ = | | | | | |
|---|---|---|---|---|---|---|
|   | 5 | 10 | 15 | 20 | 25 | 30 |
| 1·05 | 72·4 | | | | | |
| 1·1 | 65·6 | 67·0 | Detached bow-wave | | | |
| 1·2 | 56·4 | 57·5 | 60·6 | 72·5 | | |
| 1·3 | 50·5 | 51·4 | 53·4 | 58·0 | | |
| 1·4 | 45·5 | 46·3 | 48·3 | 52·8 | 59·3 | |
| 1·6 | 39·0 | 39·4 | 41·6 | 46·2 | 52·2 | 59·1 |
| 1·8 | 34·0 | 34·6 | 37·1 | 41·6 | 46·7 | 52·6 |
| 2·0 | 30·1 | 31·3 | 33·7 | 38·0 | 43·0 | 48·3 |
| 2·5 | 23·8 | 24·8 | 27·8 | 32·2 | 37·1 | 42·6 |
| 3·0 | 20·0 | 21·3 | 24·7 | 29·3 | 34·2 | 39·5 |

In some cases the Mach number may also be determined by measuring the inclinations of very weak disturbances arising from scratches made in the surface of the tunnel wall or that of the model under test. These disturbances are assumed to approximate to Mach lines and the Mach number is then found from the equation

$$M = \operatorname{cosec} \beta, \qquad (95)$$

values being given in Table 16 for the case of the wedge of zero apex angle.

## § 45. Boundary-layer transition

*Visualization.* The use of smoke for the visualization of the transition from laminar to turbulent flow in a boundary layer has been mentioned in Vol. I (1938), chap. vi, and details of the method are discussed by Preston and Sweeting† and by Salter.‡ At high speeds the quantity of smoke which must be introduced to produce a visible trace is so large that the disturbance of the flow at the point of entry is intolerable and other methods have accordingly been developed.

† 'Wood smoke as a means of visualizing boundary-layer flow at high Reynolds numbers', *J. Roy. Aero. Soc.* **47** (1943), 93.

‡ 'A multiple jet white smoke generator', *Rep. Memor. Aero. Res. Coun.*, No. 2,657 (1947).

Some of these have the advantage that they show the position of transition over the whole span instead of at one or two selected points only.

In the gas-filament technique† a gas is allowed to ooze from a hole in the surface of the body and reacts chemically with a paint placed on the surface to produce a coloured stain which, although well defined ahead of the transition point, becomes diffuse behind it. Since the method is cumulative, a very small gas flow may be used, but the time taken for a visible stain to appear at high speeds may then be objectionable.

The so-called 'contamination' techniques depend on the transport of matter from the surrounding air to the surface. In one technique‡ a small quantity of chlorine is added to the airstream and reacts chemically with a paint of starch iodide placed on the surface. A coloured stain appears first downstream of the transition point because the rate at which the chlorine reaches the surface is highest there. Similarly, if the airstream contains dust or oil the rate at which this is deposited on the surface is greater in the turbulent than in the laminar region of the boundary layer, and the transition point may be observed in this manner.

In the sublimation§,‖ and evaporation††,‡‡,‖ techniques advantage is taken of the fact that the rate at which a volatile solid or liquid is removed from the surface is greater when the boundary layer is turbulent than when it is laminar.

*The location of transition by direct-shadow observations.* Since the variation of refractive index (i.e. of density) across a laminar boundary layer differs from that across a turbulent layer, it should be possible

† Preston and Sweeting, 'An improved smoke generator for use in the visualization of airflow', *Rep. Memor. Aero. Res. Coun.*, No. 2,023 (1943); Preston, 'Visualization of boundary-layer flow', ibid. No. 2,267 (1946); Preston and Sweeting, 'Experiments on the measurement of transition position by chemical methods', ibid. No. 2,014 (1945).

‡ Gray, 'A chemical method of indicating transition in the boundary layer', *Rep. Aero. Res. Coun.*, No. 8,034 (1944), *Tech. Notes Roy. Aircraft Estb.*, No. Aero. 1,466.

§ Pringle and Main-Smith, 'Boundary layer transition indication by sublimation', *Rep. Aero. Res. Coun.*, No. 8,892 (1945), *Tech. Notes Roy. Aircraft Estb.*, No. Aero. 1,652.

‖ Holder, 'Transition indication in the N.P.L. 20 in. × 8 in. high-speed tunnel', *Rep. Memor. Aero. Res. Coun.*, No. 2,079 (1945).

†† Gray, 'A simple visual method of recording boundary layer transition', *Rep. Aero. Res. Coun.*, No. 10,028 (1946), *Tech. Notes Roy. Aircraft Estb.*, No. Aero. 1,816.

‡‡ Richards and Burstall, 'The china-clay method of indicating transition', ibid. No. 2,126 (1945).

to observe the transition position by one of the optical techniques described above. A method, based on shadowgraph observations, has been described by Pearcey,† who found that, except when transition occurred close to the leading edge, a laminar boundary layer was indicated by a bright line running parallel to, but separated from, the dark shadow of an aerofoil spanning the tunnel. This line converged on to the shadow of the aerofoil just downstream of the transition point as shown in Plate 15 (c), where the transition is at about 0·71 of the chord from the leading edge on the upper surface and 0·73 on the lower surface.

A shadowgraph photograph taken on the same aerofoil and at the same Mach number and incidence but with transition fixed artificially at the leading edge is shown in Plate 15 (d). Here the image of the turbulent boundary layer is a hard white line joining the shadow of the surface except where the boundary layer thickens or separates behind the shock waves.

*Methods for fixing transition.* In wind-tunnel tests, particularly on aerofoils fitted with control surfaces, it is sometimes desirable to fix the position of transition from laminar to turbulent flow in the boundary layer at some point fairly close to the nose. At low speeds this is often done by attaching a wire or a narrow band of rough particles to the surface at the point where transition is required to take place. The criterion for transition to occur close behind a wire is that $(U_\tau d/\nu) \doteq 20$, where $d$ is the diameter of the wire, $\nu$ the kinematic viscosity, and $U_\tau$ is the frictional velocity $(\tau_0/\rho)^{\frac{1}{2}}$, where $\tau_0$ is the surface shearing stress and $\rho$ the density. A similar criterion for transition behind a narrow band of roughness may be written $(U_\tau d/\nu) = K$, where $d$ is now the average height of the excrescences and $K$ is a constant for an assigned form of roughness. For sand or carborundum particles the value of $K$ is a little greater than 5·5, the value for which the roughness first begins to increase the resistance to flow.

For a laminar boundary layer the Pohlhausen theory gives $U_\tau x/\nu \propto (U_1 x/\nu)^{\frac{3}{4}}$, where $x$ is the distance from the leading edge and $U_1$ is the velocity outside the boundary layer. Both criteria may, therefore, be written in the form $d/x \propto (U_1 x/\nu)^{-\frac{3}{4}}$, and it follows that if the size of the wire or of the particles is chosen to be just sufficient

† 'The indication of boundary-layer transition on aerofoils in the N.P.L. 20 in. × 8 in. high-speed wind tunnel', *Current Pap. Aero. Res. Coun.*, No. 10 (1948).

to cause transition at a low speed, the disturbances which are introduced will be unnecessarily large at high speed (the kinematic viscosity remaining substantially constant or falling as the speed rises). Thus, unless the size is changed between tunnel runs, a wire which is just large enough to cause transition at the lowest Mach number of a test in a subsonic tunnel may cause very large disturbances at the higher Mach numbers. This has been confirmed experimentally by Pearcey,† who found that a strong shock wave occurred at the wire when the speed became supersonic close to the surface of the aerofoil. Wires or bands of roughness are, however, sometimes used in high-speed tunnels.

An alternative method has been developed by Fage and Sargent‡ and is such that at each Mach number the disturbance may be adjusted until it is just large enough to fix transition. The method consists of injecting minute quantities of air into the boundary layer through a spanwise row of holes drilled normal to the surface. An aerofoil with a 12-in. chord was used in the experiment and the holes were 0·0135 in. in diameter and were placed 0·075 in. apart at 0·15 chord. It was found that transition could be fixed by injecting into the boundary layer a quantity of air equal to 0·015 of the rate of mass flow in the boundary layer. No shock waves were observed close to the holes unless the rate of injection exceeded 0·04 of the rate of flow in the boundary layer.

## § 46. Analogies

A method for solving problems of potential flow by means of an analogy between the potential function of the flow and the electrical potential in a conducting layer has been described by Relf§ and has been extended to the case of two-dimensional compressible flow by Taylor and Sharman,∥ who used a conducting layer of varying thickness to simulate the variations of density in the flow. The

† 'Profile drag measurements at compressibility speeds on aerofoils with and without spanwise wires or grooves', *Rep. Memor. Aero. Res. Coun.*, No. 2,252 (1943).
‡ 'An air-injection method of fixing transition from laminar to turbulent flow in a boundary layer', ibid. No. 2,106 (1944).
§ 'An electrical method of tracing stream lines for the two-dimensional motion of a perfect fluid', ibid. No. 905 (1924); Malavard, 'The use of the rheo-electrical analogies in certain aerodynamical problems', *J. Roy. Aero. Soc.* **51** (1947), 739.
∥ 'A mechanical method for solving problems of flow in compressible fluids', *Proc. Roy. Soc.* A, **121** (1928), 194. See also *Rep. Memor. Aero. Res. Coun.*, No. 1,195 (1928).

conductor was a liquid with a free surface contained in a tank with a wax bottom which could be shaped to produce the required depth distribution. Details of the method, which is an iterative one, are given in Chap. VIII; suffice it to remark that each iteration consists of moulding a new base for the tank followed by an exploration of the electrical field. Taylor and Sharman found that the method converged as long as the conditions everywhere corresponded to subsonic flow.

An alternative method involving the use of the analogy in the hodograph plane has been suggested by Busemann† and described by Vandrey‡ and appears to be simpler than the method described above because the depth of the tank may be kept constant. The boundary conditions, however, give rise to difficulties.

The analogy (see Chap. IV) between the two-dimensional supersonic flow of a gas and the shooting flow of a shallow liquid (i.e. flow when the depth is below the critical value) with a free surface has been described by Binnie§, ‖ and Hooker§ and by Preiswerk,†† and examples of the use of the method are given in the references cited below.‡‡, §§ In the absence of strong shock waves and of surface-tension effects the analogy is exact only if the ratio of the specific heats of the gas is equal to two. For this reason the method has not been used extensively as a serious research technique though, since the power required to drive a water channel or to tow a model through water at rest is very small compared with that needed to run a supersonic wind tunnel, it is valuable for demonstration purposes.

† *Z. angew. Math. Mech.* **17** (1937), 75.

‡ 'Untersuchungen über die Behandlung ebener Unterschallströmungen mit Hilfe einer elektrischen Analogie', *A.V.A.* 44/A/10 (1944), *L.F.A. Völkenrode Transl. M.O.S.*, No. 34.

§ Binnie and Hooker, 'The flow under gravity of an incompressible and inviscid fluid through a constriction in a horizontal channel', *Proc. Roy. Soc.* A, **159** (1937), 592.

‖ Binnie, 'A possible form of high-speed water channel', *Rep. Memor. Aero. Res. Coun.*, No. 1,857 (1938).

†† 'Applications of the methods of gas dynamics to water flows with free surface. Part I. Flows with no energy dissipation', *Tech. Memor. Nat. Adv. Comm. Aero.*, No. 934, 1940; 'Part II. Flows with momentum discontinuities (hydraulic jumps)', *Tech. Memor. Nat. Adv. Comm. Aero.*, No. 935 (1940).

‡‡ Einstein and Baird, 'On the analogy between surface shock waves on liquids and shocks in compressible gases', *Hydrodyn. Lab. CALTECH. Lab. Rep.*, No. N-54 (1946).

§§ Orlin, Linder, and Bitterly, 'Applications of the analogy between water flow with a free surface and two-dimensional compressible gas flow', *Tech. Notes Nat. Adv. Comm. Aero.*, No. 1,185 (1947).

## ADDITIONAL REFERENCES

*Wind tunnels—general*

STANTON, 'On the flow of gases at high speeds', *Proc. Roy. Soc.* A, **111** (1926), 306.

―― 'The development of a high-speed wind channel for research in external ballistics', ibid. A, **131** (1931), 122.

PRANDTL, 'Herstellung einwandfreier Luftströme (Windkanäle)', *Handb. Exp. Phys.* **4** (1932), 65.

BAILEY and WOOD, 'High-speed induced wind tunnel', *Rep. Memor. Aero. Res. Coun.*, No. 1,468 (1932).

―― ――, 'Development of a high-speed induced wind tunnel of rectangular cross-section', ibid. No. 1,791 (1937).

LOCK, 'Problems of high-speed flight as affected by compressibility', *J. Roy. Aero. Soc.* **42** (1938), 193.

BAILEY and WOOD, 'Further development of a high-speed wind tunnel of rectangular cross-section', *Rep. Memor. Aero. Res. Coun.*, No. 1,853 (1938).

FERRI, 'The Guidonia High-Speed Tunnel', *Aircraft Engng.* **12** (1940), 302.

SEIPPEL, 'Supersonic wind tunnels', *Brown Boveri Rev.* **30** (1943), 176.

SMELT, 'A critical review of German research on high speed airflow', *J. Roy. Aero. Soc.* **50** (1946), 899.

HANKINS and COPE, 'The flow of gases at sonic and supersonic speeds', *Proc. Instn. Mech. Engrs.* **155** (1946), 401.

PERRING, 'High-speed performance', *Aero. Conf. Lond.* (1947), 175.

THOM and PERRING, 'The design and work of the Farnborough High-Speed Tunnel', *J. Roy. Aero. Soc.* **52** (1948), 205.

BEAVAN and HOLDER, 'Recent developments in high speed research in the Aerodynamics Division of the N.P.L.', ibid. **54** (1950), 545.


*Design of circuit*

HALL, 'Measurements of the intensity and scale of turbulence', *Rep. Memor. Aero. Res. Coun.*, No. 1,842 (1938).

TSIEN, 'On the design of the contraction cone for a wind tunnel', *J. Aero. Sci.* **10** (1943), 68.

BATCHELOR and SHAW, 'A consideration of the design of wind tunnel contractions', *A.C.A.* 4 (1944).

SMITH and WANG, 'Contracting cones giving uniform throat speeds', *J. Aero. Sci.* **11** (1944), 356.

CHEERS, 'Wind tunnel contractions', *Rep. Memor. Aero. Res. Coun.*, No. 2,137 (1945).

THWAITES, 'On the design of contractions for wind tunnels', ibid. No. 2,278 (1946).

WINGHAM, 'Design and testing of a contraction shape for a 13 ft. × 9 ft. wind tunnel', *Rep. Aero. Res. Coun.*, No. 12,122 (1948).

HARROP, 'Method for designing wind tunnel contractions', ibid. No. 11,603 (1948), *Rep. Roy. Aircraft Estb.*, No. Aero. 2251.

COLLAR, 'The effect of a gauze on the velocity distribution in a uniform duct', *Rep. Memor. Aero. Res. Coun.*, No. 1,867 (1939).

BATCHELOR, 'On the concept and properties of the idealized hydrodynamic resistance', *A.C.A.* 13 (1945).

WIRT, 'New data for the design of elbows in duct systems', *Gen. Elec. Rev.* 30 (1927), 286.

HOFMANN, 'The energy loss around 90° bends in tubes of uniform cross-section', *Mitt. hydraul. Inst. München.* 3 (1929).

PATTERSON, 'Note on the design of corners in duct systems', *Rep. Memor. Aero. Res. Coun.*, No. 1,773 (1936).

COLLAR, 'Some experiments with a cascade of aerofoils', ibid. No. 1,768 (1937).

MacPHAIL, 'Experiments on turning vanes in an expansion', ibid. No. 1,876 (1939).

YOUNG, 'Tests of high-speed flow in right-angled pipe bends of rectangular cross-section', ibid. No. 2,066 (1943).

LIGHTHILL, 'Note on the deflexion of jets by insertion of curved surfaces and on the design of bends in wind tunnels', ibid. No. 2,105 (1945).

SALTER, 'Experiments on thin turning vanes', ibid. No. 2,469 (1946).

WINTER, 'Comparative tests on thick and thin turning vanes in the 4 ft. × 3 ft. wind tunnel', ibid. No. 2,589 (1947).

COLLAR, 'The use of a freely rotating windmill to improve the flow in a wind tunnel', ibid. No. 1,866 (1938).

*Design of supersonic nozzles*

BUSEMANN, *Handb. Exp. Phys.* 4 (1931), 343.

GÖRTLER, 'Zum Übergang von Unterschall zu Überschallgeschwindigkeiten in Düsen', *Z. angew. Math. Mech.* 19 (1939), 325.

ATKIN, 'Two-dimensional supersonic channel design', *Rep. Memor. Aero. Res. Coun.*, No. 2,174 (1945).

HALLER, 'The application of a graphic method to some dynamic problems in gases', *Sulzer Tech. Rev.* No. 1 (1945), 6.

LIGHTHILL, 'The hodograph transformation in transonic flow. (1) Symmetrical channels', *Proc. Roy. Soc.* A, 191 (1947), 323–41.

SHAPIRO and EDELMAN, 'Method of characteristics for two-dimensional supersonic flow', *J. Appl. Mech.* 14 (1947), A–154.

PINKEL, 'Equations for the design of two-dimensional supersonic nozzles', *Rep. Nat. Adv. Comm. Aero.*, No. 907 (1948).

*Diffusers*

CASTAGNA, 'Experimental research on the transformation of energy of a gas flowing in a pipe'. Reproduced as *Rep. Aero. Res. Coun.*, No. 2,399 (1936).

PUCKETT, 'Final report: Model supersonic wind tunnel project'. Reproduced as ibid. No. 7,576 (1943).

LEAN, 'Report on the flow phenomena at supersonic speed in the neighbourhood of the entry of a propulsive duct', *Rep. Engng. Div. Nat. Phys. Lab.* 18/44 (1944).

YOUNG, 'Tests of high-speed flow in diffusers of rectangular cross-section', *Rep. Memor. Aero. Res. Coun.*, No. 2,201 (1944).

OSWATITSCH and BÖHM, 'Luftkräfte und Strömungsvorgänge bei angetrie-
benen Geschossen', *Forschungen und Entwicklungen des Heereswaffenamtes
Ber.* No. 1,010/2 (1944).

PLACE and SMITH, 'Supersonic diffusion in the presence of a boundary layer',
*Power Jets (R and D) Memor.*, No. M 1,071 (1945).

LEAN, 'Report on the flow phenomena at supersonic speed in the neighbourhood of the entry of a propulsive duct', *Rep. Engng. Div. Nat. Phys.
Lab.*, No. 109/45 (1945).

EGGINK, 'The pressure regain in supersonic wind tunnels', *A.V.A. Monogr.*
D.1.–5.3, *Rep. Aero. Res. Coun.*, No. 11,276 (1947).

—— 'The improvement in pressure recovery in supersonic wind tunnels',
*Rep. Roy. Aircraft Estb.*, No. Aero. 2,326, *Rep. Aero. Res. Coun.*, No.
12,527 (1949).

## Coolers

FISHENDEN and SAUNDERS, *The Calculation of Heat Transmission.* H.M.S.O.,
London (1932).

NIEHNS, 'The design of heat exchangers', *Brown Boveri Rev.* (1941), 228.

LANDER, 'Review of recent progress in heat transfer', *Proc. Instn. Mech.
Engrs.* **148** (1942), 81.

McADAMS, *Heat Transmission.* McGraw-Hill (1942).

FISHENDEN and SAUNDERS, 'Some simplified heat transfer data', *J. Inst. Fuel*,
**19** (1945), 62.

## Fans and compressors

KEARTON, *Turbo-Blowers and Compressors.* Pitman (1926).

KELLER, *Theory and Performance of Axial Flow Fans.* McGraw-Hill (1937).

COLLAR, 'Cascade theory and the design of fan straighteners', *Rep. Memor.
Aero. Res. Coun.*, No. 1,885 (1940).

—— 'The design of wind tunnel fans', ibid. No. 1,889 (1940).

CHURCH, *Centrifugal Pumps and Blowers.* Wiley (1944).

HOWELL, 'Design of axial compressors', *Proc. Instn. Mech. Engrs.* **153** (1945),
441.

## Tunnel interference at high Mach number

GOLDSTEIN and YOUNG, 'The linear perturbation theory of compressible flow,
with application to wind tunnel interference', *Rep. Memor. Aero. Res.
Coun.*, No. 1,909 (1943).

THOM, 'Tunnel wall effect on high-speed tunnel tests', *Tech. Notes Roy. Aircraft Estb.*, No. Aero 1,276 (H.S.T.), *Rep. Aero. Res. Coun.*, No. 7,050
(1943).

THOM and MAIR, 'Note on the design of a high-speed subsonic wind tunnel',
*Tech. Notes Roy. Aircraft Estb.*, No. Aero. 1,375, *Rep. Aero. Res. Coun.*,
No. 7,409 (1944).

BYRNE, 'Experimental constriction effects in high-speed wind tunnels', *A.C.
Rep. Nat. Adv. Comm. Aero.*, No. 64,607a (1944).

MAIR and GAMBLE, 'The effect of model size on measurements in the high-
speed tunnel. Part I. Drag of two-dimensional symmetrical aerofoils at
zero incidence', *Rep. Memor. Aero. Res. Coun.*, No. 2,527 (1945).

THOM 'Note on Rep. Roy. Aircraft Estb. No. Aero 2,056 "Tunnel blockage near the choking condition"', *Rep. Aero. Res. Coun.*, No. 9,095 (1945).

VINCENTI and GRAHAM, 'The effect of wall interference upon the aerodynamic characteristics of an aerofoil spanning a closed throat circular wind tunnel', *A.C. Rep. Nat. Adv. Comm. Aero.*, No. 5D21 (1945).

·SCHMITZ, 'Calculations on tunnel corrections for closed and open working sections', *Rep. Aero. Res. Coun.*, No. 9,711 (1946).

FRANKE and WEINIG, 'The correction of the speed of flow and the angle of incidence due to blockage by aerofoil models in a high-speed wind tunnel with closed working section', *M.A.P.* V335–259T (1946), *Rep. Aero. Res. Coun.* No. 10,268.

GÖTHERT, 'High-speed tests on a wing of very small dimensions in the D.V.L. High-Speed Wind Tunnel', *M.A.P.* V13–370T, Government documentary centre No. G.D.C. 286T (1946), *Rep. Aero. Res. Coun.*, No. 10,800.

FRÖSSEL, 'Experimental investigation of the compressible flow at and near a cambered wall', *M.A.P.* VG161–196T (1946), *Rep. Aero. Res. Coun.*, No. 10,465.

TOLLMIEN and SCHAEFER, 'Formation of a shock wave in the vicinity of a wall of continuous and convex curvature', *M.A.P.* VG180–316T (1946), *Rep. Aero. Res. Coun.*, No. 10,739.

FRÖSSEL, 'Experimental investigation of the compressible flow along and near a curved wall. Part III. Free flow along the circular arc profile with tangential continuation', *M.A.P.* VG29–318T (1946), *Rep. Aero. Res. Coun.*, No. 10,740.

THOM, 'Tunnel wall effect from mass flow considerations', *Rep. Memor. Aero. Res. Coun.*, No. 2,442 (1947).

THOM and KLANFER, 'Some arithmetical studies of the compressible flow past a body in a channel', ibid. No. 2,440 (1947).

ABDURAHIMAN, 'Two-dimensional compressible flow past a solid body symmetrically placed in a channel', ibid. No. 2,443 (1947).

BRITTEN, 'The use of influence functions in problems of fluid flow', ibid. No. 2,441 (1947).

WIESELSBERGER, 'Wind tunnel corrections for compressible flow', *Lilienthal-Ges. Luftfahrtforsch. Ber.*, No. LGL 127 G.D.C. 530T, *M.O.S.R. and T.*, No. 379 (1947), *Rep. Aero. Res. Coun.*, No. 11,199.

GÖTHERT, 'Wall corrections for high subsonic velocities'. *M.O.S.* (A) (*Völkenrode*) G.D.C./548T, *R. and T.*, No. 397, *Rep. Aero. Res. Coun.*, No. 11,169 (1947).

LUDWIEG, '4.2 Wind tunnel corrections for compressible flow', *A.V.A. Mongr.* D3, *Rep. Aero. Res. Coun.*, No. 11,170 (1947).

THOMPSON, 'Present methods of applying blockage corrections in closed rectangular high-speed wind tunnel', *Rep. Roy. Aircraft Estb.*, No. Aero. 2,225, *Rep. Aero. Res. Coun.*, No. 11,385 (1948).

EPSTEIN and ALBERG, 'The effect of compressibility on the two-dimensional subsonic wind tunnel constriction correction', *J. Aero. Sci.* 15 (1948), 144.

FELDMANN, 'Untersuchung von symmetrischen Tragflügelprofilen bei hohen Unterschallgeschwindigkeiten in einem geschlossenen Windkanal', *Mitt. Inst. Aerodyn. Zürich*, No. 14 (1948).

EMMONS, 'Flow of a compressible fluid past a symmetrical aerofoil in a wind tunnel and in free air', *Tech. Notes Nat. Adv. Comm. Aero.*, No. 1,746 (1948).

THOM and KLANFER, 'Tunnel wall effect on an aerofoil', *Rep. Aero. Res. Coun.*, No. 12,173 (1949).

WISE, 'Note on method of correcting for tunnel blockage', ibid. No. 12,436 (1949).

THOM, 'Note on Tech. Notes Nat. Adv. Comm. Aero. No. 1,746', *Rep. Aero. Res. Coun.*, No. 12,435 (1949).

EVANS, 'Correction to velocity for wall constraint in any 10 ft. × 7 ft. rectangular subsonic tunnel', *Rep. Memor. Aero. Res. Coun.*, No. 2,662 (1949), *Rep. Roy. Aircraft Estb.*, No. Aero. 2,307.

## Pressure measurements and manometers

OWER, *The Measurement of Air Flow*, 2nd edition. Chapman and Hall (1933).
—— 'Measurement of the flow of liquid and gases', *Trans. Inst. Chem. Engrs.* 18 (1940), 87.

MAIR, 'Review of high-speed flight research at the R.A.E.', *Rep. Memor. Aero. Res. Coun.*, No. 2,222 (1946).

KEMPER, 'Multiple measuring instruments for flight investigations', *M.A.P. Völkenrode*, M.A.P. VG26–309T, *Rep. Aero. Res. Coun.*, No. 10,543 (1946).

WEIDEMANN and STRAUSS, 'An instrument on the inductive principle for measuring static and rapidly varying pressures', *Rep. Aero. Res. Coun.*, No. 10,557 (1946).

WOLFE, MARTIN, and JUDGE, 'Condenser type indicators for fluctuating pressures', ibid. No. 9,950 (1946), *Rep. Roy. Aircraft Estb.*, No. S.M.E. 3,371.

KLEIN, 'Micromanometers', *A.V.A.* Monogr. D2, *Rep. Aero. Res. Coun.*, No. 11,391 (1947).

KERRIS and WEIDEMANN, 'Pressure capsules', *A.V.A.* Monogr. D2, *Rep. Aero. Res. Coun.*, No. 11,391 (1947).

DRESCHER, 'Measurements of unsteady pressure', *A.V.A.* Monogr. D2, *Rep. Aero. Res. Coun.*, No. 11,391 (1947).

## Balances

WINGHAM, 'An application of strain gauges to the measurement of normal force and moments in high-speed wind tunnels', *Rep. Memor. Aero. Res. Coun.*, No. 2,316 (1945).

MACPHAIL, 'The R.A.E. 11½ ft. × 8½ ft. wind tunnel', ibid. No. 2,424 (1945).

MATT, 'The High-Speed Wind Tunnel of the D.V.L.', *A.V.A.* Monogr. D1. *Rep. Aero. Res. Coun.*, No. 11,277 (1947).

KLEIN, 'Wind tunnel balances', *A.V.A.* Monogr. D2, *Rep. Aero. Res. Coun.*, No. 11,390 (1947).

MAINS, 'A strain-gauge balance system for a supersonic tunnel', *Exp. Stress Anal.* 5 (1948), 100.

*Temperature measurements*

*Temperature Measurements.* Brit. Stand. Instn. B.S. 1,041 (1943).

KING, 'Measurements of high temperature in high velocity gas streams', *Trans. Amer. Soc. Mech. Engrs.* **65** (1943), 421.

ROHSENOW and HUNSAKER, 'Determination of the thermal correction for a single-shielded thermocouple', *Annual Meeting Amer. Soc. Mech. Engrs.* (1946), Preprint No. 46–A–53.

PROBERT and SINGHAM, 'Measurement of gas temperature in turbine engines', *J. Sci. Inst.* **23** (1946), 72.

LEIST and KNORNSCHILD, 'Temperature measurements on gas-turbine motors in operation', *R.T.P. Transl.* No. 2,233 (1939).

*Optical methods and photography*

MILLER, 'The N.A.C.A. high-speed motion picture camera optical compensation at 40,000 photographs per second', *Rep. Nat. Adv. Comm. Aero.*, No. 856 (1946).

—— 'The optical system of the N.A.C.A. 400,000 frame per second motion picture camera', *Tech. Notes Nat. Adv. Comm. Aero.*, No. 1,405 (1947).

HILTON and FOWLER, 'Photographs of shock wave movement', *Rep. Memor. Aero. Res. Coun.*, No. 2,692 (1947).

FAYELLE and NASLIN, 'Photographie instantée et cinématographie ultra-rapide', *Mémor. Artille. fr.* **22** (1948), 657.

BARRY and EDELMAN, 'An improved schlieren apparatus', *J. Aero. Sci.* **15** (1948), 364.

HOLDER, NORTH, STANDRING, and LOOMS, 'A high-speed camera for the photography of shock wave oscillations in a wind tunnel', *Rep. Aero. Res. Coun.*, No. 12,543 (1949).

EDGERTON, 'Electric flash photography', *J. Soc. Mot. Pict. Engrs.*, High-Speed Photography, Part I (1949).

# FLOW PAST AEROFOILS AND CYLINDERS

## § 1. Introduction

IN this chapter we shall consider the results of wind-tunnel experiments at subsonic and supersonic speeds, including comparisons with theoretical results wherever these are possible. Most of the chapter deals with aerofoils (with sharp trailing edges), but some results for circular cylinders are also included. Except where otherwise stated the results given refer to two-dimensional flow (infinite aspect ratio). It is assumed that the flow is steady in all cases.

For the reasons given in Chap. XI, model experiments in wind tunnels become very difficult at speeds close to that of sound, and hence there are very few reliable experimental results now available for free-stream Mach numbers between about 0·85 and 1·15. Even where results are available within this speed range, their application to free-air conditions is doubtful, because of the uncertain tunnel-wall corrections at Mach numbers near 1. Moreover, except for a few special cases, there have been no theoretical investigations of flows with shock waves in which subsonic and supersonic regions exist at the same time. These mixed subsonic and supersonic flows occur with any body at free-stream Mach numbers near 1; for blunt-nosed bodies they persist throughout the supersonic range of free-stream Mach numbers. Thus very little is known either experimentally or theoretically about flows at free-stream Mach numbers near 1, and our discussion will be confined mainly to speeds above and below this range.

## § 2. Flow past aerofoils at high speeds and formation of shock waves

Before considering in detail the variations in the flow caused by changes of Mach number, aerofoil shape, and incidence, it may be useful to refer briefly to the principal changes that occur in the flow past an aerofoil, as the speed is increased gradually from zero up to a high supersonic speed. It will be shown that the type of flow changes completely as the speed is increased, and it will be found convenient to divide the whole range of speeds into several parts, each part of the speed range being associated with a different type of flow.

The first range of speeds to be considered extends from zero up to the speed at which a local Mach number of 1 is first reached at some point in the field. The Mach number corresponding to the upper limit of this range is known as the 'critical' Mach number, because above this Mach number there are local regions of supersonic flow and the formation of shock waves is possible, whereas at lower Mach numbers no stationary shock waves can be formed. On an aerofoil, shock waves can usually be observed at a Mach number which is only slightly above the critical value, but it has not yet been proved that this always occurs, and it may be possible in some cases to exceed the critical Mach number by a considerable margin without the formation of shock waves. This question is discussed further on pp. 626 and 627.

At Mach numbers below the critical value no stationary shock waves can be formed and the general features of the flow are not very different from those found at low speeds. At Mach numbers above the critical value, but still less than unity, there are large changes of pressure distribution and the shock waves which usually appear often cause separation or considerable thickening of the boundary layer. As the Mach number increases and approaches 1, the shock waves become more intense and move back towards the trailing edge. As a result the boundary-layer separation (if present) tends to become more complete, although the chordwise extent of the separated region (behind the shock waves) becomes smaller.

When the Mach number exceeds 1 a detached curved shock wave appears in front of the leading edge, and the other shock waves, which were present at subsonic speeds, usually occur at or near the trailing edge. Near the nose of the aerofoil, behind the detached shock wave, the local velocities are subsonic, but elsewhere they are supersonic. With round-nosed aerofoils this type of flow persists throughout the supersonic speed range, but with sharp-nosed aerofoils the leading-edge shock wave (or bow wave) becomes attached to the aerofoil when the Mach number exceeds a certain value. There is very little information about supersonic flow past aerofoils with detached bow waves. Except for a few special cases,† this type

† Maccoll and Codd, 'Theoretical investigations of the flow around various bodies in the sonic region of velocities', *Rep. Aero. Res. Coun.*, No. 9,315 (1945).

of flow has not been investigated theoretically, and in most of the experiments which have been made the aerofoil has been sharp-nosed and the Mach number has been high enough for the bow wave to be attached to the leading edge.

On a sharp-nosed aerofoil when the bow wave is attached, the local velocities (outside the boundary layer) are usually supersonic throughout the field. It is then usually possible to calculate the pressure distribution (for inviscid flow) either by an approximate method (Chap. VIII) or by exact theory (Chap. V). It will be shown (pp. 638 and 639) that these inviscid-flow calculations give moderately good agreement with the results of experiments in wind tunnels.

## § 3. Pressure distributions on aerofoils at subsonic speeds, below the critical Mach number

For Mach numbers below the critical value there are several approximate theoretical methods which may be used to calculate the variation of the pressure coefficients on an aerofoil with Mach number (see Chaps. VII and VIII). The simplest of these is the Prandtl–Glauert theory, which gives the result

$$C_p = \frac{C_{p0}}{\beta}, \tag{1}$$

where $C_p$ and $C_{p0}$ are defined in Fig. 178, $M_1$ is the Mach number of the free stream, and $\beta = (1-M_1^2)^{\frac{1}{2}}$.

The theory derived by von Kármán,[†] using the hodograph method, gives rather better agreement with experimental results. This leads to the expression

$$C_p = \frac{C_{p0}}{\beta + \frac{1}{2}C_{p0}(1-\beta)}. \tag{2}$$

(This may also be expressed as $(1/\beta)(1/C_p - \frac{1}{2}) = $ constant.)

It may be noted that the Kármán formula reduces to the simple Prandtl–Glauert expression when $C_{p0}$ is small. Thus for thin aerofoils at small incidences the results given by the two theories are nearly the same.

Fig. 178 shows the results of some measurements at the N.P.L. on an E.C. 1250 aerofoil.[‡] In this case the experimental results agree fairly well with the Kármán law, at Mach numbers up to the critical value, except near the trailing edge. The discrepancy near

† 'Compressibility effects in aerodynamics', *J. Aero. Sci.* **8** (1941), 337–56.
‡ Beavan and Hyde, 'Compressibility increase of lift and moment on E.C. 1250 for low speed $C_L = 0.17$', *Rep. Memor. Aero. Res. Coun.*, No. 2,055 (1942).

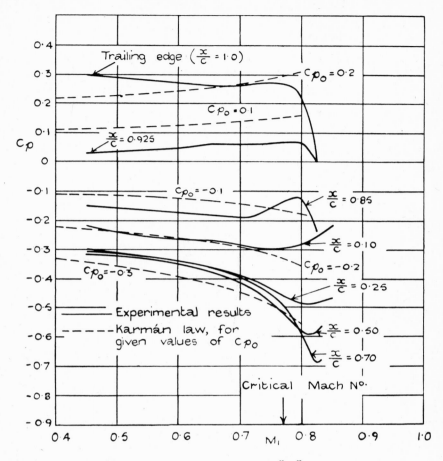

$x$ = distance from L.E. of aerofoil.    $C_p = \dfrac{p - p_1}{\frac{1}{2}\rho_1 U^2}$.

$c$ = chord of aerofoil.

$p$ = local static pressure.

$p_1$ = static pressure in free stream.    $C_{p_0}$ = value of $C_p$ at $M_1 = 0$.

(Aerofoil shape is shown in Fig. 181.)

FIG. 178. Variation of pressure coefficient with Mach number. E.C. 1250 aerofoil at $0°$ incidence ($R = 1\cdot2 \times 10^6$ to $1\cdot9 \times 10^6$).

the trailing edge is probably due to the effect of the boundary layer. The effect is more important on this aerofoil than on many others, because the unusually large trailing-edge angle makes the boundary layer rather thick near the trailing edge.

It should be noted that the variation of $C_p$ with Mach number, for a given point on an aerofoil, can only be expected to follow the Kármán law up to the critical Mach number for the aerofoil, even though sonic velocity may not be exceeded at the point under consideration until a much higher Mach number is reached.

Although for most aerofoils the variation of $C_p$ with Mach number agrees fairly closely with the Kármán law, there are some exceptional cases in which the variation with Mach number is considerably altered by separation of the boundary layer. For example in Fig. 179, which shows the results of measurements on a Frise aileron at the R.A.E.,[†] the suction coefficient at the protruding aileron nose decreases with increasing Mach number, instead of increasing as predicted by the Kármán law. The explanation of this is probably that the severe adverse pressure gradient on the lower surface, immediately behind the aileron nose, causes a separation of the boundary layer; and the extent of this separation increases with Mach number, thus causing a reduction of the peak suction coefficient.

Fig. 180 shows another exceptional case, the pressure distribution on a thin, highly cambered aerofoil at a low incidence.[‡] In this case the peak suction coefficient on the lower surface remains nearly constant at all Mach numbers up to the critical value, instead of increasing with Mach number as predicted by the Kármán law. Again, the probable explanation is that there is a separation of the (laminar) boundary layer, and this changes the effective shape of the aerofoil as the Mach number increases.

## § 4. Pressure distributions on aerofoils at high subsonic speeds. Shock waves

*Typical pressure distributions.* Figs. 181, 182 and 183 show some typical pressure distributions for aerofoils at high subsonic speeds. The measurements on E.C. 1250 and the Goldstein 'roof-top' aerofoil (Figs. 181 and 182) were made at the N.P.L.,[§] while those on

[†] Mair, Thompson, and Hutton, 'High-speed wind tunnel tests on a Spitfire type wing and aileron', *Rep. Roy. Aircraft Estb.*, No. Aero. 1,848 (1943), *Rep. Aero. Res. Coun.*, No. 7,169.

[‡] Göthert, 'Hochgeschwindigkeitsmessungen an Luftschrauben-Profilen der R.A.F. — Reihe mit verschiedenen Dickenverhältnissen', *U.M.* 1321 (1943), *M.A.P. Völkenrode R. and T.*, No. 407.

[§] Beavan and Hyde, 'Examples of pressure distribution at compressibility speeds on E.C. 1250', *Rep. Memor. Aero. Res. Coun.*, No. 2,056 (1942); Pearcey and Beavan, 'Force and pressure coefficients up to Mach No. 0·87 on the Goldstein roof-top section 1442/1547', ibid. No. 2,346 (1946); Beavan, Hyde, and Fowler, 'Pressure

PLATE 16

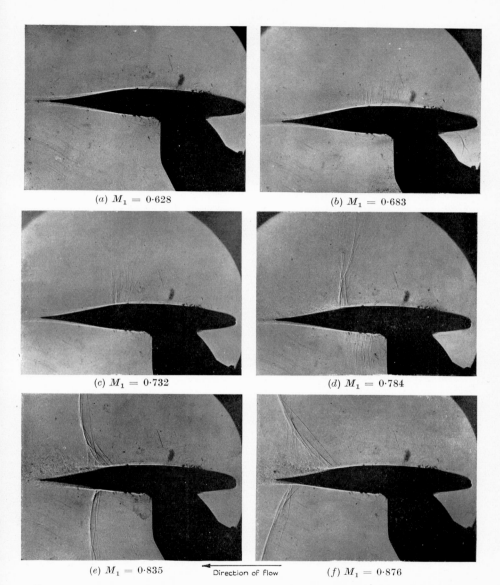

(a) $M_1 = 0.628$     (b) $M_1 = 0.683$

(c) $M_1 = 0.732$     (d) $M_1 = 0.784$

(e) $M_1 = 0.835$     Direction of flow     (f) $M_1 = 0.876$

Shadow photographs at subsonic speeds showing shock-wave formation on
Goldstein 'roof-top' aerofoil 1442/1547 at $0.5°$ incidence

(Critical Mach No. $= 0.695$)

PLATE 17

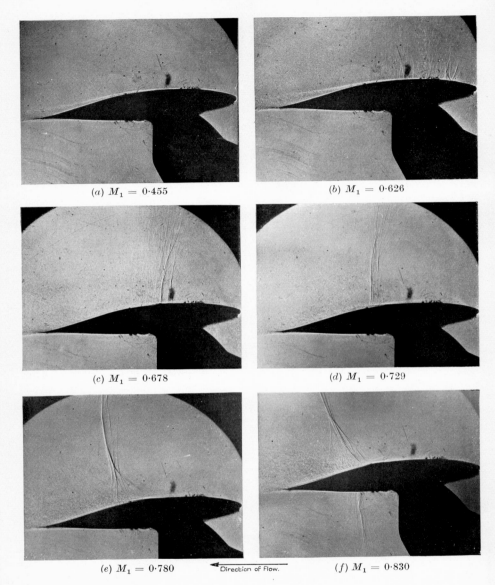

(a) $M_1 = 0.455$

(b) $M_1 = 0.626$

(c) $M_1 = 0.678$

(d) $M_1 = 0.729$

(e) $M_1 = 0.780$    ◄ Direction of Flow.     (f) $M_1 = 0.830$

Shadow photographs at subsonic speeds showing shock-wave formation on
Goldstein 'roof-top' aerofoil 1442/1547 at 6·5° incidence
(Critical Mach No. = 0·485)

N.A.C.A. 23021 (Fig. 183) were made at the R.A.E.† In most of these diagrams the pressure is expressed as the ratio $(p/H_1)$, where $p$ is the local static pressure and $H_1$ is the stagnation pressure in the free stream.‡ At high Mach numbers this form is often more convenient than the usual pressure coefficient $(C_p = (p-p_1)/\frac{1}{2}\rho_1 U^2$, see Fig. 182 (b)), because in homentropic flow the local Mach number depends only on $(p/H_1)$ and not on the free-stream Mach number. Values of the local Mach number obtained on the assumption of homentropic flow are shown on the right-hand side in Figs. 181, 182 (a), 182 (c), and 183, but it should be emphasized that these do not apply to conditions behind a shock wave or within a boundary layer. The error due to loss through the shock wave is usually small for such shock strengths as occur on aerofoils. But in the neighbourhood of a shock wave near the surface the local Mach number as calculated from the static pressure on the surface may not be even approximately equal to the value just outside the boundary layer, because of the large transverse pressure gradient in the boundary layer which occurs near a shock wave. To take a specific example, on the curve for $M_1 = 0.8$ in Fig. 182 (a), upper surface, it is probable that a shock wave occurs near $x/c = 0.7$. In front of $x = 0.6$, say, the local Mach number just outside the boundary layer is almost exactly equal to the value calculated for homentropic flow; after this point the boundary layer probably starts to thicken and the change of static pressure across it tends to distort the sudden drop in Mach number at the shock wave to the more gradual curve shown.

Figs. 182 (a) and (b) show a comparison between the two alternative methods of presentation, $(p/H_1)$ and $C_p$. In Fig. 182 (b) no scale of local Mach number has been included, because this would be different for each free-stream Mach number, but the values of local Mach number can be found from Fig. 182 (a).

*Development of shock waves.* Plates 16 and 17 show some photographs taken by Pearcey by the direct shadow method (see Chap. XI) on the Goldstein 'roof-top' aerofoil 1442/1547 in the Rectangular

and wake measurements up to Mach number 0·85 on an E.C. 1250 section with 25% control', ibid. No. 2,065 (1945); Beavan and Hyde, 'Interim report on the Rectangular High-Speed Tunnel, including some pitot traverse measurements of drag of the aerofoil E.C. 1250', ibid. No. 2,067 (1942).

† Thompson and Adamson, 'High-speed wind tunnel measurements of pressure distribution on an aerofoil of N.A.C.A. 23021 section', *Rep. Roy. Aircraft Estb.*, No. Aero. 1,985 (1944), *Rep. Aero. Res. Coun.*, No. 8,350.

‡ See footnote † on p. 554.

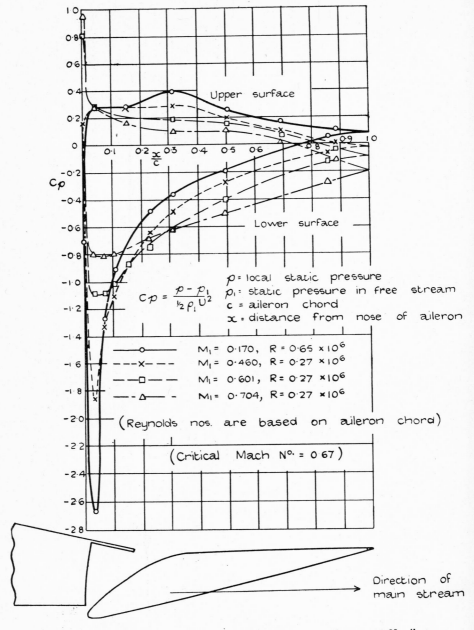

FIG. 179. Pressure distributions on Frise aileron (wing incidence = +2°, aileron angle = −15°).

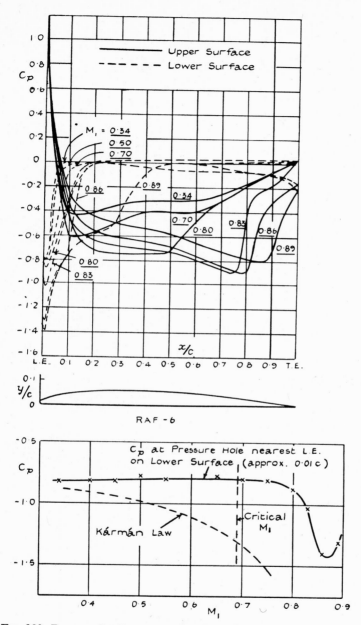

FIG. 180. Pressure distributions on R.A.F.–6 aerofoil at $\alpha = 0.5°$ approx. $(C_L = 0.2 \text{ to } 0.4)$.

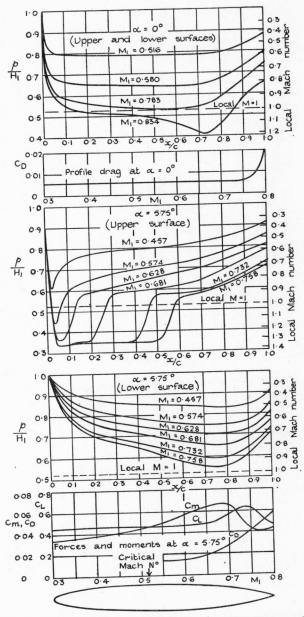

FIG. 181. Pressure distributions and forces on E.C. 1250 aerofoil.
$p$ = local static pressure.       $R = 1 \cdot 2 \times 10^6$ to $1 \cdot 8 \times 10^6$.
$H_1$ = stagnation pressure in free stream.
The local Mach-number scales are calculated from the surface pressures, assuming
homentropic flow.

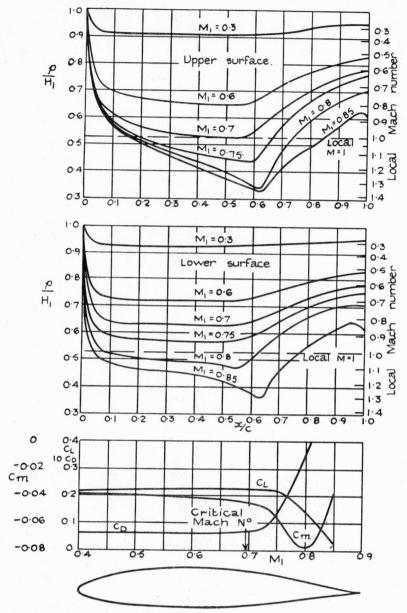

FIG. 182 (a). Pressure distributions and forces on Goldstein 'roof-top' aerofoil
1442/1547. $\alpha = +0.5°$, $R = 1.0 \times 10^6$ to $1.9 \times 10^6$. (Symbols as in Fig. 181.)
The local Mach-number scales are calculated from the surface pressures, assuming
homentropic flow.
(The same pressure distributions are given in another form in Fig. 182 (b).)

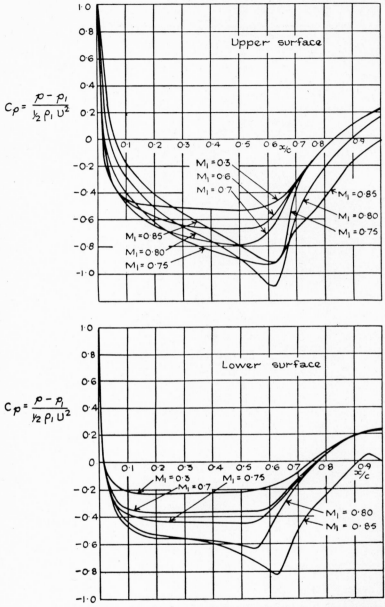

FIG. 182 (b). Pressure distributions on Goldstein 'roof-top' aerofoil 1442/1547.
$\alpha = +0.5°$.    $R = 1.0 \times 10^6$ to $1.9 \times 10^6$.    $p$ = local static pressure.
$p_1$ = static pressure in free stream.

(Fig. 182 (a) shows the same pressure distributions in another form, together with
force and moment coefficients and the aerofoil section.)

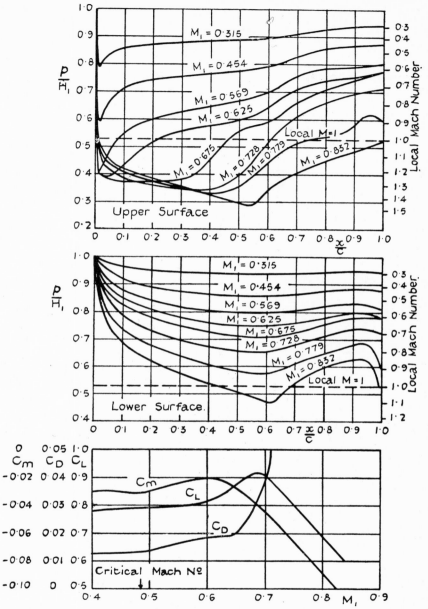

FIG. 182 (c). Pressure distributions and forces on Goldstein 'roof-top' aerofoil
1442/1547. $\alpha = +6.5°$, $R = 1.0 \times 10^6$ to $1.9 \times 10^6$. (Symbols as in Fig. 181.)
The local Mach-number scales are calculated from the surface pressures, assuming
homentropic flow.
(The aerofoil section is shown in Fig. 182 (a).)

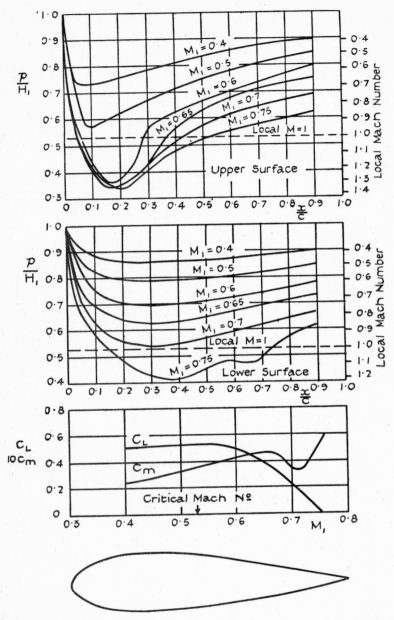

Fig. 183. Pressure distributions and forces on N.A.C.A. 23021 aerofoil. $\alpha = +5°$, $R = 2 \times 10^6$. (Symbols as in Fig. 181.)
The local Mach-number scales are calculated from the surface pressures, assuming homentropic flow.

High-Speed Tunnel at the N.P.L.† These may be compared with the pressure distributions on the same aerofoil shown in Fig. 182, but it should be noted that the tunnel conditions were not exactly the same in the two sets of experiments, so that the pressure distributions corresponding to the photographs may have been slightly different from those shown in Fig. 182. However, for a qualitative discussion of the development of shock waves, this difference is probably not important.

The light source used for these photographs was an electric spark, giving an exposure time of about $10^{-6}$ second. This time is so short that any movements of the shock waves are effectively arrested, and the photographs do not distinguish between steady shock waves and ones that are oscillating or moving steadily along the surface of the aerofoil. Thus in Plate 16 (*b*), where the Mach number is below the critical value of 0·695, the wavelets shown are probably travelling slowly towards the nose of the aerofoil, the formation of stationary shock waves being impossible at this speed.

The photographs show that as the Mach number increases the shock waves move back towards the trailing edge and become more intense. At low incidence (Plate 16) the rearward movement of the shock wave with increasing Mach number is much more pronounced on the lower surface than on the upper one; this difference is probably due to the smaller curvature of the lower surface.

The thickening or separation of the boundary layer, which occurs at high Mach numbers when the shock waves are strong, can be seen clearly in Plates 16 and 17. (The interaction between shock waves and boundary layers is discussed fully in Chap. X.) The position of the boundary layer transition on the upper surface can also be estimated roughly from these photographs. Pearcey‡ has shown that this occurs just downstream of the point of intersection of the edge of the dark shadow of the aerofoil and the bright line nearly parallel to, and well separated from, the aerofoil, which indicates a laminar boundary layer.

In the pressure distributions given for the E.C. 1250 aerofoil at 5·75° incidence (Fig. 181) the abrupt rise of pressure at the shock wave on the upper surface is clearly shown. In the other pressure

† Holder, 'The High-Speed Laboratory of the Aerodynamics Division, N.P.L.', *Rep. Memor. Aero. Res. Coun.*, No. 2,560 (1946).

‡ 'The indication of boundary layer transition on aerofoils in the N.P.L. 20 in. × 8 in. High-Speed Wind Tunnel', *Aero. Res. Coun.*, Current Paper No. 10 (1948).

distributions, however, the rise of pressure at the shock wave is more gradual, and in some cases cannot easily be distinguished from the pressure rise which occurs ordinarily on the rear part of an aerofoil, even at low speeds. These results are typical of high-speed wind-tunnel measurements, and similar effects have been found in flight.† As shown by Ackeret, Feldmann, and Rott,‡ the 'softening' of the pressure rise at the shock wave is due to the effect of the boundary layer, and if the static pressures are measured outside the boundary layer a much sharper pressure rise is observed (see Chap. X).

The results given in Figs. 181, 182, and 183 show that, as the free-stream Mach number increases above the critical value, the maximum local Mach number on the surface of the aerofoil increases up to about $1\cdot4$, and then remains roughly constant with further increase of Mach number. At the same time, the shock waves move back with increase of Mach number, the extent of this backward movement depending on the shape and incidence of the aerofoil.

In most cases the upper limiting value of the local Mach number on the surface of the aerofoil is roughly independent of incidence. The peak suction on the upper surface usually increases rapidly with incidence until the limiting value is reached, but any further increase of incidence has little effect on the peak suction. This sometimes leads to a serious limitation of the maximum lift coefficient of the aerofoil.§

It has already been pointed out that the formation of stationary shock waves is not possible when the local velocity is everywhere subsonic, i.e. below the critical Mach number. The assumption has often been made that shock waves *necessarily* occur as soon as the critical Mach number is exceeded, but there is no definite evidence to show that this assumption is correct. Theoretical solutions have been obtained for inviscid flow past aerofoils, in which local supersonic regions are present without any singularities, i.e. without shock waves (see Chap. VII). It is not known, however, whether these 'shock-free' flows are stable, or whether they can exist when viscosity

---

† Charnley and Mair, 'Measurements of pressure distribution on a Spitfire wing in flight at high speeds', *Rep. Memor. Aero. Res. Coun.*, No. 2,159 (1945).

‡ 'Untersuchungen an Verdichtungsstößen und Grenzschichten in schnell bewegten Gasen', *Mitt. Inst. Aerodyn. E.T.H. Zürich*, No. 10 (1946), *Rep. Aero. Res. Coun.*, No. 10,044.

§ e.g. Thompson and Adamson, loc. cit. on p. 617.

effects are present. It is not even certain that solutions of this kind can be obtained for all shapes of aerofoil.

It is found that these theoretical solutions break down when the Mach number exceeds a certain value; limit lines then appear in the flow and the acceleration becomes infinite on these lines. All solutions of this type so far obtained have been determined by the hodograph method, so that the shape of the aerofoil boundary changes with Mach number and singularities on the boundary appear simultaneously with the limit lines. For a given fixed boundary it has not so far been found possible to obtain theoretically an upper limit of Mach number, above which shock waves must be formed.

The actual Mach number at which shock waves first appear in the flow past an aerofoil can at present only be found by experiment. Unfortunately, when the maximum local Mach number is only slightly greater than unity, the very weak shock waves which may appear are difficult to detect, and hence there is some uncertainty about the interpretation of the experimental results. The information available at present suggests that on most aerofoils shock waves probably appear at a Mach number which is only slightly above the critical value.

On aerofoils where the peak suction coefficient occurs at a region of large curvature (e.g. near the leading edge of a thin aerofoil at a high incidence) it has been found that large changes of lift and drag do not occur until the critical Mach number has been exceeded by a considerable margin (e.g. see the curve for $C_L = 0.6$ in Fig. 189). A possible explanation of this is that in such cases no shock waves are formed until a Mach number considerably above the critical value has been reached. There is no experimental proof of this, however, and an alternative possible explanation is that although shock waves are formed at a Mach number near the critical value, they are short, with only a small supersonic region, and do not have any important effect on the pressure distribution until much higher Mach numbers are reached.

*Interaction between shock waves and boundary layers.* Experiments by Ackeret, Feldmann, and Rott,† by Liepmann,‡ and by Fage and

† Loc. cit. on p. 626.
‡ 'The interaction between boundary layer and shock waves in transonic flow', *J. Aero. Sci.* **13** (1946), 623–37.

Sargent† have shown the importance of the interaction between shock waves and boundary layers on aerofoils at high subsonic speeds (see Chap. X). It was found that the type of shock-wave formation, and its effect on the boundary layer, depended on the state of the boundary layer in front of the shock wave, and especially on whether it was laminar or turbulent. With a laminar boundary layer, at the Reynolds numbers of these experiments, the boundary layer separated in most cases and one or more forked shock waves were usually formed. (When the Mach number ahead of the shock wave was only slightly greater than 1, any separation of the laminar boundary layer was followed almost immediately by re-attachment.) With a turbulent boundary layer at moderate Mach numbers there was a single nearly normal shock wave, and the boundary layer thickened but did not separate. At higher Mach numbers the shock wave was forked and caused separation even with a turbulent boundary layer. The rise of pressure at the surface of the aerofoil in the neighbourhood of the shock wave was much more gradual with a laminar boundary layer than with a turbulent one. All these experimenters' results taken together seem to imply that in addition to changes of behaviour due to the laminar or turbulent state of the boundary layer, the Reynolds number in either or both of these cases may have an important influence on the type of shock-wave formation.

These results, with the consequent changes of pressure distribution and drag, have an important bearing on the application of high-speed wind-tunnel results to full-scale flight conditions, because the Reynolds number of a wind-tunnel test is usually much less than that of full-scale flight. Measurements at the N.P.L.‡ and in Germany§ have shown that the boundary layer on an aerofoil in a high-speed tunnel usually remains laminar as far back as the shock wave (at least for Reynolds numbers up to about $5 \times 10^6$). The position of the transition point on a wing has not been measured in full-scale flight at high Mach numbers, but observations at lower speeds suggest that transition may often occur near the leading edge. If this is so,

† 'Shock wave and boundary layer phenomena near a flat surface', *Proc. Roy. Soc.* A, **190** (1947), 1–20.

‡ Holder, 'Transition indication in the N.P.L. 20 in. × 8 in. High-Speed Tunnel', *Rep. Memor. Aero. Res. Coun.*, No. 2,079 (1945).

§ Göthert, 'Widerstandsanstieg bei Profilen im Bereich hoher Unterschall-geschwindigkeiten', *U.M.* 1167 (also *Tech. Ber.* 11, 7) (1944), *M.A.P. Völkenrode R. & T.* No. 36, *Rep. Aero. Res. Coun.*, No. 9,705.

the boundary layer will usually be turbulent in front of the shock wave in full-scale flight, and the shock-wave formation will probably differ considerably from that found in high-speed wind-tunnel tests at low Reynolds numbers, where the boundary layer is laminar immediately in front of the shock wave.

A few measurements of wing pressure distribution have been made in full-scale flight,[†] but on account of experimental difficulties it has not yet been possible to make any satisfactory comparisons with the results of wind-tunnel tests at high Mach numbers (see Chap. XI).

Some tests have been made in the R.A.E. High-Speed Tunnel to investigate the effect of Reynolds number on aerofoil pressure distributions at high subsonic Mach numbers. The tests only covered a limited range of Reynolds numbers, between about $0.5 \times 10^6$ and $3.5 \times 10^6$, but they did show a small but consistent increase in the peak suction coefficient in front of the shock wave with Reynolds number. There were also indications of changes of shape in the pressure-distribution curves, similar to those found by Ackeret, Feldmann, and Rott. Analysis of the R.A.E. results is still proceeding, and they have not yet been published.

*Effect of roughness.* Göthert[‡] has investigated the effect of surface roughness on the pressure distribution on an aerofoil at high Mach numbers. At a Reynolds number of about $4 \times 10^6$, roughness had no appreciable effect when the grain size was less than about 0.006 per cent. of the aerofoil chord. With larger grain sizes, however, the shock waves usually occurred nearer the leading edge on the rough aerofoil than on the smooth one, the difference of shock-wave position being sometimes as great as 25 per cent. of the chord. It was also found in some cases that the pressure rise at the shock wave was more gradual on the rough aerofoil than on the smooth one.

*Effect of section shape.* Only a little information is available on the effect of variations of aerofoil section on the pressure distribution at high subsonic Mach numbers. The lack of any satisfactory theory for the flow past aerofoils at high subsonic speeds, when shock waves are present, makes it difficult to derive any general conclusions from the available experimental results. Some systematic measure-

[†] Charnley and Mair, loc. cit. on p. 626.
[‡] Unpublished. Results given in *Rep. Aero. Res. Coun.*, No. 9,064 (1945). Some of these results are also given by Göthert, loc. cit. on p. 628.

ments have been made by Göthert† at the D.V.L. on a family of aerofoils based on the N.A.C.A. series,‡ but only a few of the many important variables have been explored and more extensive systematic tests are required for a full understanding of the subject. Some tentative conclusions from the results obtained by Göthert and others are given below, but in view of the complexity of the subject it should be emphasized that further work may make it necessary to revise these conclusions.

At low incidences, increasing the thickness ratio of an aerofoil causes an increase in the suction coefficients (and local Mach numbers), for a given incidence and free-stream Mach number. Thus a given local Mach number is reached at a lower value of the free-stream Mach number on a thick aerofoil than on a thin one, so that the critical Mach number, and the Mach number at which large changes of lift and drag occur, are also lower for a thick aerofoil.

On a cambered aerofoil at a positive lift, the peak suction coefficients at high Mach numbers are usually greater on the upper surface than on the lower one, even when the incidence is less than the 'design' value. As a result, the critical Mach number is usually a maximum for an incidence giving roughly zero lift, and not for the 'design' incidence. The Mach number at which large changes of lift and drag occur is sometimes a maximum for an even lower incidence, giving a negative lift.

As the position of the maximum thickness is moved back on an aerofoil with small camber at a low incidence, the position of the shock wave (for a given Mach number) also moves back. The critical Mach number of an aerofoil is usually increased slightly by moving the maximum thickness back, but the effect of a shock wave in causing separation or thickening of the boundary layer is sometimes

† Loc. cit. on p. 629; id., 'Profilmessungen im Hochgeschwindigkeitskanal 2·7 m. D.', *F.B.* 1490 (1941), *M.A.P. Völkenrode R. & T.*, No. 410; id. 'Druckverteilungs- und Impulsverlust-Schaubilder für das Profil N.A.C.A. (00xx–1.1 30) bei hohen Unterschallgeschwindigkeiten', *F.B.* 1505/1–5 (1941), *M.A.P. Völkenrode R. & T.*, No. 404; id. 'Hochgeschwindigkeitsmessungen an Profilen gleicher Dickenverteilung mit verschiedener Krümmung im D.V.L. Hochgeschwindigkeitskanal', *F.B.* 1910/1 and 1910/6 (1943), *M.A.P. Völkenrode R. & T.*, Nos. 400, 402; id. 'Hochgeschwindigkeitsmessungen an Profilen der Reihe N.A.C.A. 230 mit verschiedenen Dickenverhältnissen', *U.M.* 1259/1–3 (1944), *M.A.P. Völkenrode R: & T.*, No. 409; id. 'Druckverteilungsschaubilder für das Profil N.A.C.A. 230 — bei hohen Unterschallgeschwindigkeiten', *U.M.* 1260/1–3 (1944), *M.A.P. Völkenrode R. & T.*, No. 403.

‡ Jacobs, Ward, and Pinkerton, 'The characteristics of 78 related airfoil sections from tests in the variable density wind tunnel', *Tech. Rep. Nat. Adv. Comm. Aero.*, No. 460 (1933).

greater when it occurs far back on an aerofoil, so that the Mach number at which important changes of lift and drag occur may not be increased appreciably by moving back the position of maximum thickness.

*Effects of incidence and control flaps.* The effect of changing incidence on aerofoil pressure distributions at high Mach numbers can be seen from Figs. 181 and 182. At high incidences and low Mach numbers there is a sharp suction peak near the leading edge on the upper surface, but at higher Mach numbers this flattens out, giving a fairly large region of approximately constant suction. With increasing Mach number the shock wave moves back and the region of high suction becomes larger, but the maximum local Mach number remains roughly constant. For a given Mach number, as the incidence increases, the shock wave moves forward on the upper surface and backward on the lower surface. It has been shown by Göthert† that these shock-wave movements with changing incidence, which have important effects on the lift and pitching moment, can be reduced by modifying the rear part of the aerofoil so as to reduce the trailing-edge angle.

Fig. 184 shows the results of some measurements of pressure distribution on an aerofoil with a control flap, in the High-Speed Tunnel at the N.P.L.‡ At Mach numbers below the critical value changes of flap angle have considerable effects on the pressures in front of the hinge, but at high Mach numbers, when shock waves occur at or behind the hinge line, the pressures in front of the hinge are nearly independent of the flap angle. This result is to be expected, because at high Mach numbers there is a large supersonic region, extending forward from the shock wave towards the leading edge, and changes due to movements of the flap cannot be transmitted upstream through this supersonic region. The loss of control effectiveness due to this phenomenon is discussed later (p. 660).

Another important phenomenon, which takes place over a fairly narrow range of Mach number around 0·85, has been observed recently.§ In general, when there is a well-developed supersonic region on one surface of an aerofoil with a control flap, this is

† Loc. cit. on p. 629.
‡ Beavan, Hyde, and Fowler, loc. cit. on p. 616.
§ Shaw, 'Changes in control characteristics with changes in flow pattern at high subsonic speeds. Tests on an E.C. 1250 aerofoil with 25% concave control flap', *Rep. Memor. Aero. Res. Coun.*, No. 2,436 (1948).

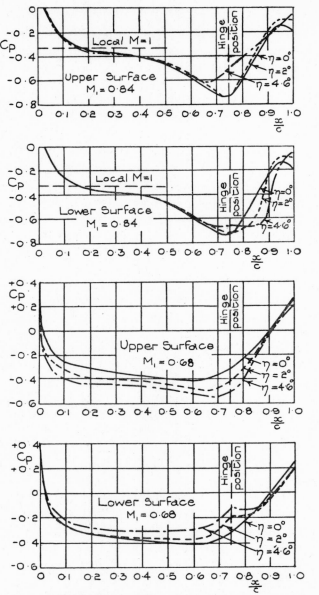

Fig. 184. Pressure distributions on E.C. 1250 aerofoil with 25 per cent. control flap. Incidence $= 0°$, $R \approx 1.8 \times 10^6$.

$x =$ distance from L.E. of aerofoil.  $C_p = \dfrac{p-p_1}{\frac{1}{2}\rho_1 U^2}$.  $\eta =$ flap angle.

$e =$ chord of aerofoil.  $p =$ local static pressure.

$p_1 =$ static pressure in free stream.  (Aerofoil shape is shown in Fig. 181.)

PLATE 18

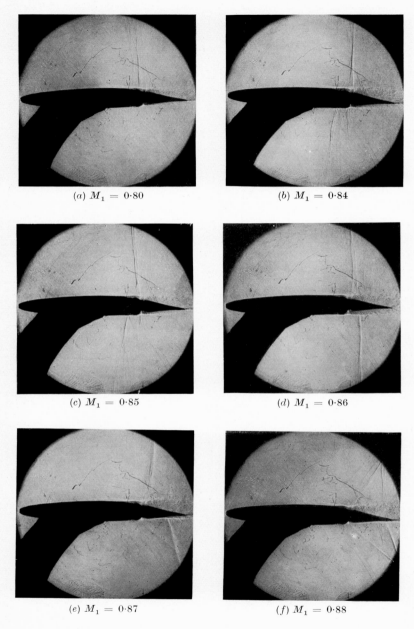

(a) $M_1 = 0{\cdot}80$          (b) $M_1 = 0{\cdot}84$

(c) $M_1 = 0{\cdot}85$          (d) $M_1 = 0{\cdot}86$

(e) $M_1 = 0{\cdot}87$          (f) $M_1 = 0{\cdot}88$

Aerofoil E.C. 1250 with 25 per cent. concave control flap, $\alpha = 0°$,
$\eta = 5°$

terminated by a normal shock at the control hinge, with severe thickening (possibly separation) of the boundary layer there. It appears that it may often happen that at a slightly higher Mach number the flow behind the hinge reattaches itself to the surface, the necessary turning of the flow at the hinge occurring through an oblique shock wave of suitable magnitude (or even in some cases through a Prandtl–Meyer expansion). A normal shock wave with thickening of the boundary layer then occurs farther back along the control and may even be delayed to the trailing edge.

Pressure distributions and corresponding direct-shadow photographs of the flow for a typical case are shown in Fig. 185 and Plate 18. (The sudden changes of pressure shown in Fig. 185 for $M_1 = 0.87$ and $0.88$ are drawn to correspond to the shock waves shown at the hinge in Plate 18.)

It has been verified that this effect is not dependent on the state of the boundary layer before the hinge, since very similar changes occurred in an experiment when the stream ahead of the aerofoil was made turbulent by a wire. It seems necessary that the pressure distribution ahead of the hinge should be favourable (i.e. accelerating flow) and that a high local Mach number, about $1.4$ for an oblique shock wave, $1.25$ for a Prandtl–Meyer expansion, should be reached.

*Effect of a small bulging of the surface.* At low speeds the change in the pressure distribution on an aerofoil surface is severe even for quite a small bulging, such as may occur in flight under load or on wind-tunnel models not made to the highest degree of accuracy.† Some measurements have been made at speeds above the critical to observe the pressure distribution in the presence of bulges having a height about 1/40th of their length.‡ Photographs of the shock waves were also taken.

Two examples of the development of the pressure distributions and shock-wave systems and the resultant force-changes are shown in Figs. 186 and 187. The first is the case of zero incidence on an otherwise symmetrical aerofoil, and shows that the low-speed type of pressure distribution is maintained, despite the presence of a

---

† Fage, 'The smallest size of a surface bulge, ridge or hollow which affects the drag of a laminar flow aerofoil', *Rep. Memor. Aero. Res. Coun.*, No. 2,120 (1943).

‡ Beavan and Rogers 'High-speed wind tunnel tests on an aerofoil with and without spanwise bulges', *Rep. Aero. Res. Coun.*, No. 13,786 (1951).

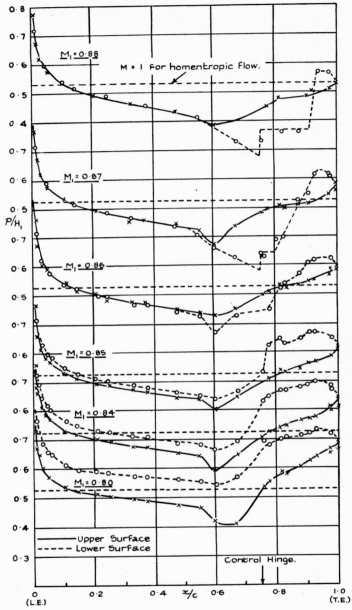

FIG. 185. Pressure distributions on aerofoil E.C. 1250 with 25 per cent. concave control flap. $\alpha = 0°, \eta = 5°$.

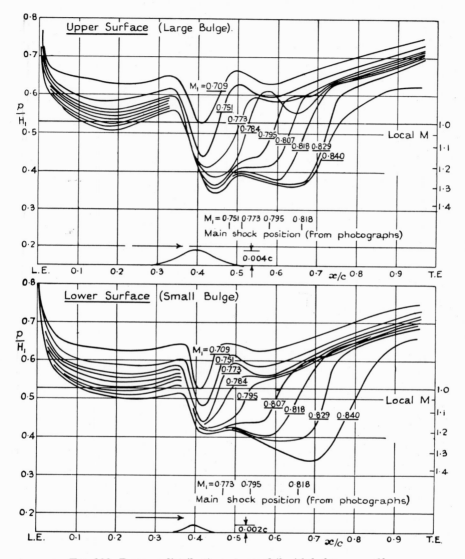

Fɪɢ. 186. Pressure distributions on aerofoil with bulges. $\alpha = 0°$.
The local Mach-number scales are calculated from the surface pressures, assuming
homentropic flow.

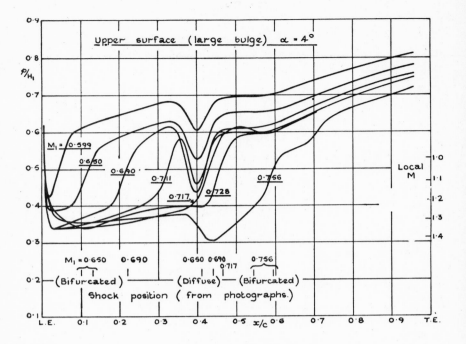

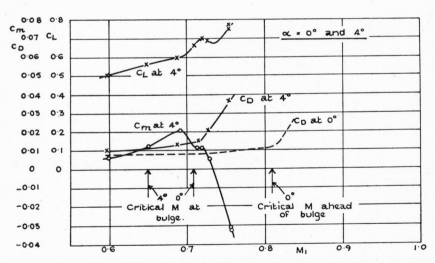

FIG. 187. Pressure distributions on upper surface, and force changes—aerofoil with bulges.

The local Mach-number scale on the upper figure is calculated from the surface pressures, assuming homentropic flow.

shock wave at the rear of the bulge, to a Mach number 0·04 above the critical value on the bulge. The shock wave then begins to move downstream; somewhat later the boundary layer thickens and the sharp rise of drag begins. The tests were made, as indicated in Fig. 186, in the presence of a second bulge of half the height and width on the lower surface. It can be seen that the effects due to this bulge, which at low speed gives the same peak disturbance in the pressure, are very similar to those on the upper surface.

The second case is at an incidence of 4°, where the suction peak that is now present near the nose is higher than that at the bulge. When the Mach number is increased, normal shock waves form both on the bulge and near the nose. The latter develops in the usual way, starting to move back along the chord at a speed considerably above the critical; but that on the bulge remains in position until the other coalesces with it, which happens rapidly with quite a small increase in speed. It is only then that the boundary layer begins to thicken and the steep drag-rise begins, as the combined shock wave continues the movement towards the trailing edge.

## § 5. Aerofoils at supersonic speeds

*Pressure distributions.* For an aerofoil with sharp leading and trailing edges the pressure distributions at supersonic speeds can be calculated with fair accuracy by the use of Busemann's[†] second-order theory (see Chap. VIII), provided that the Mach number is high enough for the attachment of the shock wave at the nose and that the inclination of the aerofoil surface to the stream is small at all points. If the bow wave is detached from the nose of the aerofoil, either because the nose is rounded or because the Mach number is relatively low, no theoretical method is available for calculating the pressure distribution.

Lock[‡] has considered the application of Busemann's theory to the calculation of pressure distributions and forces on aerofoils of

† 'Aerodynamischer Auftrieb bei Überschallgeschwindigkeit', *Proc. 5th Volta Congr. Rome (1935)*; also *Luftfahrtforsch.* 12 (1935), 210–20, translated as *Rep. Aer. Res. Coun.*, No. 2,844.

‡ 'Examples of the application of Busemann's formula to evaluate the aerodynamic force coefficients on supersonic aerofoils', *Rep. Memor. Aero. Res. Coun.*, No. 2,101 (1944).

simple shape, and has pointed out that for some simple sections the second-order terms have no effect on the lift or drag (see p. 669). Hence in these cases, when only the overall forces are required, it is sufficient to use the first-order theory given by Ackeret.† In cases where the inclination of the aerofoil surface to the stream is not small enough at all points to make the third-order and higher terms negligible, the exact theory as given by Lighthill‡ may be used (provided the shock wave is attached at the nose).§ However, since all these theories refer only to inviscid flow, and since in a real fluid viscosity has important effects on the pressure distribution, there is in practice hardly ever any justification for using any theory more exact than Busemann's second-order one. In fact, as will be shown later, the effects of the neglected third-order and higher terms are counteracted to some extent by the effects of viscosity.

A few measurements of pressure distribution have been made on aerofoils at supersonic speeds,‖, †† for comparison with calculations by Busemann's method. Some typical results, obtained by Ferri‖ on a symmetrical bi-convex aerofoil $(t/c = 0.10)$, are given in Fig. 188. The agreement with the theoretical calculations by Busemann's method (shown by dotted lines) is good except at points near the rear of the aerofoil where the theory predicts a high suction. Schlieren photographs (taken on a slightly different aerofoil) showed that this discrepancy between theory and experiment at the rear of the aerofoil was due to separation of the boundary layer. The separation occurs near the point at which the experimental pressure-distribution curve begins to depart seriously from the theoretical curve. At the same point there is a weak inclined shock wave. The rear shock wave, which would start at the trailing edge in the absence

† 'Luftkräfte auf Flügel die mit größerer als Schallgeschwindigkeit bewegt werden', *Z. Flugtech.* 16 (1925), 72–74; Taylor, 'Applications to aeronautics of Ackeret's theory of aerofoils moving at speeds greater than that of sound', *Rep. Memor. Aero. Res. Coun.*, No. 1,467 (1932).

‡ 'Two-dimensional supersonic aerofoil theory', ibid. No. 1,929 (1944).

§ Strictly, the exact theory becomes inapplicable when the Mach number immediately behind the nose shock-wave falls below 1. For a given aerofoil and incidence, this occurs at a Mach number very slightly greater than that at which the bow wave becomes detached, but the difference between the two limits is not important in practice.

‖ Ferri, 'Alcuni risultati sperimentali riguardanti profili alari provati alla Galleria Ultrasonora di Guidonia', *Atti Guidonia*, No. 17 (1939). (Part of this paper has been translated as *M.A.P. Transl.* No. 1,115, *Rep. Aero. Res. Coun.*, No. 4,780.)

†† Valensi and Pruden, 'Some observations on sharp nosed profiles at supersonic speed', *6th Int. Congr. Appl. Mech. Paris* (1946), *Rep. Memor. Aero. Res. Coun.*, No. 2,482 (1947).

PLATE 19

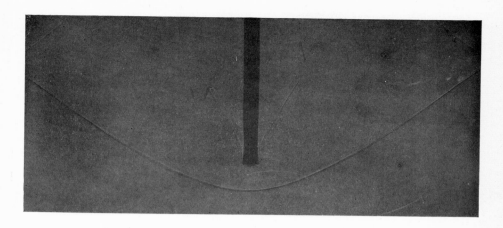

Shadow and schlieren photographs for a flat plate with square nose
$M_1 = 1\cdot6$

PLATE 20

Shadow and schlieren photographs of aerofoil
E.C. 1250. $M_1 = 1.8$

of viscosity, actually starts at a point near the trailing edge but outside the wake from the separated boundary layer.†

It may be noted that this discrepancy between theory and experiment only occurs when the theory predicts a pressure falling appreciably below that of.the free stream, with a shock wave at the trailing edge. For example, in Fig. 188 the theoretical results for the lower surface at $\alpha = 8°$ show a pressure coefficient only slightly below zero at the trailing edge, and in this case there is hardly any discrepancy.

Apart from discrepancies of the kind discussed above, caused by separation of the boundary layer, the Busemann theory gives a fairly reliable indication of the pressure distribution on an aerofoil at supersonic speeds. In some cases the agreement with experiment is fairly good even at incidences and Mach numbers at which the theory is not strictly applicable (i.e. when the shock wave is detached from the nose).

The forces on aerofoils at supersonic speeds are considered in § 9.

*Flow about rounded leading edges at supersonic speeds.* Some observations have recently been made‡ of the detached bow wave and other features accompanying the flow at supersonic speeds past rounded leading edges. Schlieren and shadowgraph pictures were taken at Mach numbers of 1·45, 1·6, and 1·8 for (i) flat plates with elliptic noses of axis ratio varying from zero (a square nose) to eight, (ii) a circular cylinder, and (iii) an aerofoil of section E.C. 1250. Typical photographs are shown in Plates 19 and 20.

With noses blunter than a semicircle there is a separation of the boundary layer near the shoulder, with subsequent reattachment, and the shape and position of the bow wave do not vary much with nose shape. The photographs show a second shock wave at the point of reattachment of the boundary layer.

Estimates of the position of the detached shock wave by theory based on the squares method§ and otherwise‖ did not agree with the

---

† Recent experiments by H. W. Liepmann (unpublished) have shown that the separation found by Ferri only appears when the boundary layer is laminar. With a turbulent boundary layer there is no appreciable separation. The rear shock waves then start very near the trailing edge and the pressure distribution agrees much better with the theoretical results.

‡ Holder, Tomlinson, and Rogers, 'Preliminary experiments on blunt nosed plates in supersonic airstreams', *Rep. Aero. Res. Coun.*, No. 12,418 (1949).

§ Maccoll and Codd, loc. cit. on p. 613; Drougge, 'Flow around conical tips in the upper transonic range', *F.F.A. Meddelande*, No. 25 (1948).

‖ Dugundji, 'An investigation of the detached shock in front of a body of revolution', *J. Aero. Sci.* **15** (1948), 699; Lin and Rubinov, 'On the flow behind curved shocks', *J. Math. Phys.* **27** (1948), 105.

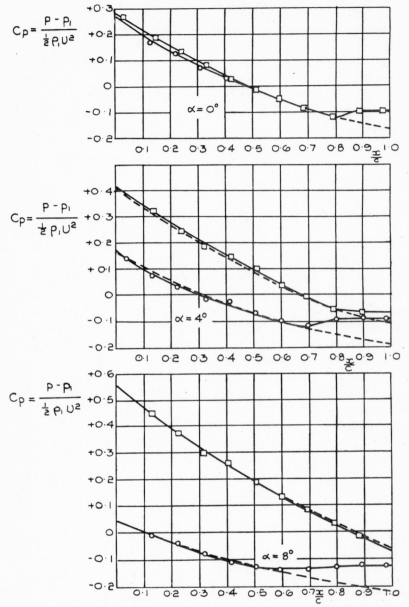

FIG. 188. Pressure distributions on symmetrical bi-convex aerofoil at $M_1 = 2.13$.
$t/c = 0.10$, $R = 6.4 \times 10^5$.
Experimental results: —○— upper, —□— lower surface.
Theoretical results for Busemann's second-order theory: - - - .
$p$ = local static pressure. $p_1$ = static pressure in free stream.

observations, although the shapes of the waves were similar. Later measurements of pressure distribution by Holder and Chinneck (not yet published) have shown reasonably good agreement with the theoretical results obtained by Maccoll and Codd.[†]

## § 6. Drag.  Subsonic speeds

*Typical experimental results.* Fig. 189 shows the variation of profile drag coefficient with Mach number for a typical symmetrical aerofoil. The measurements were made in the D.V.L. High-Speed Tunnel,[‡] using an aerofoil with end plates to simulate infinite aspect ratio.

The results show that the drag coefficient is roughly constant at Mach numbers up to about 0·7, with a rapid increase of drag at higher Mach numbers. The Mach number $(M_D)$ at which the drag starts to rise rapidly, which is often called the 'drag critical' Mach number, decreases slightly with increase of lift coefficient. The critical Mach number, at which local sonic velocity is first reached, is indicated by an arrow on each of the curves. It is clear that there is no simple relation between the critical Mach number and the drag critical Mach number $M_D$.

It may be noted that all the curves show little or no change of drag at Mach numbers below the critical value. Young and Winterbottom[§] have shown theoretically that at Mach numbers below the critical value, when no shock waves can be formed, only a very small change of drag coefficient with Mach number is to be expected. Most of the available experimental results agree very well with this conclusion, the only exceptions being cases in which an increase of drag is caused by forward movement of the transition point or by separation of the boundary layer. (The slight increase of drag shown for $C_L = 0$ in Fig. 189, between $M_1 = 0·65$ and $M_1 = 0·75$, is probably caused by forward movement of the transition point due to increase of tunnel turbulence with speed.)

*Effect of shock waves.* At low lift coefficients the results given in Fig. 189 show a rapid rise of drag coefficient soon after the critical Mach number is exceeded. This rise of drag coefficient is caused by

---

† Loc. cit. on p. 613.

‡ Göthert, 'Hochgeschwindigkeitsmessungen an Profilen gleicher Dickenverteilung mit verschiedener Krümmung im D.V.L. Hochgeschwindigkeitskanal', *F.B.* 1910/1 and 1910/6 (1943); *M.A.P. Völkenrode R. & T.*, Nos. 400 and 402.

§ 'Note on the effect of compressibility on the profile drag of aerofoils in the absence of shock waves', *Rep. Memor. Aero. Res. Coun.*, No. 2,400 (1940).

the formation of shock waves, probably accompanied by thickening or separation of the boundary layer. At higher lift coefficients there is a much greater difference between the critical Mach number and

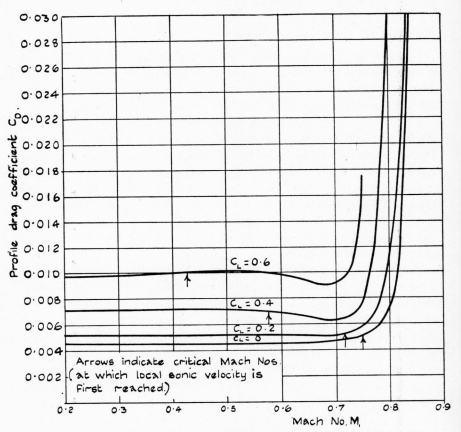

Fig. 189. Variation of profile drag coefficient with Mach number. N.A.C.A. 0012–0·5540 aerofoil (infinite aspect ratio). ($R = 4·5 \times 10^6$ at $M_1 = 0·8$.)

Max. thickness = 12 per cent. chord at 40 per cent. chord from L.E.
Camber = 0.  L.E. radius = $0·55(t/c)^2 c = 0·8$ per cent. $c$.

the drag critical Mach number. Measurements of pressure distribution, made at the same time as the drag measurements, showed that shock waves were probably formed at a Mach number not much above the critical value, even for these high lift coefficients, but apparently the shock waves did not cause much thickening or separation of the boundary layer until a much higher Mach number was reached. On a thin symmetrical aerofoil at a high incidence, the shock wave forms first on the upper surface near the leading edge, at a region of high curvature, and it appears that the absence of any serious effect on the boundary layer may be associated with the high surface curvature at the position of the shock wave.

The explanation of the slight decrease of drag coefficient above the critical Mach number, shown in Fig. 189 for high lift coefficients, is that the shock wave moves back with increase of Mach number and the transition point moves back with it.† (This is because the pressure gradient is usually favourable as far back as the shock wave.) Thus there is a reduction of drag due to the farther back transition, and this outweighs the small increase of drag due to the loss of energy at the shock wave. (If there were any separation of the boundary layer, this would of course give a large increase of drag.)

Beavan‡ has analysed the results of a large number of drag measurements on aerofoils in the N.P.L. High-Speed Tunnels, and has found that the rate of increase of drag with Mach number, after the drag starts to rise rapidly, is roughly the same for all the aerofoils considered and for all incidences. He found that the average value of $(\partial C_D/\partial M_1)_\alpha$ was about $0.45$, for values of $C_D$ between $0.015$ and $0.030$ and for a Reynolds number of about $1.8 \times 10^6$. Measurements in the R.A.E. High-Speed Tunnel, at about the same Reynolds number, give values of $(\partial C_D/\partial M_1)_\alpha$ agreeing fairly well with Beavan's figure.§ Göthert's measurements at the D.V.L., at a Reynolds number of about $4.5 \times 10^6$, also give values of $(\partial C_D/\partial M_1)_\alpha$ of the same order (e.g. Fig. 190). The value of $(\partial C_D/\partial M_1)_{C_L}$ is usually considerably greater than $(\partial C_D/\partial M_1)_\alpha$ (e.g. Fig. 189) because at high Mach numbers the incidence has to be increased with the Mach number in order to keep $C_L$ constant.

*Effect of section shape and incidence.* Measurements made in high-speed tunnels at the D.V.L.‖ and elsewhere have shown that the

---

† Holder, loc. cit. on p. 628; Göthert, loc. cit. on p. 628.

‡ 'Note on rise of drag above the critical Mach number—results in the N.P.L. High-Speed Tunnels', *Rep. Aero. Res. Coun.*, No. 8,682 (1945).

§ e.g. Mair and Gamble, 'The effect of model size on measurements in the R.A.E. High-Speed Tunnel. Drag of two-dimensional symmetrical aerofoils at zero incidence', *Rep. Memor. Aero. Res. Coun.*, No. 2,527 (1944).

‖ Göthert, 'Profilmessungen im Hochgeschwindigkeitskanal 2·7 m. D.', *F.B.* 1490 (1941), *M.A.P. Völkenrode R. & T.* No. 410; also, 'Druckverteilungs- und Impulsverlustschaubilder für das Profil N.A.C.A. (00xx—1.1 30) bei hohen Unterschallgeschwindigkeiten', *F.B.* 1505/1–5 (1941), *M.A.P. Völkenrode R. & T.*, No. 404.

thickness/chord ratio is a most important variable affecting the drag of an aerofoil at high Mach numbers, especially at low incidences. Fig. 190 shows some typical results from measurements made at the D.V.L. At zero incidence, reduction of the thickness ratio gives a considerable increase in the drag critical Mach number. For high Mach numbers, and for the range of thicknesses considered in Fig. 190, the Mach number corresponding to a given drag coefficient varies approximately linearly with $t/c$, the slope being given roughly by

$$\left(\frac{\partial M_1}{\partial(t/c)}\right)_{C_D} = -1\cdot2. \tag{3}$$

(It may be noted that this is not in accordance with the transonic similarity law given by von Kármán,† probably because the Mach numbers considered in these experimental results were not very near to unity.)

At higher incidences the rise of drag with Mach number is not so much affected by changes of aerofoil thickness, and in the particular case shown for $\alpha = 4°$ in Fig. 190 the drag at high Mach numbers is roughly the same for all values of $t/c$ between 0·09 and 0·18. It is not yet known whether similar results would be obtained on other families of aerofoils, because there have been very few systematic tests at high Mach numbers to investigate the effects of varying thickness. It may be noted, however, that the results given for $\alpha = 4°$ in Fig. 190 refer to aerofoils at the same *incidence*. If the comparison had been made at the same *lift coefficient*, the drag of the thicker aerofoils would have appeared relatively greater.

The effect of camber on the drag of aerofoils at high Mach numbers has also been investigated at the D.V.L.,‡ some typical results being shown in Figs. 191 and 192. The drag critical Mach number decreases with increasing camber, for all lift coefficients up to 0·6, although for the higher lift coefficients the critical Mach number increases with camber. These results show that the usual low-speed conception of 'design incidence' for a cambered aerofoil has no meaning at high Mach numbers when shock waves are present. This point is illustrated further in Fig. 192, in which the incidence for minimum drag is plotted against Mach number for aerofoils of different camber. At low Mach numbers the drag is a minimum approximately at the

† 'The similarity law of transonic flow', *J. Math. Phys.* **26** (1947), 182–90.
‡ Göthert, loc. cit. on p. 641.

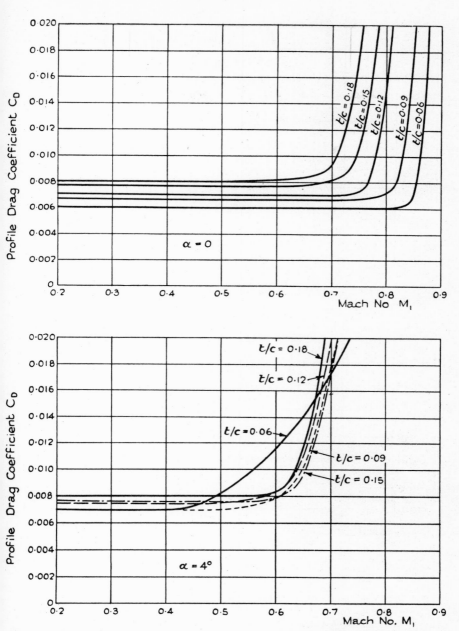

FIG. 190. Variation of drag coefficient with Mach number, for symmetrical aerofoils of different thickness-ratio.

(Infinite aspect ratio.)        $R = 4\cdot5 \times 10^6$ at $M_1 = 0\cdot8$.

Position of max. thickness = 30 per cent. chord.    L.E. radius = $1\cdot1(t/c)^2c$.

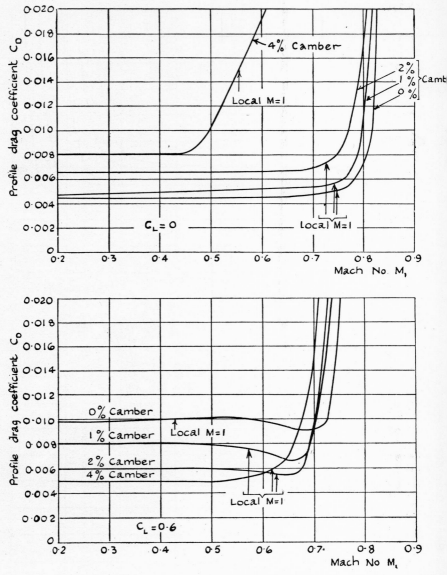

Fig. 191. Variation of drag coefficient with Mach number, for aerofoils of different camber.

(Infinite aspect ratio.) $R = 4 \cdot 5 \times 10^6$ at $M_1 = 0 \cdot 8$.
Max. thickness = 12 per cent. chord at 40 per cent. chord from L.E.
Position of max. camber = 35 per cent. chord from L.E.
L.E. radius = $0 \cdot 55(t/c)^2c = 0 \cdot 8$ per cent. $c$.

'design incidence', but at high Mach numbers the incidence for minimum drag changes suddenly to a negative value, returning nearly to zero at still higher Mach numbers.

It may be noted that the large increase of drag below the critical Mach number, shown in Fig. 191 for the 4 per cent. cambered aerofoil at $C_L = 0$, is due to a separation of the boundary layer on the lower

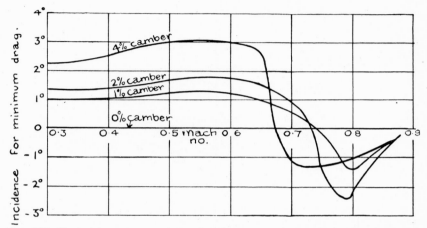

FIG. 192. Variation of incidence for minimum drag with Mach number. Cambered aerofoils of infinite aspect ratio. (For details see Fig. 191.)

surface near the leading edge. As the Mach number increases, the adverse pressure gradient also increases, and hence the separation becomes more serious. This is an example of a case in which Young and Winterbottom's theory[†] for the variation of drag below the critical Mach number does not apply. (The theory assumes, of course, that there is no separation of the boundary layer.)

Some tests have also been made at the D.V.L.[‡] to investigate the effect of varying the position of the maximum thickness on the drag of an aerofoil at high Mach numbers. Fig. 193 shows some of the results of these tests. At zero lift the drag critical Mach number does not vary much between the three aerofoils, but it is slightly greater for the aerofoil with maximum thickness at 40 per cent. chord than for the other two. At $C_L = 0.4$, however, there is a considerable increase in the drag critical Mach number as the maximum

† Loc. cit. on p. 641.
‡ Göthert, loc. cit. on p. 629.

thickness is moved back, although the critical Mach number at this value of $C_L$ actually decreases as the maximum thickness is moved back.

It should be noted that the fairly large differences of drag coefficient shown at low Mach numbers in Figs. 191 and 193 are mainly due to differences in the position of the transition point. At higher Reynolds numbers (e.g. in full-scale flight) the differences of drag between the various aerofoils at low Mach numbers would probably be much smaller.

Tests made at the D.V.L. on aerofoils with different leading-edge radii[†] showed that, at low incidences, variation of leading-edge radius had only a small effect on the drag coefficient at any Mach number. However, the tests only covered a small range of leading-edge radius, from 0·8 to 1·6 per cent. $c$, and it is possible that the effects on drag might be larger with radii outside this range. At higher incidences (e.g. $\alpha = 6°$), the drag at high Mach numbers decreased as the leading edge radius was reduced.

*Roughness and Reynolds number effects.* The effect of surface roughness on aerofoil pressure distributions at high Mach numbers has already been discussed (p. 629). When the grain size (at $R = 4 \times 10^6$) is less than about 0·006 per cent. of the chord, roughness has no effect, either on the pressure distribution or on the drag.[†] With larger grain sizes, however, roughness slightly reduces the drag critical Mach number, and hence increases the drag for a given Mach number.

Tests made on an aerofoil of N.A.C.A. 0012 section at the R.A.E.,[‡] to investigate the effect of surface roughness on drag over a range of Reynolds and Mach numbers, showed that the increase of drag due to roughness was independent of Mach number up to $M_1 = 0·7$, i.e. below the critical Mach number.

Experiments have been made at the R.A.E. to investigate the effect of Reynolds number on the drag of an aerofoil at high Mach numbers.[§] The work of Ackeret, Feldmann, and Rott[||] has shown, however, that the position of the transition point may be at least as important as the actual Reynolds number, so that the results of

[†] Göthert, loc. cit. on p. 629.
[‡] A. D. Young, Green, and E. Young, 'High-speed wind tunnel tests of the effect of camouflage paint roughness on drag', *Rep. Aero. Res. Coun.*, No. 8,152 (1944).
[§] Mair and Gamble, loc. cit. on p. 643.
[||] Loc. cit. on p. 626.

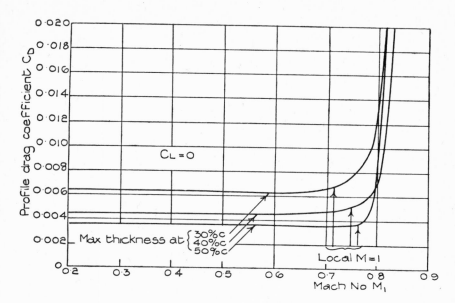

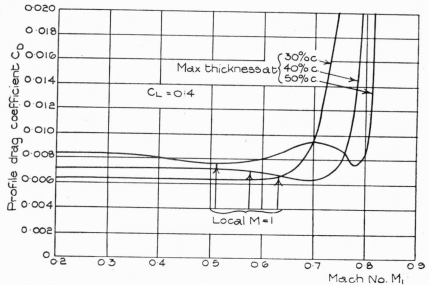

FIG. 193. Variation of drag coefficient with Mach number, for aerofoils having different positions of maximum thickness.

(Infinite aspect ratio.) $R = 4 \cdot 5 \times 10^6$ at $M_1 = 0 \cdot 8$.
Symmetrical aerofoils with max. thickness = 12 per cent. chord.
L.E. radius = $0 \cdot 55(t/c)^2 c = 0 \cdot 8$ per cent. $c$.

N

these experiments, in which no attempt was made to control or determine the position of the transition point, may not have much significance. Fig. 194 shows the variation of drag coefficient with

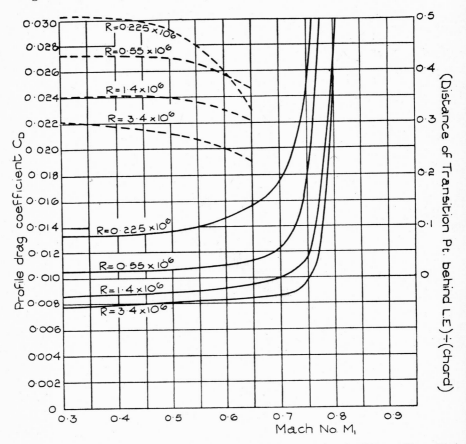

FIG. 194. Variation of profile drag coefficient with Mach number for different Reynolds numbers. N.A.C.A. 0015 aerofoil (symmetrical) at zero incidence. (Dotted lines show theoretical transition-point positions, calculated from measured drag coefficients.)

Mach number for the same aerofoil at several Reynolds numbers. There appears to be a considerable scale effect on the drag at high Mach numbers, especially between Reynolds numbers of $0.55 \times 10^6$ and $1.4 \times 10^6$. The position of the transition point, which was not measured in these tests, has been calculated from the measured drag coefficients for Mach numbers up to 0.65 (i.e. when there were no shock waves), using the method given by Squire and Young† and neglecting the effect of compressibility. (For Reynolds numbers below $10^6$ the results given by Squire and Young have been extrapolated.) The results of these calculations, shown by the dotted lines in Fig. 194, indicate that there was a considerable forward movement of the transition point with increase of Reynolds number. Fig. 195 shows a comparison between the drag of an aircraft in flight

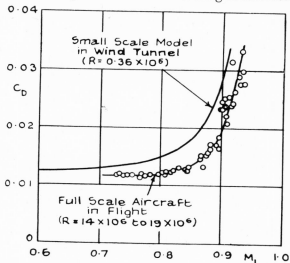

Fig. 195. Drag of D.H. 108 aircraft as measured in wind tunnel and in flight. (The fin was not represented on the wind-tunnel model.)

and that of a small-scale model in a wind tunnel.‡ There is a large difference of Reynolds number between the two sets of measurements and this probably accounts for most of the difference between the two curves. The aircraft has swept-back wings and no horizontal tail. There was a swept-back vertical tail fin on the full-scale aircraft, but this was not represented on the wind-tunnel model. However, the area of this fin was small compared with that of the wing, so that its effect on the total drag coefficient was probably not important. The Reynolds numbers are based on the mean wing-chord measured in the line of flight.

† 'The calculation of the profile drag of aerofoils', *Rep. Memor. Aero. Res. Coun.*, No. 1,838 (1937).

‡ Unpublished measurements by the De Havilland Aircraft Co. Ltd., and the Royal Aircraft Establishment.

The results given in Fig. 195 show that in this case the rapid rise of drag occurs at a higher Mach number when the Reynolds number is increased. It is not yet known whether this result is generally true for other wings and bodies.

*Causes of the drag rise at high subsonic Mach numbers.* As already mentioned, the large increase of drag coefficient which occurs at high subsonic Mach numbers is caused by the formation of shock waves. The total increase of drag due to the shock waves may be considered in two parts, as follows:

(a) The drag due to degradation of mechanical energy at the shock waves.

(b) The increase of drag due to the effect of the shock waves on the boundary layer.

For convenience, the first part may be called the 'shock' drag, while the total drag due to other causes, i.e. the sum of the low-speed drag and the drag increase due to the effect of the shock waves on the boundary layer, may be called the 'basic' drag.

When the profile drag of an aerofoil is measured by the wake-traverse method (Chap. XI), using a comb which is placed fairly close behind the trailing edge, it is possible to estimate roughly the relative contributions of the 'shock' and 'basic' drag to the total drag increase at high Mach numbers. This is illustrated in Figs. 196, 197, and 198, taken from some measurements made at the R.A.E. at a section of a three-dimensional model 'Spitfire' wing.† Fig. 196 shows the distribution of total head across the wake at a high Mach number. It is clear that the outer parts of the wake must be caused by the total-head loss at the shock waves, while the large total-head loss near the centre must be associated with the boundary layer. Although the dividing line between the two regions cannot be specified exactly, it is possible to distinguish roughly between the areas associated with 'basic' and 'shock' drag, as shown by the shading in the diagram.

Figs. 197 and 198 show the 'basic' and 'shock' drag, plotted against Mach number, for the 'Spitfire' wing section at two different incidences. These results show that on this particular wing the greater part of the drag increase at high Mach numbers is due to direct shock-wave loss, especially at the lower incidence (Fig. 197).

† Thompson and Port, 'High-speed wake traverse drag measurements on a model Spitfire half wing', *Rep. Memor. Aero. Res. Coun.*, No. 2,152 (1945).

The 'Spitfire' wing section used for these measurements had a thickness/chord ratio of only about 11 per cent. It is possible that on wings of greater thickness/chord ratio separation or thickening of the boundary layer may have a more important effect on the drag rise, i.e. the rise of 'basic' drag may be relatively greater than

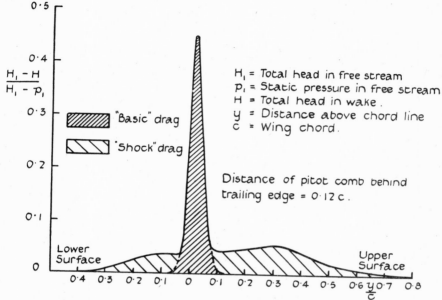

FIG. 196. Loss of total head behind model 'Spitfire' wing, showing rough division into 'basic' and 'shock' drag. ($R = 1.8 \times 10^6$, $\alpha = -1°$, $M_1 = 0.846$.)

on the 'Spitfire' wing. There is little definite information on this point, however, because in most of the wake-traverse drag measurements which have been made at high speeds the traverse has been too far behind the trailing edge to enable even a rough analysis into 'basic' and 'shock' drag to be made. In some cases the measured pressure distribution on the surface of the wing shows evidence of separation of the boundary layer behind the shock wave, as indicated by a low and nearly constant pressure on the rear part of the aerofoil (e.g. Fig. 204).

*Effect of boundary-layer suction.* Some consideration has been given to the possibility of reducing the drag of an aerofoil at high Mach numbers by sucking away the boundary layer near the shock waves. The improvement to be expected from boundary-layer suction

depends on the relative contributions of 'basic' and 'shock' drag to
the total drag increase, because although suction may be expected
to reduce the 'basic' drag considerably, it probably has little effect

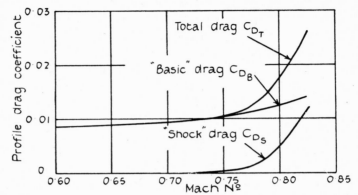

FIG. 197. Analysis of 'Spitfire' wing drag into 'basic' and 'shock' drag.
($R = 1{\cdot}8 \times 10^{6}$, $\alpha = -1°$.)

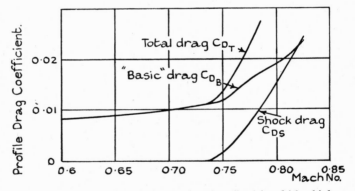

FIG. 198. Analysis of 'Spitfire' wing drag into 'basic' and 'shock' drag.
($R = 1{\cdot}8 \times 10^{6}$, $\alpha = +0{\cdot}9°$.)

on the drag due to direct shock-wave loss. (There is, however, some
doubt about the latter point; suction may affect the shock-wave
position and formation and hence affect the direct 'shock' drag.)

Experiments have been made at the N.P.L.† to investigate the
effect of boundary-layer suction on the drag (as measured by wake
traverse) of a N.A.C.A. 0020 aerofoil at high Mach numbers. With
suction at 50 per cent. chord, the drag was reduced by about 40 to

† Fage and Sargent, 'Effect on aerofoil drag of boundary layer suction behind
a shock wave', *Rep. Memor. Aero. Res. Coun.*, No. 1,913 (1943).

50 per cent. at all Mach numbers up to 0·735, but the Mach number $(M_D)$ at which the drag started to rise was not much affected by suction. The rate of drag rise above this Mach number was slightly reduced by suction at $\alpha = 4°$ but was unaffected at $\alpha = 0°$. It was found that the drag coefficient observed on the aerofoil without suction at the Mach number $M_D$ was reached on the aerofoil with suction at a Mach number about 0·1 greater than $M_D$. In these experiments the power saved by the reduction of drag was about the same as the power absorbed by the suction pump, but at higher Reynolds numbers (e.g. in full-scale flight) the power used by the suction pump would be probably relatively smaller.

## § 7. Lift. Subsonic speeds

*Typical experimental results.* Fig. 199 shows some results obtained by Göthert† at the D.V.L. on a 15 per cent. thick symmetrical aerofoil. The variation of lift coefficient with Mach number for an incidence of 5° is given, together with the corresponding pressure distributions for eight different Mach numbers. From this diagram it can be seen how the changes of lift are related to the changes of pressure distribution of the kind discussed in § 4.

At $M_1 = 0·58$ the critical Mach number has only just been exceeded, and up to this speed the pressure coefficients all increase roughly in accordance with the Prandtl–Glauert law, with a corresponding increase of lift coefficient. At higher speeds there is a local supersonic region on the upper surface and a shock wave is formed, and for this particular aerofoil this leads to a *smaller* increase of lift than is given by the Prandtl–Glauert law, for Mach numbers up to 0·7. (As discussed below, the changes of lift on thinner aerofoils are different; for these aerofoils the increase of lift with Mach number immediately above the critical value is usually *greater* than is given by the Prandtl–Glauert law.) In this range of Mach numbers, up to about 0·1 above the critical value, changes of lift are produced mainly in two ways. There may be a tendency for the lift coefficient to fall, caused by reduction of the peak suction coefficients on the upper surface, either because of separation of the boundary layer or because the upper limiting value of the local Mach number has been reached (see p. 626). There may also be a tendency for the lift coefficient to rise, because of rearward movement of the shock wave

† Loc. cit. on p. 629.

on the upper surface and an extension of the supersonic region along
the chord. In the case of the aerofoil of Fig. 199 the first of these
effects appears to be predominant up to $M_1 = 0.7$, and between
Mach numbers of 0·58 and 0·7 the increase of $C_L$ is less than is given
by the Prandtl–Glauert law. (For thinner aerofoils the second effect
is often more important, and the lift may increase rapidly with Mach
number above the critical value.)

For the aerofoil considered in Fig. 199 there is a considerable
rearward movement of the shock wave and extension of the supersonic region on the upper surface as $M_1$ increases from 0·70 to 0·75,
and this leads to a fairly rapid increase of lift coefficient. As $M_1$
increases from 0·75 to 0·82 there is very little further rearward movement of the shock wave on the upper surface, and the peak suction
coefficient decreases with increase of $M_1$ because the upper limiting
local Mach number has been reached. As a result, and additionally
because of the formation of a supersonic region (with high suction)
on the lower surface, the lift coefficient falls rapidly. When $M_1$ increases above 0·82 there is a rapid rearward movement of the shock
waves on both surfaces, but the movement is especially important
on the upper surface and this leads to a sudden increase of lift
coefficient. It may be noted that the pressure distribution shown
in Fig. 199 for $M_1 = 0.855$ bears some resemblance to those found
at supersonic speeds on other aerofoils (e.g. Fig. 188).

Fig. 200 shows the variation of lift-curve slope with Mach number
for several symmetrical aerofoils of different thickness tested at the
D.V.L.† For the thinner aerofoils of this series the lift-curve slope
is approximately proportional to $1/\beta$ (as given by the Prandtl–
Glauert theory) for all Mach numbers up to the critical value or
slightly above. At higher Mach numbers the increase of lift-curve
slope for the thinner aerofoils is greater than is given by the Prandtl–
Glauert theory, because of the extension of the supersonic region
on the upper surface with increase of Mach number, as explained
above. For the thinner aerofoils there is a sudden reduction of lift-
curve slope when the Mach number exceeds the critical value by
about 0·1. This is caused by a reduction of the peak suction coefficient on the upper surface and an extension of the supersonic region
on the lower surface. For the thicker aerofoils the reduction of lift-
curve slope starts at a Mach number below the critical value, and

† Göthert, loc. cit. on p. 643.

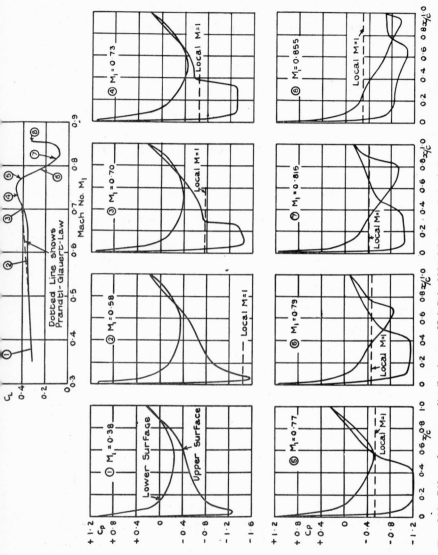

FIG. 199. Lift and pressure distributions on N.A.C.A. 0015–1·1 40 aerofoil at 5° incidence. (Infinite aspect ratio.) Max. thickness = 15 per cent. chord at 40 per cent. chord from L.E. Zero camber. $R = 6 \cdot 5 \times 10^6$ at $M_1 = 0 \cdot 8$.

there is little or no increase of lift-curve slope up to this Mach number. This different behaviour of the thicker aerofoils is probably connected with the formation of thick boundary layers on these aerofoils.

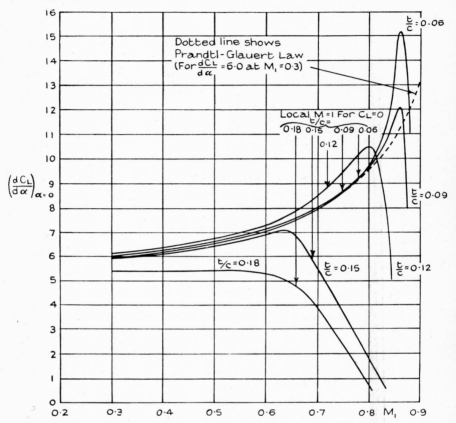

FIG. 200. Variation of lift-curve slope with Mach number, for symmetrical aerofoils of different thickness.
Infinite aspect ratio.   $R = 4 \cdot 5 \times 10^6$ at $M_1 = 0 \cdot 8$.
Position of max. thickness = 30 per cent. chord. (Slope measured at zero incidence.)

Fig. 201 shows the variation with Mach number of the incidence for zero lift, for several aerofoils of different camber tested at the D.V.L.† For a symmetrical aerofoil the incidence for zero lift should of course be zero at all Mach numbers, and the variations shown in Fig. 201 for zero camber must be caused either by lack of symmetry

† Göthert, loc. cit. on p. 641.

in the model or by irregularities in the wind-tunnel stream. For the cambered aerofoils the incidence for zero lift is roughly constant for all Mach numbers up to the critical value or a little greater, but there

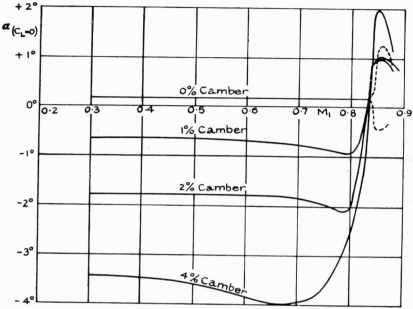

FIG. 201. Variation of zero-lift incidence with Mach number, for aerofoils of different camber (for details see Fig. 191).

is a sudden increase at higher Mach numbers. At Mach numbers approaching unity the incidence for zero lift appears to be between $0°$ and $+1°$ for all the aerofoils. The constancy of the incidence for zero lift at Mach numbers below the critical value is in accordance with the Prandtl–Glauert theory, since for a given incidence the pressure coefficients increase in the same ratio at all points. Thus if the lift is zero at a low Mach number it will remain zero at all Mach numbers up to the critical value.

As illustrated in Fig. 199, the lift coefficient of an aerofoil at a given incidence usually falls rapidly as the Mach number increases in a range well above the critical value. This rapid fall is usually more marked for a cambered aerofoil than for a symmetrical one, because in the former case the increase of zero-lift incidence at high Mach numbers makes an extra contribution to the fall of lift coefficient for a given incidence.

For some aerofoils it is found that the lift–incidence curves at high Mach numbers are not even approximately straight lines. An example of this is given in Fig. 203, which shows the results of lift measurements on the aerofoil N.A.C.A. 23015 at the D.V.L.† Although the behaviour of this aerofoil is complicated by the non-linearity of the curves, changes of lift-curve slope and zero-lift incidence similar to those shown in Figs. 200 and 201 can be seen. The curve for $M_1 = 0.848$ is particularly interesting, because at this Mach number the lift-curve slope is negative for a range of incidences near zero and positive for higher incidences. Fig. 204 shows the pressure distributions for $M_1 = 0.848$ at incidences of $-4°$ and $+4°$, the lift in both these cases being about zero. At $\alpha = -4°$ the shock wave occurs at about 50 per cent. chord on the lower surface and near the trailing edge on the upper surface. Since a region of high suction always occurs before a shock wave, this leads to a considerable positive lift on the rear part of the aerofoil which counteracts the negative lift on the front part. At $\alpha = +4°$ the upper and lower surface shock-wave positions are interchanged, and the positive lift on the front part of the aerofoil is counteracted by negative lift on the rear part.

*Effect of control flaps.* Fig. 202 shows the variation of control-flap effectiveness with Mach number for the aerofoil and flap‡ whose pressure distributions are given in Fig. 184. As already noted in discussing the pressure distributions, the effectiveness of the flap as a control decreases to zero at high Mach numbers. This loss of control is explained by the fact that, at high Mach numbers, the pressures on the part of the aerofoil in front of the hinge are not affected by changes of flap angle (Fig. 184). Thus changes of flap angle at high Mach numbers can only affect the lift on the flap itself, and cannot affect the lift on the front part of the aerofoil. The *reversal* of control effectiveness, shown in Fig. 202 for Mach numbers above 0.81, is caused by fore and aft movements of the shock waves on the flap, an effect similar to that shown in Fig. 204 for a plain aerofoil.

† Göthert, 'Hochgeschwindigkeitsmessungen an Profilen der Reihe N.A.C.A. 230 mit verschiedenen Dickenverhältnissen', *U.M.* 1259/1–3 (1944), *M.A.P. Völkenrode R. & T.*, No. 409; also, 'Druckverteilungsschaubilder für das Profil N.A.C.A. 230 — bei hohen Unterschallgeschwindigkeiten', *U.M.* 1260/1–3 (1944), *M.A.P. Völkenrode R. & T.*, No. 403.

‡ Beavan, Hyde, and Fowler, loc. cit. on p. 616.

Mention should also be made here of the phenomenon discussed on p. 633, which may also lead to reversal of control at even higher Mach numbers.

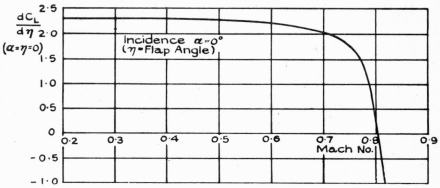

FIG. 202. Variation of control-flap effectiveness with Mach number. E.C. 1250 aerofoil with 25 per cent. control flap. Infinite aspect ratio. $(R = 1.0 \times 10^6$ to $1.8 \times 10^6.)$

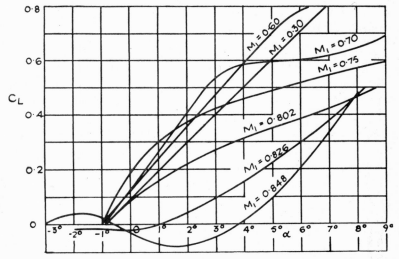

FIG. 203. Variation of lift coefficient with incidence for N.A.C.A. 23015 aerofoil (15 per cent. thick, 1·8 per cent. camber). Infinite aspect ratio. $(R = 4.5 \times 10^6$ at $M_1 = 0.8.)$

*Maximum lift coefficients.* Measurements have been made in several wind tunnels to investigate the variation of maximum lift coefficient with Mach number, but unfortunately in many of these experiments the results were confused by the effects of varying Reynolds number.

Fairly comprehensive measurements† have been made, however, on the aerofoil N.A.C.A. 0012–63, and some of the results are shown in Fig. 205. In this diagram the curve drawn through the group of experimental points shows the estimated variation of $C_{L\max}$ with Mach number at a constant Reynolds number of about $3 \times 10^6$. It is probable that the curves for other Reynolds numbers would have the

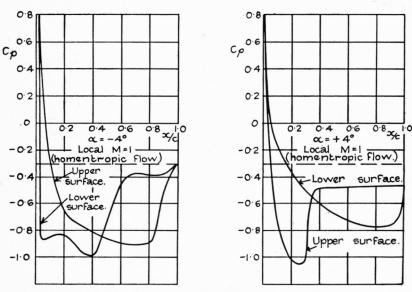

Fig. 204. Pressure distributions on N.A.C.A. 23015 aerofoil at $M_1 = 0.848$, showing small change of lift with incidence. ($R = 4.6 \times 10^6$.) (Aerofoil 15 per cent. thick, 1.8 per cent. camber.)

same general shape, but there is evidence‡ that for some aerofoils the reduction of $C_{L\max}$ with increasing Mach number may be less severe at higher Reynolds numbers.

The reduction of $C_{L\max}$ with increasing Mach number, shown in Fig. 205, may be attributed mainly to the limitation of maximum local Mach number discussed on p. 626. For a given value of $(p/H_1)$, or of local Mach number, the value of the suction coefficient $(-C_p)$ decreases as $M$ increases. At high incidences this only occurs on the

† Göthert, loc. cit. on p. 629; Muse, 'Some effects of Reynolds and Mach numbers on the lift of a N.A.C.A. 0012 rectangular wing in the N.A.C.A. 19 ft. pressure tunnel' (A.C. Bull. Nat. Adv. Comm. Aero.), *Rep. Aero. Res. Coun.*, No. 7,054 (1943).

‡ Mair, Hutton, Gamble, 'High-speed wind tunnel tests on the Welkin', *Rep. Aero. Res. Coun.*, No. 7,388 (1943); Dickinson, 'Welkin F. Mk I D.X. 279. Effect of Mach number on dive and recovery characteristics', *Rep. Aero. Res. Coun.*, No. 7, 854 (1944).

upper surface, and hence there is a steady reduction of $C_{L\max}$ with increasing Mach number. At very high Mach numbers, however, rearward movement of the upper-surface shock wave with increasing Mach number may cause $C_{L\max}$ to increase again, as in Fig. 205 at Mach numbers above 0·8.

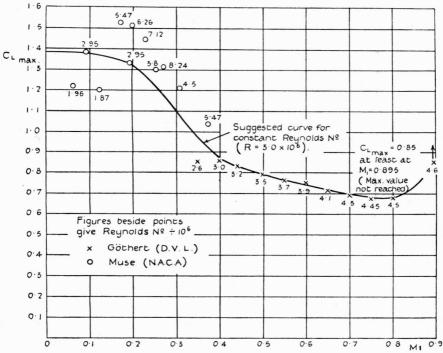

FIG. 205. Variation of maximum lift coefficient with Mach No. (N.A.C.A. 0012–63 aerofoil).

Recent measurements at the N.P.L.† have shown that the maximum lift coefficient of an aerofoil at high Mach numbers is considerably increased by even a small amount of camber. There were also some indications that the maximum lift coefficient at high Mach numbers was increased by moving the position of maximum camber farther back. These tests were made at a low Reynolds number (about $0·7 \times 10^6$), but the beneficial effect of camber is probably associated

† Beavan, Sargent, and Burrows, 'Measurements of maximum lift on 19 aerofoil sections at high Mach number', *Rep. Memor. Aero. Res. Coun.*, No. 2,678 (1947).

with the positions of the shock waves on the upper and lower surfaces, and is therefore probably not much affected by Reynolds number.

*Effect of roughness.* Experiments at the D.V.L.† have shown that the maximum lift coefficient and lift-curve slope of an aerofoil at high Mach numbers may be considerably reduced by roughening the surface. On a rough aerofoil the upper-surface shock wave usually occurs nearer the leading edge than on a smooth one, so that the region of high suction on the upper surface is smaller, and this leads to a reduction of lift. As in the case of drag and pressure distribution, roughness appears to have little or no effect if the grain size is less than about 0·006 per cent. chord.

## § 8. Pitching moment.  Subsonic speeds

*Typical experimental results.* Fig. 206 shows the results of some pitching-moment measurements at the D.V.L. on a typical cambered aerofoil. The pitching-moment coefficients $C_m$ are plotted against Mach number at constant values of the lift coefficient, but the general shape of the curves would be similar if they were plotted at constant incidence instead of constant lift coefficient. Since the curves for the different lift coefficients all have roughly the same shape, only the zero-lift curve will be considered in detail.

At zero lift there is a gradual increase of $(-C_m)$ as the Mach number rises to a value a little above the critical, followed by a more rapid rise of $(-C_m)$ at higher Mach numbers. As the Mach number rises above about 0·8, $(-C_m)$ falls rapidly to zero and $C_m$ then becomes positive.

The first part of the change considered above, i.e. the gradual rise of $(-C_m)$ with Mach number, up to the critical value, is caused by a numerical increase of pressure coefficient at all points on the aerofoil, approximately in accordance with the Prandtl–Glauert theory. The theory is strictly applicable only to a thin aerofoil of small camber, and for this case the numerical increase of $C_p$ would be in the ratio $1/\beta$ at all points, and $(-C_m)$ would increase in the same ratio.

The more rapid increase of $(-C_m)$ which occurs after the critical Mach number has been exceeded is caused by the development of supersonic regions and shock waves on both the upper and lower surfaces. The most important effect is due to the formation of a

† Göthert, loc. cit. on p. 629.

supersonic region on the upper surface, extending back to about the half-chord point. This leads to high suction between the quarter- and half-chord points, and thus causes a considerable increase of $(-C_m)$.

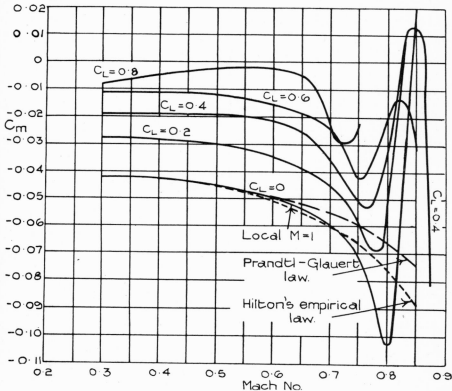

FIG. 206. Variation of pitching-moment coefficient with Mach number. Aerofoil N.A.C.A. 2 35 12–0·55 40 (2 per cent. camber, 12 per cent. thickness). $R = 4·5 \times 10^6$ at $M_1 = 0·8$. Infinite aspect ratio. ($C_m$ measured about $\frac{1}{4}$ chord point.)

Hilton† has suggested an empirical formula for the variation of $C_m$ (at zero lift) with Mach number, which he found to give better agreement with experimental results than the Prandtl–Glauert theory, for aerofoils between about 10 and 20 per cent. thick. Hilton's formula is:

$$(C_{m0})_{\text{II.S.}} = (C_{m0})_{\text{L.S.}}\left(\frac{1}{\beta} + 5·9 M_1^5 \frac{t}{c}\right), \tag{4}$$

† 'Empirical laws for the effect of compressibility on moment coefficient and for the choice of an aerofoil with small compressibility effects on centre of pressure', *Rep. Memor. Aero. Res. Coun.*, No. 2,195 (1943).

o

where $(C_{m0})$ H.S. and $(C_{m0})$ L.S. are values of $C_m$ for zero lift at Mach numbers $M_1$ and 0 respectively, $t/c$ is the thickness/chord ratio of the aerofoil, and $\beta = (1-M_1^2)^{\frac{1}{2}}$. (For zero $t/c$ this formula reduces to the simple Prandtl–Glauert law.)

Theoretical curves according to the Prandtl–Glauert law and Hilton's empirical law are also shown in Fig. 206, for comparison with the experimental results. In this case the agreement with Hilton's law is very good up to a Mach number about 0·1 above the critical value. In many other cases Hilton's law gives good agreement with experimental results up to the Mach number at which $(-C_m)$ starts to fall. (The law is of course not intended to apply beyond this point.)

Hilton[†] has also suggested a general empirical rule for calculating the variation of $C_m$ with Mach number at any value of $C_L$, but the agreement with experimental results is not as good for positive values of $C_L$ as for zero lift. In Fig. 206 the curves for positive values of $C_L$ are similar in shape to that given for $C_L = 0$, but even at low Mach numbers the spacing between the curves varies with Mach number and $C_L$ in a rather irregular manner. Thus it is not surprising that no general rule for the variation of $C_m$ with Mach number has yet been found which gives good agreement with experimental results.

Fig. 207 shows the variation of $dC_m/dC_L$ with Mach number, for several symmetrical aerofoils tested at the D.V.L.[‡] For moderate Mach numbers there is a gradual increase of $dC_m/dC_L$ with Mach number, indicating a forward movement of the aerodynamic centre.[§] At higher Mach numbers the thinner aerofoils show a sudden reduction of $dC_m/dC_L$. Since it is known from theory that $dC_m/dC_L$ is about $-0·15$ or $-0·20$ for most aerofoils at supersonic speeds (measuring $C_m$ about the quarter-chord point), it is probable that the thicker aerofoils considered in Fig. 207 would also show a large reduction of $dC_m/dC_L$ if sufficiently high Mach numbers were reached.

At low Mach numbers it is known that $dC_m/dC_L$ depends mainly on trailing-edge angle, and hence it is possible that the differences shown in Fig. 207, between aerofoils of different thickness, may be

[†] Loc. cit. on p. 665.

[‡] Göthert, 'Profilmessungen im Hochgeschwindigkeitskanal 2·7 m. D.' F.B. 1490 (1941), *M.A.P. Völkenrode R. & T.* No. 410.

[§] The aerodynamic centre is defined as the point about which the pitching moments would have to be measured in order to make $dC_m/d\alpha$ zero. (This is equivalent to making $dC_m/dC_L$ zero, except in the special case when $dC_L/d\alpha$ is also zero.) For a symmetrical aerofoil, $C_m = 0$ when $C_L = 0$ and the aerodynamic centre then coincides with the centre of pressure.

due more to differences of trailing-edge angle than to differences of thickness.

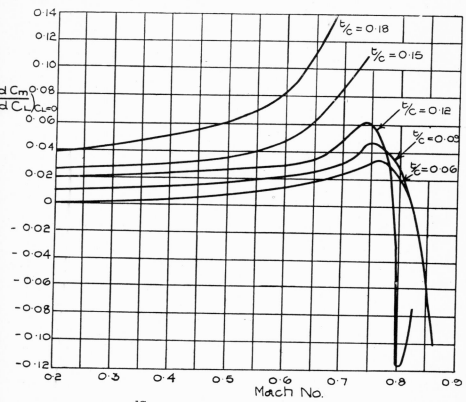

FIG. 207. Variation of $\dfrac{dC_m}{dC_L}$ with Mach number, for symmetrical aerofoils of different thickness. ($R = 4.5 \times 10^6$ at $M_1 = 0.8$.) Infinite aspect ratio. Position of max. thickness = 30 per cent. chord. Slope measured at $C_L = 0$. $C_m$ measured about $\frac{1}{4}$ chord point.

*Causes of changes of pitching moment at high subsonic Mach numbers.* The causes of the pitching-moment changes considered above can be seen by considering pressure distributions such as those shown in Fig. 182 (*b*). As the Mach number increases up to the critical value (about 0.7 in the case of Fig. 182 (*b*)), the suctions increase steadily all over the aerofoil and $(-C_m)$ increases according to the Prandtl–Glauert law (or, more exactly, according to Hilton's law). With further increase of Mach number, up to about 0.8 in Fig. 182 (*b*), the value of $(-C_p)$ decreases on the upper surface near the leading edge but continues to increase gradually elsewhere, thus leading to a more rapid rise of $(-C_m)$ with $M_1$. The decrease of $(-C_m)$ which occurs at still higher Mach numbers is caused by the rearward movement of the lower-surface shock wave, leading to a large increase of suction on the lower surface towards the trailing edge.

On thin aerofoils (and probably also on thick ones) there is a sudden reduction of $dC_m/dC_L$ at high Mach numbers, i.e. a rearward movement of the aerodynamic centre. This change occurs as the shock waves move back towards the trailing edge and the pressure distribution approaches that found at supersonic speeds (e.g. Fig. 188).

On thicker aerofoils this reduction of $dC_m/dC_L$ is preceded, at a slightly lower Mach number, by a considerable increase of $dC_m/dC_L$ (i.e. a forward movement of the aerodynamic centre). The explanation of this effect can be seen by considering the pressure distributions shown in Fig. 204. In the first diagram $(\alpha = -4°)$ $C_m$ is obviously negative, while in the second diagram $(\alpha = +4°)$ $C_m$ is positive. Although there is a change of incidence of $8°$ between the two diagrams, there is only a small increase of lift, and hence $dC_m/dC_L$ has a large positive value.

## § 9. Forces and moments at supersonic speeds

*Theoretical methods.* As explained in Chaps. V and VIII and on p. 637, the pressure distribution on a sharp-nosed aerofoil at supersonic speed can be calculated theoretically for inviscid flow, provided the Mach number is high enough for the front shock wave to be attached to the leading edge. If the inclination of the aerofoil surface to the stream is small at all points, it is sufficiently accurate to use Busemann's second-order theory. If this condition is not satisfied the exact theory† may be used, but in practice this is hardly ever justified because the effects of boundary-layer separation (which are neglected in all the theories) are usually more important than the neglected third-order and higher terms.

The lift and pitching moment on an aerofoil at supersonic speed can be found directly from the theoretical pressure distribution by integration. The wave drag can be found in the same way, but in order to determine the total drag it is necessary to add the drag

† Lighthill, loc. cit. on p. 638.

due to boundary-layer effects. For aerofoils which are symmetrical about the chord line and about the normal to the chord line through its centre (and also for some aerofoils having other kinds of symmetry) the second-order terms have no effect on the lift or drag.[†] Thus for these aerofoils, when only the lift and drag are required, Ackeret's linear theory can be used for calculating the pressure distributions. For calculating pitching moments, however, Busemann's theory should always be used, because the second-order terms have an important effect on $C_m$.

*Comparisons between experimental and theoretical results.* Figs. 208, 209, and 210 (a) show the results of measurements of lift, drag, and pitching moment by Ferri[‡] on a 10 per cent. symmetrical bi-convex aerofoil at $M_1 = 2 \cdot 13$. (Pressure distributions on this aerofoil are shown in Fig. 188.) These diagrams also show the calculated values given by the first- and second-order theories. The second-order terms have no effect on the lift and drag (Figs. 208 and 209), because the aerofoil is symmetrical about both axes, but Fig. 210 (a) shows that these terms have an important effect on the pitching moment at high incidences, even when the aerofoil is symmetrical. Fig. 210 (b) shows the results of pitching-moment measurements on a plano-convex aerofoil at the same Mach number. (In Figs. 210 (a) and (b) $C_m$ is the pitching-moment coefficient measured about the leading edge, whereas in the other parts of this chapter, dealing with sub-sonic speeds, $C_m$ is measured about the quarter-chord point.)

Fig. 208 shows that the observed lift-curve slope of the symmetrical bi-convex aerofoil is slightly less than the theoretical one. This discrepancy is caused by the boundary-layer separation which occurs near the trailing edge, especially on the upper surface. The effect of the separation is to reduce the suction on the upper surface at high incidences, and thus to reduce the lift (Fig. 188). The exact theory would give a lift-curve slope increasing with incidence, and even greater values of $C_L$ at high incidences than the approximate theory. Thus the approximate theory gives better agreement with the experimental results than the exact theory. This is because the third and higher-order terms, which are neglected in the approximate second-order theory, have an effect on lift which is opposite in direction to the effect of the boundary-layer separation.

† Lock, loc. cit. on p. 637.
‡ Loc. cit. on p. 638.

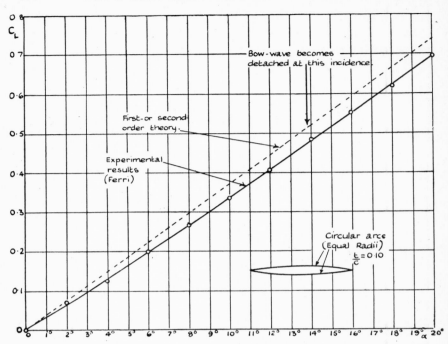

FIG. 208. Lift curves for 10 per cent. symmetrical bi-convex aerofoil at $M_1 = 2 \cdot 13$
$(R = 6 \cdot 4 \times 10^5)$. (Infinite aspect ratio.)

Fig. 209 shows that the observed drag coefficient of this aerofoil
at low incidences is about $0 \cdot 008$ greater than the theoretical form
drag coefficient, the difference increasing to about $0 \cdot 013$ at $\alpha = 14°$.
Since the skin-friction drag coefficient would probably be about $0 \cdot 01$
at this Reynolds number, these figures show that the observed drag
coefficients agree fairly well with the calculated values, when an
allowance is made for skin friction. This result is rather surprising,
because Fig. 188 shows that the suction actually observed at the rear
of the aerofoil is less than that given by the theory, so that the
observed form drag ought to be less than the theoretical form drag.
Measurements made by Ferri† on other aerofoils have shown that
in some cases the observed total drag is actually less than the
theoretical form drag, so that when allowance for skin friction is
made the experimental drag is considerably less than that given by
the theory.

† Loc. cit. on p. 638.

It is interesting to note that at supersonic speeds separation of the boundary layer at the rear of an aerofoil causes a *reduction* of drag, whereas at subsonic speeds it causes an *increase* of drag.

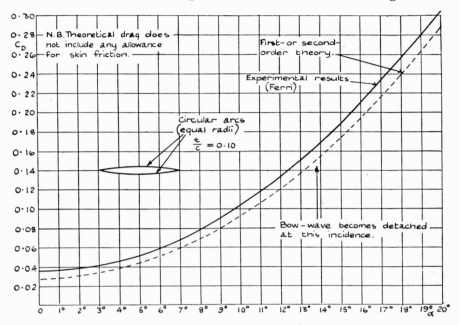

FIG. 209.   Drag of 10 per cent. symmetrical bi-convex aerofoil at $M_1 = 2\cdot13$
$(R = 6\cdot4 \times 10^5)$.  (Infinite aspect ratio.)

Fig. 210 shows a comparison between theory and experiment for the pitching moments of two aerofoils. The experimental $C_m$–$C_L$ curve for the symmetrical bi-convex aerofoil agrees very well with the curve given by the second-order theory, for all incidences up to that at which the bow wave becomes detached. This means that the effect of the boundary-layer separation is counteracted by the neglect of the third and higher-order terms in the theory. For the plano-convex aerofoil the agreement is not quite so good, but even in this case the effect of the neglected third-order terms must be largely counteracted (at high incidences) by the boundary-layer separation. On this aerofoil at zero incidence the upper surface at the leading edge makes an angle of 20° with the stream, and this rather large angle probably explains the poor agreement between theory and experiment at low incidences.

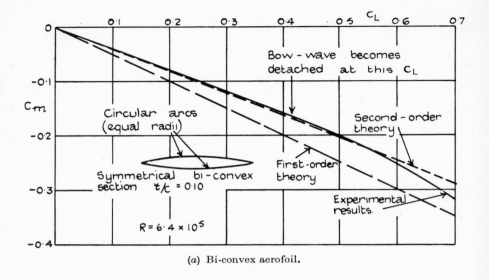

(a) Bi-convex aerofoil.

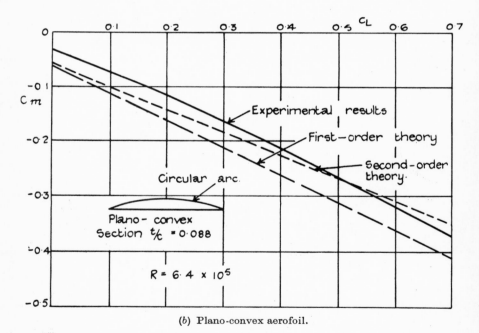

(b) Plano-convex aerofoil.

FIG. 210. Pitching moments on aerofoils at supersonic speed ($M_1 = 2 \cdot 13$) (measured about leading edge).

It may be noted that the agreement between the second-order theory and the experimental results shown in Fig. 210 would not appear to be as good if the results were presented as $C_m$–$\alpha$ curves instead of $C_m$–$C_L$ curves.

The differences between the results given by the first and second-order theories are fairly small at low incidences (Fig. 210), but they become larger at higher incidences where the second-order terms have a more important effect.

Measurements made at the N.P.L. on a number of aerofoils,[†] at Mach numbers up to about 1·5, have given values of $C_L$, $C_D$, and $C_m$ which agreed fairly well with calculations based on Busemann's second-order theory. In the case of the drag measurements it was found that the observed values of $C_D$ were about 0·008 greater than the theoretical form drag coefficients, so that if this amount was added to the theoretical values to allow for skin friction, good agreement was obtained. Thus these measurements agreed with the results given in Fig. 209 in showing that boundary-layer separation appeared to have little effect on the drag.

## § 10. Aerofoils of finite aspect ratio

*Subsonic speeds.* With the exception of the 'Spitfire' wing drags given in Figs. 196, 197, and 198, all the results given so far in this chapter have referred to aerofoils for which the flow is effectively two-dimensional (i.e. aerofoils of infinite aspect ratio). Most of these results are also applicable, with only slight modifications, to aerofoils of finite aspect ratio, provided the aspect ratio is not less than about 5 and there is no appreciable sweep-back or sweep-forward.

It can be shown by lifting-line theory and the linear theory of subsonic flow‡ (assuming an elliptical lift distribution) that the lift-curve slope $a$ of an aerofoil of aspect ratio $A$ at a Mach number $M_1$ is given by

$$\frac{1}{a} = \frac{\beta}{a_{i0}} + \frac{1}{\pi A}, \tag{5}$$

† Hilton and Pruden, 'Subsonic and supersonic high-speed tunnel tests of a faired double-wedge aerofoil', *Rep. Memor. Aero. Res. Coun.*, No. 2,057 (1943); Hilton, 'Subsonic and supersonic tests on a 7½% bi-convex aerofoil', ibid. No. 2,196 (1944); Pruden, 'Tests of a double-wedge aerofoil with a 30% control flap over a range of supersonic speeds', ibid. No. 2,197 (1945).

‡ Young, 'Note on the effect of compressibility on the lift-curve slope of a wing of finite span', *Rep. Aero. Res. Coun.*, No. 7,046 (1943).

where $a_{i0}$ is the lift-curve slope at a low Mach number for an aerofoil of infinite aspect ratio having the same section and $\beta = (1 - M_1^2)^{\frac{1}{2}}$. (It is assumed that $M_1$ is not greater than the critical Mach number.) Although this equation is based on the assumption of elliptical lift distribution, wind-tunnel tests have shown that it gives nearly the correct values for the lift-curve slopes of rectangular or straight-tapered aerofoils, provided the aspect ratio is not less than about 5. For aerofoils of smaller aspect ratio the assumptions of the lifting-line theory are no longer even approximately correct, so that eqn. (5) over-estimates both the lift-curve slope and its rate of increase with Mach number.

No systematic tests have been made at high subsonic Mach numbers to investigate the effect of aspect ratio on the pressure distribution at a section of an aerofoil. The available information suggests, however, that the pressure distribution for a given section lift coefficient is not much affected by changes of aspect ratio, provided the section under consideration is not too near the tip. For a given geometrical incidence changes of aspect ratio do of course have important effects on the lift and pressure distribution at a section of an aerofoil, as indicated by eqn. (5).

Tests made at the D.V.L.† on an aerofoil of very small aspect ratio ($A = 1\cdot15$) have shown that the changes which occur at high Mach numbers are quite different from those found on aerofoils of larger aspect ratio. This is illustrated by the results shown in Figs. 211 and 212. The first diagram in Fig. 211 shows that the lift-curve slope is almost independent of Mach number up to $M_1 = 0\cdot9$. This result is qualitatively in agreement with eqn. (5), which gives a lift-curve slope independent of Mach number as the aspect ratio tends to zero, but since lifting-line theory is not applicable to an aerofoil of such small aspect ratio, no useful quantitative comparison with the theory can be made. It is remarkable that no sudden loss of lift-curve slope occurs at any Mach number up to 0·9, although for an aerofoil of this thickness (12 per cent.) with a larger aspect ratio there would be a considerable loss of lift-curve slope at a Mach number of about 0·8 (see Fig. 200).

The second diagram in Fig. 211 shows the change of centre of pressure position with Mach number, for the same aerofoil. (The

† Göthert, 'Hochgeschwindigkeitsmessungen an einem Flügel kleiner Streckung', F.B. 1846 (1943), M.A.P. Völkenrode R. & T., No. 18.

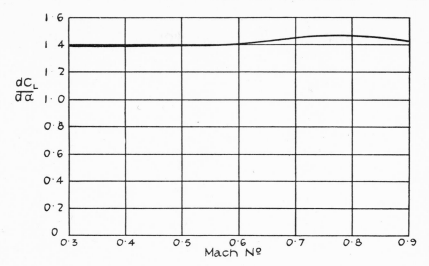

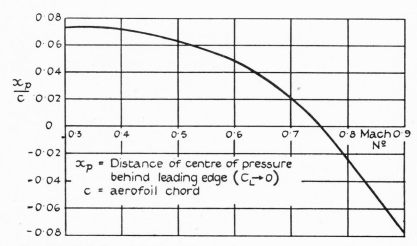

FIG. 211. Variation of lift-curve slope and centre of pressure position with Mach number.  Rectangular aerofoil: aspect ratio 1·15, section N.A.C.A. 0012–1·1 30 (symmetrical).  $(R = 4\cdot3 \times 10^6$ at $M_1 = 0\cdot8$.)

aerofoil is symmetrical, and thus the centre of pressure position at zero lift is given directly by $dC_m/dC_L$.)  Even at low Mach numbers the centre of pressure is much farther forward than the normal position for aerofoils of large aspect ratio (about 25 per cent. chord), and at high Mach numbers the centre of pressure moves in front of the leading edge. The movement of centre of pressure with increasing Mach number is not yet fully understood, but a partial explanation is given by the linear theory of subsonic flow (Chap. VIII). It is known from this theory that the flow past a given aerofoil at a high Mach number can be related to the flow past an aerofoil of

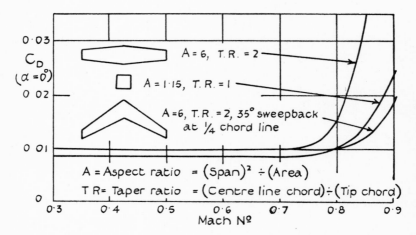

FIG. 212. Variation of aerofoil drag with planform and Mach number. Incidence = 0°. ($R = 4\cdot3\times10^6$ at $M_1 = 0\cdot8$.) (Section N.A.C.A. 0012–1·1 30.)

smaller aspect ratio at a low Mach number. Thus since a reduction of aspect ratio (at low Mach number) causes a forward movement of the centre of pressure, it is to be expected that an increase of Mach number should also cause a forward movement of the centre of pressure.

Fig. 212 shows the drag of the aerofoil of aspect ratio 1·15 compared with the drag of an aerofoil of the same section having an aspect ratio of 6. The results show that reduction of the aspect ratio to a very small value causes a considerable increase in the drag critical Mach number. Also, the rate of increase of drag above this Mach number is less for the aerofoil of small aspect ratio than for the (unswept) aerofoil of normal aspect ratio. The reduction of drag coefficient at high Mach numbers due to reducing the aspect ratio is nearly as great as that caused by a sweep-back of 35° (see Fig. 212 and p. 681).

*Supersonic speeds.* Some tests have been made at the N.P.L. on aerofoils of small aspect ratio at supersonic speeds.† Pressure distributions were measured on aerofoils of 10 per cent. symmetrical double-wedge section, for aspect ratios from 0·75 to 1·5 and for Mach numbers from 1·3 to 2·3. The aerofoils were rectangular in planform and were mounted on the wall of the wind tunnel, so that one end of the aerofoil was within the boundary layer on the tunnel wall. The observed pressure distributions were integrated to obtain lift, drag, and centre of pressure, and these were then compared with the results of calculations by first-order theory (see Chap. VIII).‡

In Fig. 213 (a) the ratio of the observed lift-curve slope for finite aspect ratio $A$ to the theoretical lift-curve slope for infinite aspect ratio is plotted against $A\sqrt{(M_1^2 - 1)}$. Most of the experimental points lie slightly below the theoretical curve, probably because of the boundary layer on the tunnel wall.

In Fig. 213 (b) the difference between the drag at incidence $\alpha$ and that at zero incidence is divided by the theoretical value of this difference for infinite aspect ratio and plotted against $A\sqrt{(M_1^2 - 1)}$. (The theoretical curve for this case is exactly the same as in Fig. 213 (a).) For a given aspect ratio and Mach number the experimental results for the different incidences were rather scattered. The extreme values have therefore been indicated in Fig. 213 (b), in addition to the average values shown by the points.

The results of these tests showed that as the aspect ratio was reduced the lift and drag coefficients (for a given incidence) decreased and the centre of pressure moved forward and slightly outward from the tunnel wall. All these effects of varying aspect ratio became more pronounced as the Mach number was reduced.

## § 11. Yawed and swept-back aerofoils

The critical changes of lift, drag, and pressure distribution which occur on a normal wing at high subsonic speeds can be delayed to higher Mach numbers by sweeping the wing either back or forward (see Fig. 214). The effect of sweep-back at high Mach numbers was

---

† Orman, Rae and Ward, 'Wind tunnel test of a wing of finite aspect ratio of symmetrical double wedge section at supersonic speeds', *Proc. Roy. Soc.* A, **209** (1951), 309–24.

‡ Busemann, 'Infinitesimale kegelige Überschallströmung', *D.A.L. Jahrbuch 7.B* (1943), 105–22, translated as *Tech. Memor. Nat. Adv. Comm. Aero.*, No. 1,100; Gunn, 'Linearized supersonic aerofoil theory', *Philos. Trans.* **240** (1947), 327–75; R. T. Jones, 'Properties of low aspect-ratio pointed wings at speeds below and above the speed of sound', *Rep. Nat. Adv. Comm. Aero.*, No. 835 (1946).

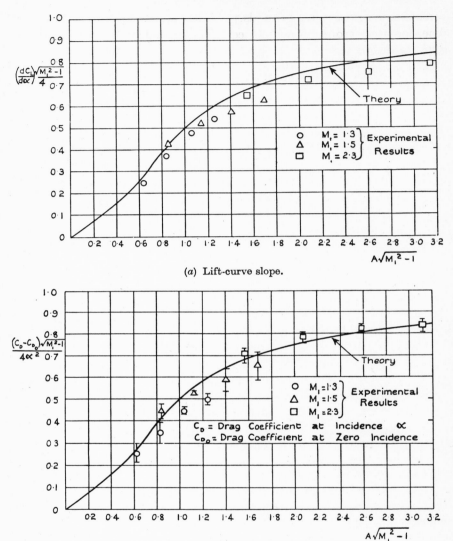

(a) Lift-curve slope.

(b) Drag.

FIG. 213. Rectangular aerofoils of finite aspect ratio at supersonic speeds. (Symmetrical double-wedge section, $R = 0.5 \times 10^6$ to $0.8 \times 10^6$.)

first considered by Busemann† in 1935; since then the subject has attracted a considerable amount of attention as a means of postponing undesirable compressibility effects to higher Mach numbers.

† Loc. cit. on p. 637.

*Theory of the infinite yawed aerofoil.* The simplest case to consider is that of an infinitely long aerofoil of constant chord, whose leading edge makes an angle $\phi$ with the normal to the undisturbed stream

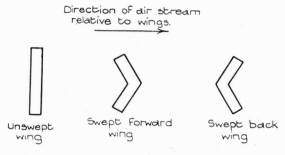

Fig. 214. Swept-forward and swept-back wings.

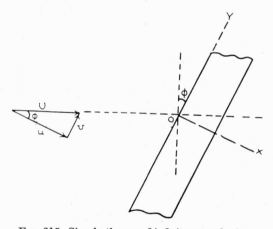

Fig. 215. Simple theory of infinite yawed wing.

(Fig. 215). Let the free-stream velocity $U$ be resolved into components $u$ and $v$, parallel to the axes $OX$ and $OY$. If viscous effects are neglected the forces on the aerofoil depend entirely on the component $u$ and are independent of $v$. The pressure coefficient $C'_p$ at any point on the yawed aerofoil, at a Mach number $M'_1$, is therefore related to the value $C_p$ at the same point on a similar unyawed aerofoil, at a Mach number $M_1 = M'_1 \cos\phi$, by the equation:

$$C'_p = C_p \cos^2\phi \qquad (6)$$

(since $u = U \cos\phi$).

The above equation is correct if the incidence of the unyawed aerofoil is the same as that of the yawed aerofoil measured in a plane normal to the leading edge. In considering swept-back wings, however, it is more usual to measure the incidence in a plane parallel to the direction of the free stream. If $\alpha'$ is the incidence of the yawed aerofoil, measured in this way, and $\alpha$ is the incidence of the unyawed aerofoil, then eqn. (6) will still be correct if we make

$$\alpha' = \alpha \cos \phi. \tag{7}$$

It can be shown from eqn. (6) that the coefficients of lift and pitching moment for the yawed aerofoil ($C'_L$ and $C'_m$), at a Mach number $M'_1$, are related to the coefficients $C_L$ and $C_m$ for the unyawed aerofoil at a Mach number $M_1$ by the equations:

and
$$\left. \begin{array}{l} C'_L = C_L \cos^2\phi \\ C'_m = C_m \cos^2\phi \end{array} \right\}. \tag{8}$$

In defining the coefficient $C'_m$ for the yawed aerofoil, the chord is measured in a direction parallel to the free stream and the pitching moments are measured about an axis perpendicular to this chord line.

In the case of the drag coefficient the ratio of $C'_D$ to $C_D$ is $\cos^3\phi$ instead of $\cos^2\phi$, because the resultant force in the plane of the yawed aerofoil acts along $OX$, whereas only the component of this force in the direction of the free stream affects the drag. (This simple theory can only apply to form drag, because non-viscous flow has been assumed.)

*Experimental results.* For comparison with the above theory, measurements on a yawed aerofoil spanning the working section of a wind tunnel have been made by Göthert,[†] by Koch,[‡] and by Lock, Beavan, and others[§] at the N.P.L. Göthert's measurements were made only at low speeds, and showed that the pressure coefficients on the yawed wing were almost exactly $\cos^2\phi$ times the values

[†] Göthert, 'Hochgeschwindigkeitsmessungen an einem Pfeilflügel', *F.B.* 1813 (also *Lilienthal Ges. Luftfahrtforsch. Ber.* 156 (1942)), *M.A.P. Völkenrode R. & T.*, No. 73.

[‡] 'Druckverteilungsmessungen am schiebenden Tragflügel', *Lilienthal Ges. Luftfahrtforsch. Ber.* 156 (1942), *M.A.P. Völkenrode R. & T.*, No. 363.

[§] Lock and Fowler, 'Yaw and sweep-back at high Mach number', *Rep. Aero. Res. Coun.*, No. 8,718 (1945); Beavan and Bumstead, 'Tests on yawed aerofoils in the 20 in. × 8 in. high-speed tunnel', *Rep. Memor. Aero. Res. Coun.*, No. 2,458 (1947).

on the unyawed wing, as given by eqn. (6). In Koch's experiments the pressure distributions were measured over a range of Mach numbers up to about 0·85, and again the results agreed well with eqn. (6). In the N.P.L. experiments only the drag was measured (by the pitot-traverse method). It was found that yawing the aerofoil raised the Mach number for a given increase of $C_D$, but only by about 80 per cent. of the amount predicted by the simple theory. It is, of course, not surprising that the full reduction of drag given by the theory is not realized in practice, because the boundary layer obviously has an important effect on the form drag at high Mach numbers and this is neglected in the theory.

In any aeronautical application of swept wings it is probably necessary to use a 'V' planform, either flying with the central point first (swept-back) or with the tips in front (swept-forward). For a wing of this planform the conditions are quite different from those considered in the simple theory of the infinite yawed wing, especially at the centre and tips of the 'V'. It is found in practice that on a 'V' wing the Mach number at which large changes of lift and drag occur is only increased by about half the amount given by the simple theory. Nevertheless, there are considerable advantages in using wings of this planform for high-speed flight, as is shown by the D.V.L. wind-tunnel results† given in Figs. 212, 216, and 217.

In Fig. 212 it is shown that the Mach number at which the drag has risen to double the low-speed value is increased by about 0·09 by 35° of sweep-back, compared with 0·18 given by the simple theory. The theoretical reduction of form drag coefficient in the ratio $\cos^3 \phi$ has no effect on the drag at low speeds, which is nearly all due to skin friction, but it does cause a reduction in the rate of rise of drag at high Mach numbers.

Fig. 216 shows that the collapse of lift-curve slope at high speeds is also delayed to higher Mach numbers by the use of sweep-back. The results given in Fig. 216 do not include high enough Mach numbers to show the magnitude of this effect, but other tests‡ have shown that the increase in the Mach number at which $dC_L/d\alpha$ starts to fall is about half that given by the simple theory.

The Mach number at which a sudden movement of the centre of

† Göthert, loc. cit. on p. 680.
‡ e.g. results of experiments by Walchner reproduced by Schomerus in discussion of a paper by Helmbold: 'Statische Längsstabilität bei hohen Fluggeschwindigkeiten', *Schriften D.A.L.* 1031/41g (Berlin), 1941.

pressure occurs is increased by about 0·10 by 35° sweep-back (Fig. 217); again this is about half the increase given by the simple theory.

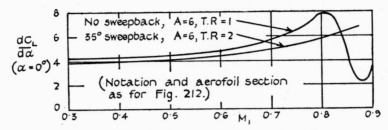

FIG. 216. Variation of lift-curve slope with Mach number, for aerofoils with and without sweepback. $(R = 4\cdot3 \times 10^6$ at $M_1 = 0\cdot8.)$

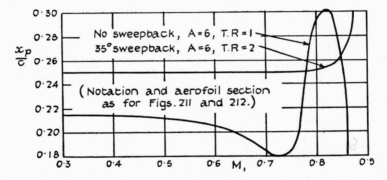

FIG. 217. Variation of centre of pressure position with Mach number, for aerofoils with and without sweepback. $(R = 4\cdot3 \times 10^6$ at $M_1 = 0\cdot8.)$

Only a few experiments have been made on swept-back wings at supersonic speeds, and most of these have been concerned with particular applications. A considerable amount of theoretical work has been done on supersonic flow past aerofoils of small aspect ratio (i.e. $A < 3$) with highly swept-back leading edges; an account of this is given in Chap. VIII.

## § 12. Circular cylinders

At low Mach numbers the pressure distribution on a circular cylinder changes considerably with Reynolds number (see Vol. I (1938)). In particular, there are important changes at the 'critical'

Reynolds number, between about $2 \times 10^5$ and $4 \times 10^5$, the drag coefficient being much lower at Reynolds numbers above this critical value than at lower Reynolds numbers.

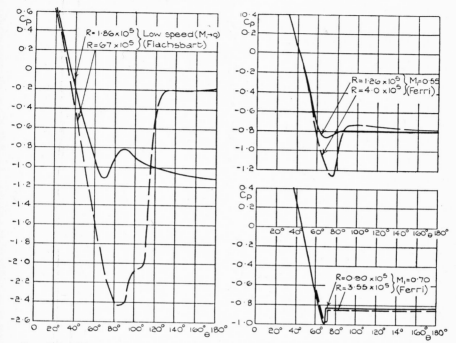

FIG. 218. Effect of Reynolds number on pressure distributions on circular cylinders. $C_p = (p-p_1)/\frac{1}{2}\rho_1 U^2$.   $\theta =$ angular distance from front stagnation point.

N.B. The usual value of the 'critical' Reynolds number is about $3 \times 10^5$. Thus the pressure distribution (for $M_1 \to 0$) at $R = 4 \times 10^5$ would be nearly the same as that given for $R = 6.7 \times 10^5$.

Ferri[†] has measured drag and pressure distribution on circular cylinders over a fairly wide range of Reynolds and Mach numbers. The results of some of Ferri's pressure measurements are given in Fig. 218, together with some results obtained at low speeds by Flachsbart and reproduced by Muttray.[‡] These results show that the large change of pressure distribution which occurs at low Mach numbers, when the Reynolds number rises through the 'critical' value, no longer occurs at Mach numbers above about 0·6. At low

† 'Influenza del numero di Reynolds ai grandi numeri di Mach', *Atti Guidonia*, Nos. 67, 68, 69 (1942).

‡ *Handbuch Exp.-Phys.* (Leipzig), **4**, pt. 2 (1932), 316.

Mach numbers the 'critical' change of pressure distribution is due to a change from a laminar to a turbulent boundary layer, causing the separation point to move farther back. At high Mach numbers the separation point is probably fixed by the presence of shock waves, so that it cannot move any farther back when the laminar boundary layer changes to a turbulent one.

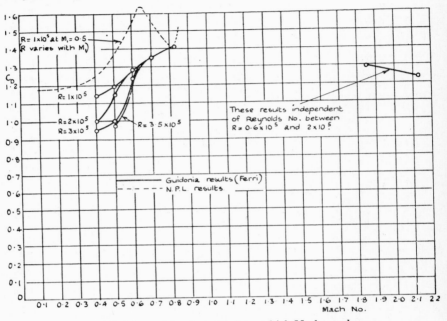

FIG. 219. Drag of circular cylinders at high Mach numbers.

Fig. 219 gives the results of some of Ferri's drag measurements, showing that the change of drag at the 'critical' Reynolds number also disappears at Mach numbers above about 0·6.

It may be noted that the results given in Fig. 219 do not show a very low drag coefficient at the highest Reynolds number of the tests, even at a Mach number as low as 0·4. Thus it appears possible that a 'critical' change of drag might have been observed at high Mach numbers if the tests had been extended to higher Reynolds numbers. This is not very likely, however, because at low Mach numbers, when the stream turbulence is small, the reduction of $C_D$ with increasing Reynolds number usually starts at a Reynolds number of about $2 \times 10^5$ and is complete at a Reynolds number of about

$4 \times 10^5$. (In a turbulent stream the 'critical' Reynolds number is lower.) If these Reynolds numbers are high enough to cause the transition point to move forward at low Mach numbers, this should .also be true at moderately high Mach numbers. Also, measurements on circular cylinders made by Matt† at the D.V.L. gave high values of $C_D$ (about $1 \cdot 2$ to $1 \cdot 3$) at Mach numbers above $0 \cdot 6$, even at Reynolds

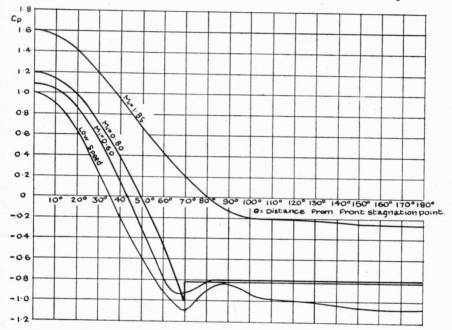

FIG. 220. Pressure distributions on circular cylinders at $R = 1 \times 10^5$ to $2 \times 10^5$.

numbers as high as $11 \times 10^5$. Ferri's experiments on spheres‡ showed no sign of a 'critical' drop of $C_D$ at high Mach numbers, even at Reynolds numbers as high as $7 \times 10^5$. (The 'critical' Reynolds number for a sphere at low Mach numbers is about $3 \cdot 5 \times 10^5$ to $4 \times 10^5$.) Thus it may be concluded that at Reynolds numbers of $7 \times 10^5$ or more the results obtained on circular cylinders would probably be similar to those given in Figs. 218 and 219 for $R = 3 \times 10^5$ to $4 \times 10^5$.

The probable explanation of the small change of $C_D$ with $R$, shown

† 'Hochgeschwindigkeitsmessungen an Rund- und Profilstangen verschiedener Durchmesser', *Lilienthal Ges. Luftfahrforsch. Ber.* 156 (1942), *M.A.P. Völkenrode R. & T.*, No. 368.

‡ Loc. cit. on p. 683.

for the lowest Mach number in Fig. 219, is that compressibility effects are causing a large increase of drag (at high Reynolds numbers) even at a Mach number as low as 0·4. That is, if the tests at $R = 3·5 \times 10^5$ had been extended down to very low Mach numbers, much lower values of $C_D$ would probably have been found.

The dotted curve in Fig. 219 shows the results of some drag measurements made on circular cylinders at the N.P.L.† In these experiments the Reynolds number changed with Mach number, the cylinder diameter and stagnation pressure being kept constant. The agreement with Ferri's results is not good, the most noticeable difference being the maximum in the N.P.L. curve at a Mach number of about 0·65, which is not shown in Ferri's results.

Fig. 220 shows the results of Ferri's measurements of pressure distribution, for a range of Mach numbers up to 1·85. As already mentioned, the effect of Reynolds number is believed to be small for Mach numbers above 0·6, so that the curves given in Fig. 220 for high Mach numbers are probably correct for a fairly wide range of Reynolds numbers.

## Symbols used in Chapter XII

| | |
|---|---|
| $A$ | aspect ratio. |
| $a$ | $= dC_L/d\alpha$ lift-curve slope. |
| $a_{i0}$ | value of $a$ for zero Mach number and infinite aspect ratio. |
| $c$ | aerofoil chord. |
| $C_D$ | drag coefficient. |
| $C_L$ | lift coefficient. |
| $C_{L\max}$ | maximum lift coefficient. |
| $C_m$ | pitching-moment coefficient (about quarter-chord point except where otherwise stated). |
| $C_{m0}$ | value of $C_m$ for $C_L = 0$. |
| $C_p$ | $(p-p_1)/\frac{1}{2}\rho U^2$ pressure coefficient. |
| $C_{p0}$ | value of $C_p$ for $M = 0$. |
| $C'_L,\ C'_D,\ C'_m,\ C'_p$ | coefficients for yawed aerofoil. |
| $H$ | total head at any point in wake. |
| $H_1$ | total head in undisturbed stream. |
| $M$ | Mach number. |
| $M_1$ | Mach number in undisturbed stream. |

† Knowler and Pruden, 'On the drag of circular cylinders at high speeds', *Rep. Memor. Aero. Res. Coun.*, No. 1,933 (1944).

$M_D$      drag critical Mach number, i.e. Mach number at which drag starts to rise rapidly.

$p$      static pressure.

$p_1$      static pressure in undisturbed stream.

$R$      Reynolds number (based on aerofoil chord except where otherwise stated).

T.R.      taper ratio.

$t$      aerofoil thickness.

$U$      velocity of undisturbed stream.

$u$      velocity component along $x$-axis.

$v$      velocity component along $y$-axis.

$x$      distance behind leading edge of aerofoil.

$x_p$      distance of centre of pressure behind leading edge of aerofoil.

$\alpha$      angle of incidence.

$\theta$      angular distance from front stagnation point (on circular cylinder).

$\eta$      control flap angle.

$\rho_1$      air density in undisturbed stream.

$\phi$      angle of yaw.

# XIII

## FLOW PAST BODIES OF REVOLUTION

### § 1. Introduction

RECENT developments, and particularly the spectacular rise in the maximum speed of aircraft, have made it easy to forget that certain branches of supersonic research are very old. In fact, it is probably true to say that the determination of the drag coefficients of solids of revolution with particular application to projectiles has as long a history as almost any branch of aerodynamic research. In particular the drag coefficient of spheres up to a Mach number of about 2 was determined by Robins in 1742. Gunnery is a very specialized subject having contacts with many branches of engineering and physics but close relations with none and it is subject to security restrictions; so developments in external ballistics were to some extent shrouded in secrecy and it is only in the last few decades that these particular applications have begun to be at all closely linked with other branches of high-speed flow.

In this chapter attention will be concentrated on spin stabilized projectiles of the conventional type. There have been spectacular developments during the last decade in rockets and fin stabilization, but, although the necessary extensions to ballistic theory have been published,† the practical applications can only be mentioned here in passing.

The general character of the flow about the most used body of revolution—a projectile or shell—is well illustrated in the series of photographs reproduced in Plates 21 and 22.

In Plate 21 (a), at a Mach number just above the lower critical (see p. 689), the presence of a locally supersonic field of flow is indicated by the shocks near the base. Calculation, confirmed by such measurements as exist, predicts that the forward boundary of the supersonic region is on the ogival head near to the shoulder.

In Plate 21 (b), at a Mach number just above but very near to unity, the complicated nature of the field is obvious at a glance.

† For a general history, see Willy Ley, *Rockets and Space Travel*, Viking (1948). For theory see Knight, 'The elementary mathematics of the rocket', *Math. Gaz.* **82** (1948), 187; Rosser, Newton, and Gross, *Mathematical Theory of Rocket Flight*, McGraw-Hill (1947); Rankin, 'The mathematical theory of the motion of rotated and unrotated rockets', *Philos. Trans.* **241** (1949), 457.

PLATE 21

(a) $M_1 = 0 \cdot 86$

(b) $M_1 = 1 \cdot 01$

(c) $M_1 = 1 \cdot 26$

Shadowgraphs of projectile in flight

PLATE 22

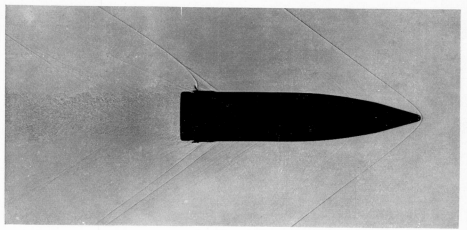

(a) $M_1 = 1 \cdot 76$

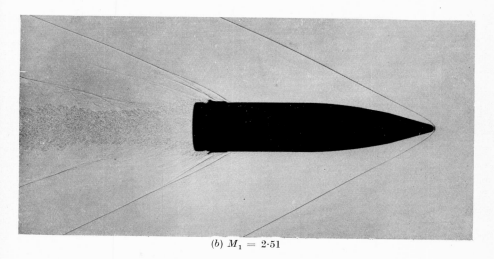

(b) $M_1 = 2 \cdot 51$

Shadowgraphs of projectile in flight

The main shock (or bow wave) is well ahead of the nose, there is a second shock (or rather system) near the shoulder, a third shock of some strength a little in front of the driving band, and finally there is a fourth emanating from the wake. In addition, many wavelets indicate where the flow, having become subsonic through the shock, has again become supersonic. Altogether there are three (or perhaps four) regions in which the flow changes from supersonic to subsonic and then reverts to supersonic, and the picture gives a good idea of the enormous difficulties inherent in making any calculations in the transonic regions.

In Plate 21 (c), at a Mach number of about $1\frac{1}{4}$, the presence of wavelets indicates that, except right at the nose, the field is everywhere supersonic and it would be fair to describe this Mach number as at or above the upper critical (see p. 690). The wave system now consists of a head shock, a shock from the driving band, and an imperfectly integrated shock system in the wake.

In Plate 22 (a), at a Mach number of about $1\frac{3}{4}$, the picture is much as in Plate 21 (c), except that the shock system in the wake has more or less coalesced in a single shock and that the wake itself is beginning to neck down.

In Plate 22 (b), at a Mach number of about $2\frac{1}{2}$, the process has continued and the wave system near the base can now fairly be described as a single shock pointing at the neck of the wake.

Notice also how the wave system folds back more and more on the projectile as the Mach number increases and thus demonstrates visually that the disturbance is more and more confined to the neighbourhood of the projectile and its wake.

Calculation predicts and photographs confirm that the wave system decays very slowly. Plate 24 (a) (facing p. 701) shows the wave system as far as about 8 calibres from the body and other photographs have shown that the pattern persists with little visual change as far as about 40 calibres transversely from the body.

In the foregoing paragraphs the expressions 'lower critical', 'upper critical', and 'transonic' have been used; they represent a departure from the previous nomenclature and are defined as follows.

The 'lower critical' (elsewhere termed the 'critical') Mach number is the Mach number (less than unity) of a field of flow such that if a body be immersed in it the local velocity at some point attains, but at no point exceeds, the local speed of sound at that point.

The 'upper critical' (Mach number) is the Mach number (greater than unity) of a field of flow such that if a body be immersed in it the local velocity at some point decreases to, but at no point (neglecting boundary layers) falls below, the local speed of sound.

'Transonic' flow is a flow whose Mach number lies between the upper and lower critical.

A field of flow whose Mach number is less than the 'lower critical' will be described as 'subsonic': and one whose Mach number is above the 'upper critical' as 'supersonic'.

In practice almost all projectiles have slightly rounded noses, which implies a normal shock in this region and its concomitant subsonic flow. Strictly speaking, therefore, the field of flow round a projectile is never supersonic. But a glance at Plates 21 (c) to 22 (b) will show that this region is very local and that the difference between Plate 21 (b) and, say, Plate 21 (c) is for all practical purposes one of kind and not of degree, and therefore it is customary to neglect this small region. The field of Plate 21 (b), therefore, would be described as transonic but that of Plate 21 (c) as supersonic, with a great gain in convenience but a loss of logical precision.

The numerical values to be attached to the various terms obviously depend on the shape of the body; in the case of a cone the change from supersonic to transonic flow (the upper critical) occurs when the shock becomes detached from the nose.

The definitions and the notation for some of the quantities customarily used in external ballistics differ from those used in aerodynamics; we shall here use ballistic notation defined as follows.

Drag coefficient $\qquad f_R \equiv R^*/\rho U^2 r_1^2.$

Cross-wind force $\bigg\}$ coefficient $f_L \equiv L/\rho U^2 r_1^2 \sin \delta = m^* k/\rho U r_1^2.$
Lift

Moment coefficient $\qquad f_M \equiv M^*/\rho U^2 r_1^3 \sin \delta = A^2 N^2/4 B s \rho U^2 r_1^3.$

Yawing moment coefficient $\quad f_H \equiv H/\rho U \omega r_1^4 = B h/\rho U r_1^4.$

Magnus couple coefficient $\quad f_J \equiv J/\rho U N r_1^4 \sin \delta = A \gamma/\rho U r_1^4.$

Where: $R^* \equiv$ drag, the force opposing motion.

$L \equiv$ cross-wind force or lift, the force at right angles to motion in the plane of yaw.

$M^* \equiv$ moment $= \mu \sin \delta.$

$H \equiv$ yawing moment due to yawing.

$J \equiv$ Magnus couple.

$\rho \equiv$ density of the fluid.

$U \equiv$ velocity of centre of gravity of the body.

$r_1 \equiv$ radius of the cylindrical portion of the body.

$\delta \equiv$ yaw, the angle between the axis of the body and the direction of motion of its centre of gravity.

$\omega \equiv$ resultant transverse angular velocity of the body.

$N \equiv$ spin of the body about its axis.

$m^* \equiv$ mass of the body.

$A \equiv$ longitudinal moment of inertia.

$B \equiv$ transverse moment of inertia at the C. G.

$\Omega \equiv AN/B.$

Stability coefficient $s \equiv A^2 N^2/4B\mu = \Omega^2 B/4\mu.$

Damping factors $\begin{cases} k \equiv L/m^* U \sin\delta, \\ h \equiv H/B\omega, \\ \gamma \equiv J/AN \sin\delta. \end{cases}$

The drag, lift, and moment are defined precisely by the following considerations. The resultant of the normal and tangential forces acting on the body is, of course, a force in a certain direction, and it is customary to define the intersection of the line of action of this force with the axis of the body as the centre of pressure. It is also customary to transfer this force to the centre of gravity of the body and there resolve it along and perpendicular to the line of travel of the C.G. As a result it is usual to speak of drag (the force opposing motion), lift (the force at right angles to motion in the plane of yaw), and moment. But before considering these forces and couple as such it is both more convenient and logical to consider the detailed distribution on the body. Also it is better to deal with the cases of yaw (defined above) and no yaw separately.

## § 2. Pressure distribution at no yaw

*Effect of head shape.* In Figs. 221–4 and 225–8 are shown the pressure distributions on a series of models.† The pressures at the model surface and in the free stream are denoted by $p_s$ and $p_1$, respectively. The measurements were made in the N.P.L. Engineering Division $4\frac{1}{2}$ in. open jet and in the 5 in. × 2 in. flexible wall induction tunnels at Mach numbers of about 0·9 and 1·3 and are therefore typical of conditions somewhere near the lower and upper criticals respectively. The latest series of measurements are shown as dots.

† *Rep. Engng. Div. Nat. Phys. Lab.* (unpublished).

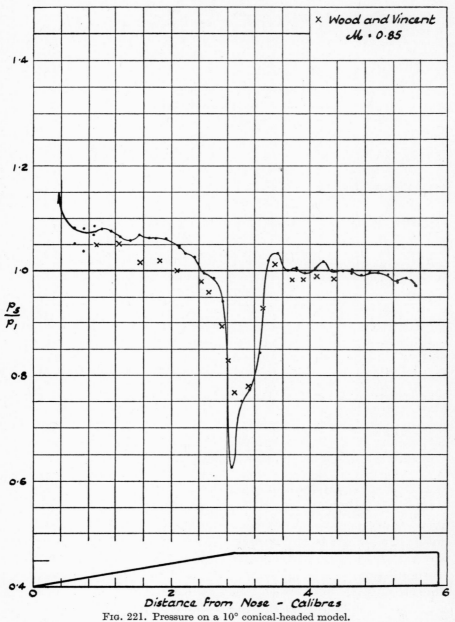

FIG. 221. Pressure on a 10° conical-headed model.

[The free-stream Mach number for the latest measurements (shown by dots) was 0·90.]

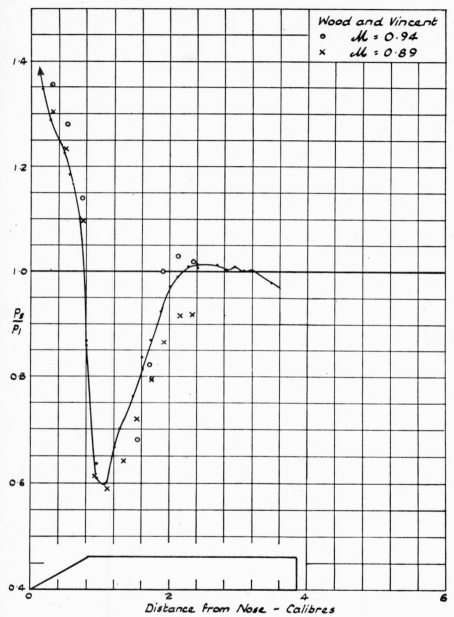

Fig. 222. Pressure on a 30° conical-headed model.

[The free-stream Mach number for the latest measurements (shown by dots) was 0·89.]

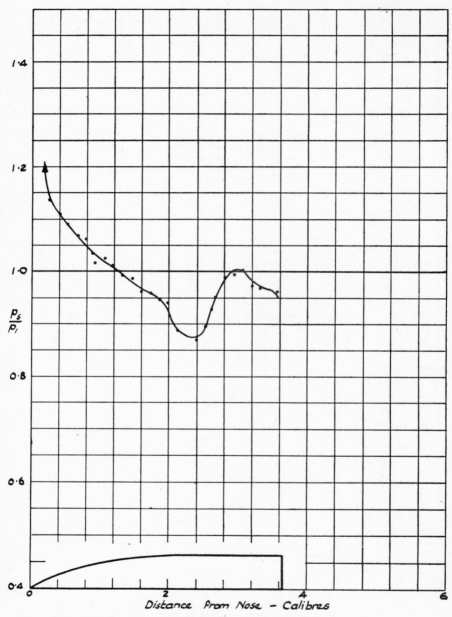

FIG. 223. Pressure on a 5/10 C.R.H. model at a Mach number of 0·89.

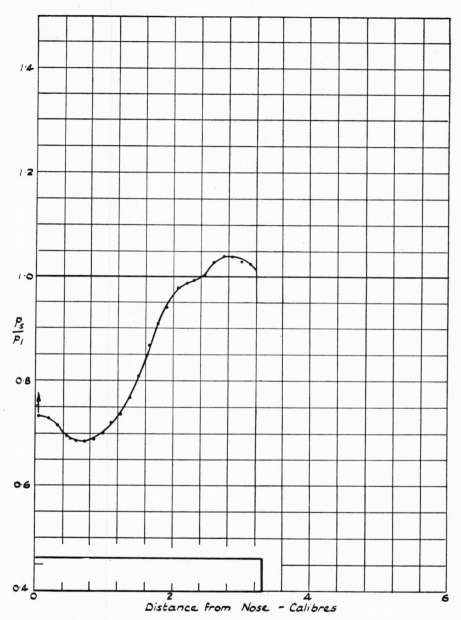

FIG. 224. Pressure on a flat-headed model at a Mach number of 0·88.

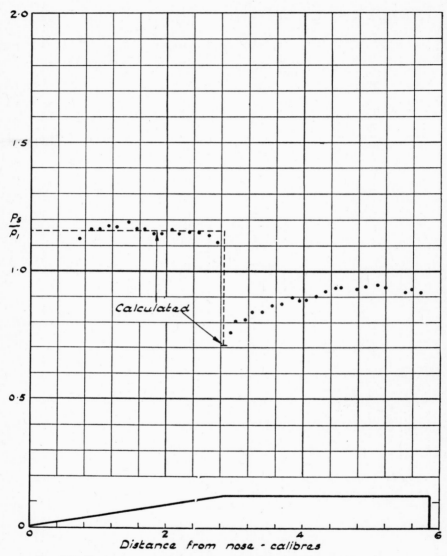

FIG. 225. Pressure on a 10° conical-headed model at a Mach number of 1·32.

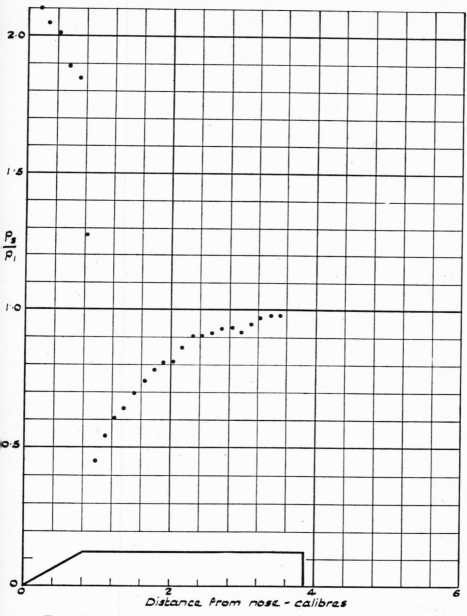

FIG. 226. Pressure on a 30° conical-headed model at a Mach number of 1·34.

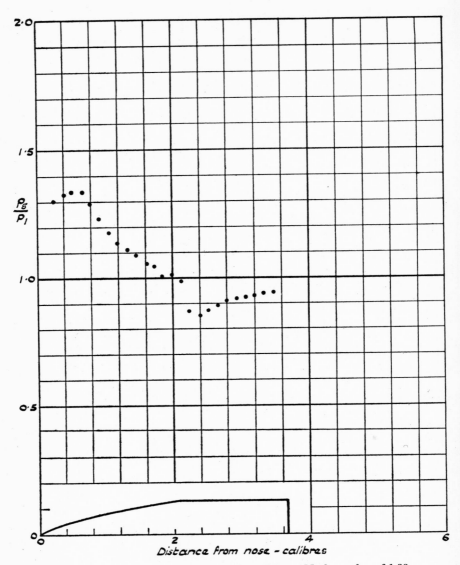

FIG. 227. Pressure on a 5/10 C.R.H. model at a Mach number of 1·33.

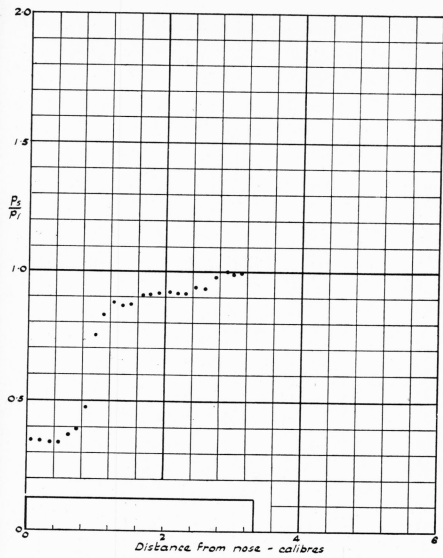

FIG. 228. Pressure on a flat-headed model at a Mach number of 1·37.

The series comprised conical-headed models of 10°, 20°, and 30° semi-angle, a model with a 5/10 C.R. head and one with a flat head. From these the results on the models with the two extreme values of cone angle, the 5/10 C.R.H. model and the flat-headed model, have been selected.

In general the two sets of results at high subsonic speeds are in good accord although they were made at very different dates and in tunnels of different types, and the agreement with calculation where the latter has been made is reassuring. The chief points to notice are: firstly, the abrupt decrease in pressure in coming from the head to the parallel portion, if the junction of the two be a sharp corner. (For instance Fig. 221 shows that, as the fluid passes the corner, the pressure drops abruptly by nearly half its value, whereas Fig. 223 shows a drop which is neither so abrupt nor so large. A comparison of Figs. 225 and 227 reveals the same kind of behaviour.) Secondly, there is the rapid recovery of pressure along the parallel portion to a value not far removed from the free-stream static pressure; and, thirdly, the excellent agreement with calculation where the latter exists (Fig. 225): this agreement was also found for the 20° cone. The régime for the 10° and 20° cones was supersonic at the higher Mach number; in all the other cases it was transonic. The pressure on the head of the flat-headed model was also measured; these results are discussed later (§ 5). Photographs taken by the schlieren method of the flow near a 30° cone for Mach numbers between 0·81 and 0·94 are reproduced as Plate 23; they show the growth with increasing Mach number of the shock system.

The pressure on a conical head, with the shock attached to the cone, is one of the few cases in which an exact solution of the equations of motion is possible, and for which therefore the pressure can be calculated *ab initio*. The details are given in Chap. V, § 11.

*Base pressure.* At the inception of supersonic wind-tunnel research on projectiles, and for many years after, it seems to have been tacitly assumed that the base pressure of a projectile was a function of Mach number only. It was appreciated that the nature and position of the supports had a profound effect, and indeed some of Sir Thomas Stanton's earliest work seems to have been directed to this end. But the effect of Reynolds number was ignored; indeed, so long as a tunnel works, as the early ones did, at one stagnation pressure only, no variation of Reynolds number was obtainable by pressure

PLATE 23

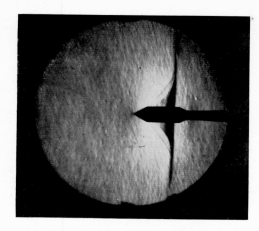

Test No. 1.
Mach number = 0·94

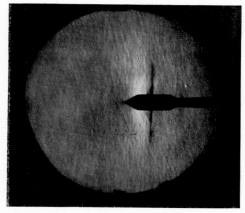

Test No. 2.
Mach number = 0·895

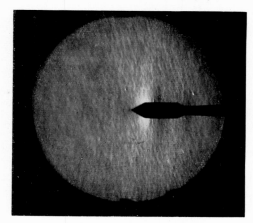

Test No. 3.
Mach number = 0·815

Schlieren photographs of a conical-headed projectile

PLATE 24

(*a*) Shadowgraph of Mark VII 0·303 rifle bullet. $M = 2·15$

(*b*) Shadowgraph showing boundary layer growth. $M = 2$. Yaw 10° (approx.)

XIII. 2]   FLOW PAST BODIES OF REVOLUTION   701

variation and the small size of the tunnels practically compelled the use of the largest possible model, which even then was only $\frac{1}{4}$ in. diameter.

The advent of the closed-circuit tunnel capable of working over a range of stagnation pressures radically altered the situation, and some measurements made in the 11 in. tunnel† demonstrated beyond cavil that the base pressure ratio was a function of stagnation pressure and therefore presumably of Reynolds number. Moreover, the variation was quite large, being of the order of $2:1$ over the range covered by the tunnel. The need for some sort of working theory, even if only approximate, is therefore great.

Fig. 229 is plotted from the original series of measurements. Plate 22 shows that the flow near the base is very complicated if considered in detail, but if the Mach number be considerably greater than unity and the effect of the driving band be neglected, a picture rather like that of Plate 24 $(a)$, which is a photograph of a rifle bullet, can be regarded as typical. This, in its turn, can be simplified to Fig. 230, and from this simplified picture it is possible to calculate the base pressure comparatively easily.‡

For a projectile of diameter $d$ and length $l$ ($= K_1 d$), so that $K_1$ is the length in calibres, and with $\delta$ now denoting the thickness of the boundary layer at the base, the field of flow (see Fig. 230) can be described thus. Immediately behind the base the wake 'necks down' to form a frustum of a cone $ABB_1A_1$; the height $h$ ($= K_2 d$) of the cone is of the same order as $d$ and the angle ($\phi$) which the side makes with the axis of the projectile is comparatively small (up to $15°$). From near $BB_1$ a shock wave emerges whose angle is comparable with the nose wave. Behind $BB_1$ the wake proper becomes approximately of constant width and changes markedly in appearance. Along $AB$ or $A_1B_1$ the edge is clearly defined and nearly straight: behind $BB_1$ the edge is much more irregular and appears to be bounded by vortices regularly arranged. In short, it looks very like a subsonic wake. Immediately behind the base there is a region of still air; it is not always visible in photographs, but its

† Hankins, 'Experiments of Reynolds number effect on projectiles at supersonic speeds', *Rep. Engng. Divn. Nat. Phys. Lab.*, No. 221/46; *6th Int. Congr. appl. Mech., Paris* (1946).

‡ Cope, 'Calculations of Reynolds number effect on projectiles at supersonic speeds', *Rep. Engng. Div. Nat. Phys. Lab.*, No. 222/46; *6th Int. Congr. appl. Mech., Paris* (1946).

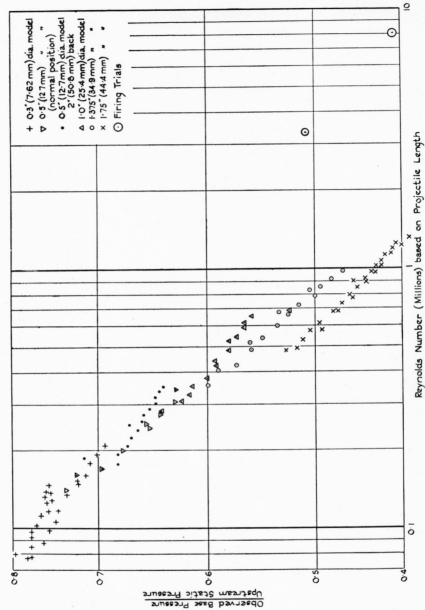

Legend (reading within the plot):
+ 0·3" (7·62 mm) dia. model
▽ 0·5" (12·7mm) " (normal position)
● 0·5" (12·7mm) dia. model 2" (50·8 mm) back
▲ 1·0" (25·4 mm) dia. model "
○ 1·375" (34·9 mm) " "
× 1·75" (44·4 mm) " "
⊙ Firing Trials

Vertical axis: Observed Base Pressure / Upstream Static Pressure

Horizontal axis: Reynolds Number (Millions) based on Projectile Length

FIG. 229.

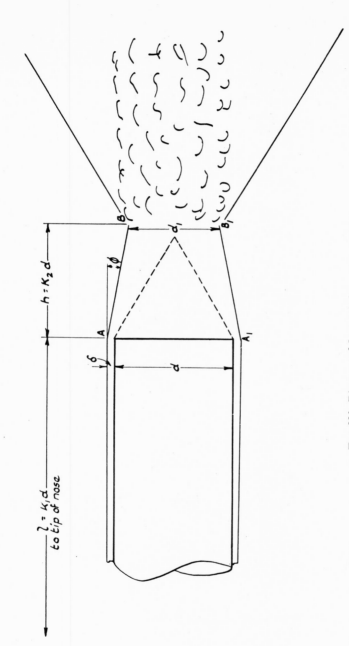

Fig. 230. Diagram of flow near base of projectile.

presence has been verified by wind-tunnel tests. An example is given later in this chapter (Fig. 242).

As the Mach number approaches 1 (from above) this simplification becomes less accurate (see, for instance, Plate 21 (b)). The principal changes are that the edges $AB$, $A_1B_1$ of Fig. 230 become less clearly defined and that the shock wave starts farther from the neck and appears to be generated by the concurrence of wavelets emerging from $AB$.

The general idea underlying the present treatment is that $AB$ and $A_1B_1$ are traces of a vortex sheet across which there is a velocity but not a pressure difference. The boundary layer expands from the annulus $AA_1$ to fill the circle $BB_1$; the main stream turns through an angle $\phi$. At $BB_1$ a compression occurs which results in the shock waves from the neck and wake farther downstream. Broadly speaking, this picture amounts to saying that the projectile streamlines itself by adding the frustum $ABB_1A_1$ of still air to its (cylindrical) base and that the pressure on $BB_1$ is $p_b$. The angle ($\phi$) of the stream-lining is fixed by the fact that changing it has an opposite effect on $p_b$ as calculated from the flow in the main stream and from the boundary layer respectively. The bigger $\phi$ is the smaller is $p_b/p_A$ calculated from the main stream: but $d_1$ is decreased by increasing $\phi$, so that the boundary layer expands less and therefore $p_b/p_A$ calculated from it increases. It should be noticed that this treatment yields a change in $p_b$ although the state of the boundary layer is unchanged and therefore differs essentially from the treatment typified by the sphere, in which a change of state of the layer alters the position of the point of separation.

It follows immediately from the above that $p_b$ is a function of the thickness of the boundary layer at the base of the projectile and therefore of $R$. And it is possible to predict qualitatively its changes with $R$. Begin with a low value of $R$ (say 100,000)† and for the moment ignore the fact that $p_A$ is not quite equal to the static pressure in the free stream ($p_1$). The boundary layer will be completely laminar and fairly thick. Therefore $p_b/p_1$ will be 'large'. Increasing $R$ will decrease $p_b/p_1$ comparatively rapidly, so long as the layer remains laminar, since $\delta\sqrt{R}$ is a constant and therefore $\delta$ decreases sharply as $R$ increases. With further increase in $R$ the layer will become turbulent and sooner or later, perhaps after a

† Based on projectile length.

transition period, a stage will be reached in which it can be treated as turbulent right to the nose of the projectile. When this stage is reached the layer will be much thicker so $p_b/p_1$ will again be 'large'. Thereafter $p_b/p_1$ will again decrease but will be much less sensitive to increase of $R$ since now $\delta R^{1/m}$ is a constant where $m$ is of the order of 5. The range of $R$ which constitutes the transition zone for a boundary layer when the main stream is supersonic is as yet imperfectly known, but it appears to be approximately the same as the range for a subsonic main stream for which the limits of the zone are some hundreds of thousands and a few million. Finally since base drag and base pressure are connected by the relations

$$f_B = \frac{\pi}{\gamma M^2}\left(1 - \frac{p_b}{p_1}\right), \qquad \frac{p_b}{p_1} = 1 - \frac{\gamma M^2}{\pi} f_B,$$

$f_B$ will decrease as $p_b/p_1$ increases.

To sum up: in terms of $f_B$ which is the practically important quantity, the above discussion leads to the following conclusions. $f_B$ is a function of $R$ since it depends on the thickness of the boundary layer. For sufficiently low values of $R$ this layer is laminar and $f_B$ increases (possibly quite sharply) with $R$. At some value of $R$, provisionally fixed at about $\frac{1}{2}$ million, the layer begins to become turbulent. The transition zone may last until $R$ is a few million, when the layer can be regarded as completely turbulent. It is now very much thicker, so $f_B$ has decreased considerably. Thereafter it increases with $R$ but much more slowly than in the laminar region. Broadly speaking, projectiles operate at Reynolds numbers above the transition zone and supersonic wind tunnels within it. To a first approximation, therefore, $f_B$ would be a constant in free flight, but would vary in a wind tunnel in a manner which might be settled by the flow conditions in that particular tunnel.

The translation of the above ideas into symbols, and the numerical calculation of $p_b/p_1$ for comparison with measurements, is carried out using standard inviscid theory for the main-stream flow and existing boundary-layer theory for the flow in the annulus. The result of the calculation contains one disposable constant $K_2$; it cannot be calculated from the momentum for the frustum because the contribution from the conical portion is unknown; indeed, for this reason, the momentum equation cannot be used. $K_2$ therefore is determined by range photographs as described later.

The Prandtl–Meyer two-dimensional solution of the flow round a corner has been used to calculate $p_b/p_1$ in the main stream since no analogous three-dimensional solution is known. $\phi$ is usually small, so that it is reasonable to hope that no large error is introduced. It seems probable that the values of $p_b/p_1$ thus obtained will be too small.

The calculation of $p_b/p_1$ from the boundary-layer standpoint proceeds as follows:

The mass flow (in unit time) through the circle $BB_1$ is

$$\tfrac{1}{4}\pi d_1^2 \rho_b U_b$$

and the mass flow (also in unit time) passing $AA_1$ is

$$\pi d \int_0^\delta \rho u \, dy = \pi d l \rho_A U_A \left(1 - \frac{\delta_1}{\delta}\right)\frac{\delta}{l},$$

where the symbols have their usual boundary-layer meanings.

Equating the mass flows and substituting $K_1 d$ for $l$,

$$\frac{\rho_b}{\rho_A} = 4K_1 \frac{U_A}{U_b}\left(1 - \frac{\delta_1}{\delta}\right)\frac{\delta}{l}\frac{d^2}{d_1^2}.$$

From the geometry of Fig. 230,

$$\frac{d}{d_1} = \frac{1}{1 - 2K_2 \tan \phi}.$$

Therefore     $$\frac{\rho_b}{\rho_A} = \frac{U_A}{U_b}\left(1 - \frac{\delta_1}{\delta}\right)\frac{\delta}{l}\frac{4K_1}{(1 - 2K_2 \tan \phi)^2}.$$

Across $BB_1$ the energy is

$$\tfrac{1}{2}U_b^2 + c_p T_b \equiv c_p T_b\left(1 + \frac{\gamma - 1}{2}M_b^2\right).$$

Therefore     $$\frac{T_b}{T_A} = \frac{1 + \tfrac{1}{2}(\gamma - 1)M_A^2}{1 + \tfrac{1}{2}(\gamma - 1)M_b^2}$$

on the assumption that the total energy per unit mass is the same at $AA_1$ and at $BB_1$.

Combining with the equation of continuity

$$\frac{p_b}{p_A} = \frac{\rho_b T_b}{\rho_A T_A} = \frac{1 + \tfrac{1}{2}(\gamma - 1)M_A^2}{1 + \tfrac{1}{2}(\gamma - 1)M_b^2}\frac{U_A}{U_b}\left(1 - \frac{\delta_1}{\delta}\right)\frac{\delta}{l}\frac{4K_1}{(1 - 2K_2 \tan \phi)^2}.$$

Now $p_A < p_1$; it is a function of the length of the body and it will be taken on the general evidence of wind-tunnel work as about $0.92p_1$. So that finally:

$$\frac{p_b}{p_1} = \left\{0.92\frac{1+\frac{1}{2}(\gamma-1)M_A^2}{1+\frac{1}{2}(\gamma-1)M_b^2}\frac{U_A}{U_b}\right\}\left(1-\frac{\delta_1}{\delta}\right)\frac{\delta}{l}\frac{4K_1}{(1-2K_2\tan\phi)^2}.$$

Consider now in order the various terms on the right-hand side; first the terms within { }. The multiplier $0.92$ has already been considered and

$$\frac{1+\frac{1}{2}(\gamma-1)M_A^2}{1+\frac{1}{2}(\gamma-1)M_b^2} > 1, \text{ since } M_A > M_b.$$

In what follows $M_A$ is taken as $1.1M_b$; $M_b = M_1$. Over the range considered it varies from $1.02$ to $1.07$ and tends asymptotically to $1.1$ for large $M$.

$\dfrac{U_A}{U_b} = \dfrac{U_A}{C_3}\Big/\dfrac{U_b}{C_3}$, where $C_3$ is the velocity of efflux into a vacuum at the stagnation conditions appropriate to the flow. The ratio is therefore determinate when $M_A$ and $M_b$ are known. It varies from $1.08$ for $M_1 = 1$ to $1.03$ for $M_1 = 3$ and tends asymptotically to $1$ for large $M$.

Thus the several terms within { } are all near unity and moreover their values are in some cases slightly above and in others below it. So the value of the { } is quite close to unity (its mean value is $1.014$) and its effect on base pressure can be neglected. The variation of $p_b/p_1$ comes from the remaining terms, which will now be considered.

$1-(\delta_1/\delta)$ and $\delta/l$ are known functions of $M$ once the velocity distribution in the boundary layer is known. In the calculations the sinusoidal distribution has been assumed for laminar flow and the '1/7th power law' for turbulent flow. The calculation yields an equation of the form $(\delta/x)R_x^{1/m} = $ constant, where the constant is a function of $M$. It is given in Figs. 231 and 232.

$K_1$ is the length of the projectile in calibres. $K_1 = 4$ has been used in the calculations as a typical figure.

$K_2$ is the distance in calibres of the 'neck' from the base of the projectile. Available information on its value is scanty and not very accurate. Examination of such as is available plotted as Fig. 233 suggests that $K_2 = 1$ for $R > 1\frac{1}{2}$ million and for $M > 2$, but that it increases to about $1\frac{1}{2}$ for $R = \frac{1}{2}$ million and to about $1\frac{1}{4}$ for $M = 1$. Values read from the curves have been used in the calculations, but

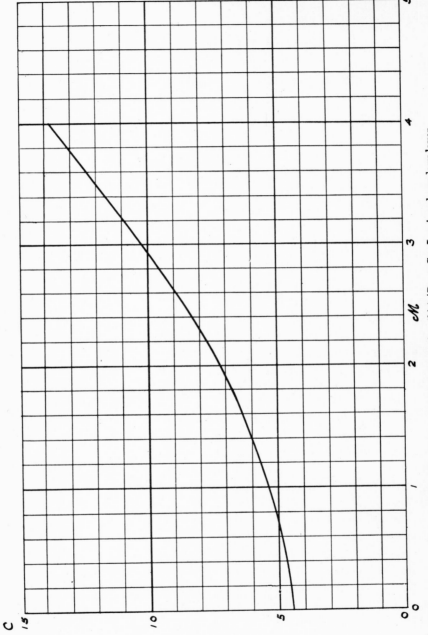

FIG. 231. Value of $C$ in the equation $(\delta/x)\sqrt{R_x} = C$. Laminar boundary layer.

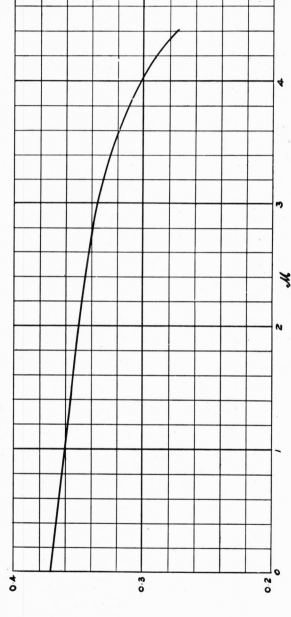

FIG. 232. Value of $C$ in the equation $(\delta/x)R_x^{\frac{1}{5}} = C$. Turbulent boundary layer $u \propto y^{\frac{1}{7}}$.

they must be regarded as tentative; in particular, the variation of $K_2$ with $R$ has had to be based almost entirely on observations made at Mach numbers greater than 2.

The analysis thus yields an expression for $p_b/p_1$, in terms of $\phi$ and

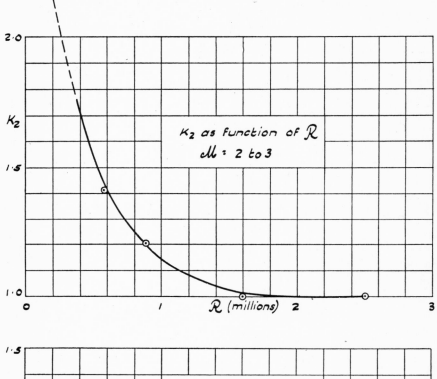

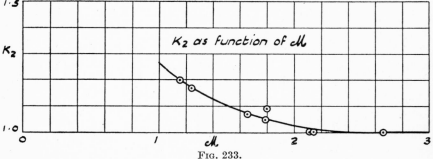

Fig. 233.

quantities which can be regarded as known in a convenient form for computing.

Similarly, the Prandtl–Meyer theory yields an expression for $p_b/p_1$ in terms of $\phi$ quite simply. The method of obtaining numerical results, therefore, is to plot $p_b/p_1$ for the boundary layer and for the free stream against $\phi$. The intersection of the two curves gives the required value of $p_b/p_1$. Fig. 234 is a sample of the type of curve obtained in the course of the calculations.

Calculations have been carried out for $M = 2 \cdot 4$ over the whole range of $R$ (from $\frac{1}{4}$ million to 100 million) likely to be attained. The results are plotted as Fig. 235. The mean line of the N.P.L. results† in the 11 in. tunnel is also plotted and such results from firing trials as are available. The agreement is as good as could be expected and makes it reasonably certain that the simplification depicted in Fig. 230 is at least a satisfactory qualitative explanation. At lower Mach numbers (e.g. $1\frac{1}{2}$) the calculated and measured curves are approximately parallel but the numerical agreement is less good. This is to be expected since the flow pattern at the base appears not to attain its final form until the Mach number is well above unity.

Projectiles have been fitted with streamline bases, or 'boat tails', for many years. Linearized theory predicts a rise of pressure, and so a reduction of drag, if the section of a body of revolution tapers towards the rear, and measurements confirm this qualitatively. But a detailed quantitative comparison is difficult because this rise in pressure constitutes an adverse pressure gradient from the point of view of the boundary layer. The behaviour of the layer must therefore be known, and in particular any regions where there is separation must be known and excluded from the comparison of calculation and measurement.

*Skin friction.* With ordinary spun projectiles skin friction is comparatively unimportant, contributing at most about 20 per cent. to the total resistance; fin-stabilized bodies (such as V2) tend to be much longer and here an accurate knowledge of skin friction is much more important. Since the whole question has been treated in Chap. X it is not necessary to deal with it here.

*Drag.* The sum of the head resistance, skin friction, and base drag is of course the total resistance to motion or drag at no yaw. This has been calculated for two hypothetical bodies having $10^\circ$ and $20^\circ$ conical heads and 4 calibres length, and the results are shown in Table 1 and plotted in Fig. 236. The head drag was calculated by the method of Chap. V, the skin friction by the method of Chap. X with

† Hankins, loc. cit. on p. 701.

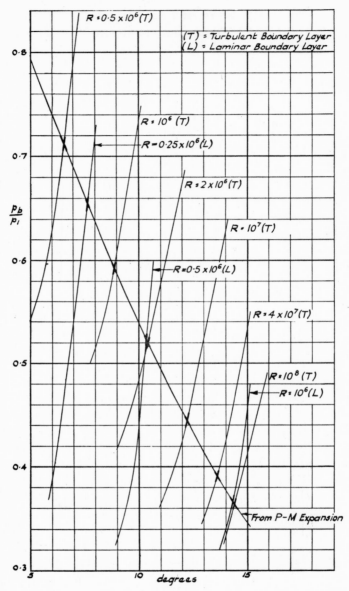

FIG. 234. $p_b/p_1$ as a function of $\phi$ calculated from boundary expansion and from Prandtl–Meyer expansion.

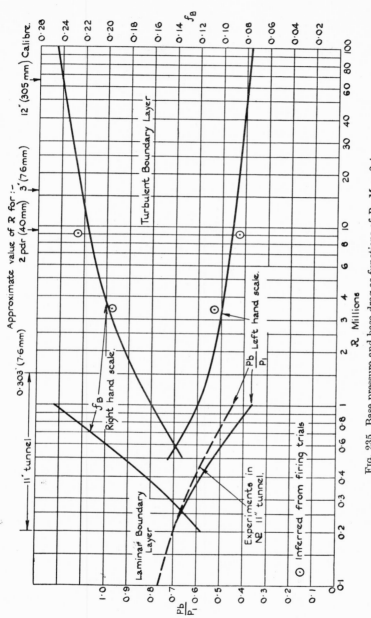

Fig. 235. Base pressure-and base drag as functions of $R$; $M = 2.4$.

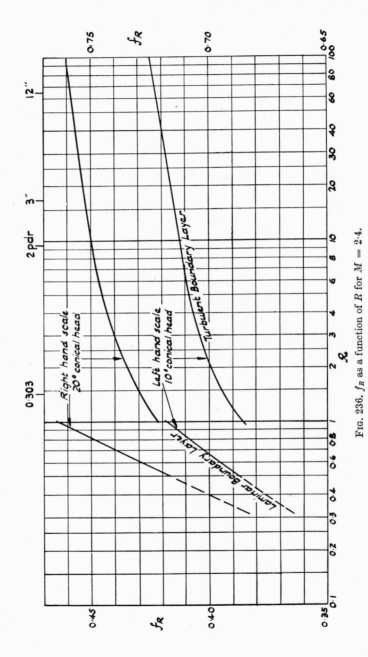

Fig. 236. $f_R$ as a function of $R$ for $M = 2.4$.

allowance for the decrease of skin friction with Mach number, and the base drag by the method of this chapter. The results bear out the remarks just made about the comparatively small importance of skin friction. They also show that over most of the range of Reynolds number occurring in external ballistics the change of drag is so small that its detection would require special measurements of very high accuracy. On the other hand, it is also apparent that the results obtained in a small wind tunnel might easily be some 10 per cent. lower than the results obtained in firing trials with 2 pdr. or 3 in. projectiles and this was in fact a puzzling feature of early measurements.

## TABLE 1

*Contribution to Drag Coefficient from Friction*

| $M$ | $R$ (millions) | Base drag | Friction drag | Head drag† | Sum $\equiv f_R$ 10° cone | 20° cone |
|---|---|---|---|---|---|---|
| 2·4 | ½ | 0·186 (L) | 0·044 | For | 0·381 | 0·717 |
| | 1 | 0·245 (L) | 0·033 | 10° cone | 0·419 | 0·765 |
| | | 0·157 (T) | 0·078 | 0·151 | 0·386 | 0·722 |
| | 2 | 0·184 (T) | 0·065 | and for | 0·400 | 0·736 |
| | 10 | 0·212 (T) | 0·050 | 20° cone | 0·413 | 0·749 |
| | | | | 0·487 | | |
| | 40 | 0·232 (T) | 0·037 | .. | 0·420 | 0·756 |
| | 100 | 0·243 (T) | 0·031 | .. | 0·425 | 0·761 |

(L) With laminar boundary layer.    (T) With turbulent boundary layer.

† Independent of $R$, *ex hypothesi*.

## § 3. Pressure distribution at yaw

If there is no yaw then the pressure distribution at any section of the body will be uniform, but with yaw this ceases to be so and the distribution of pressure around the body as well as along it needs investigation. This greatly increases both the number of observations necessary and the numerical work of reduction, and so comparatively few series of measurements exist. Figs. 237, 238, and 239 have been selected from two such series as typical of the distributions existing.‡

The most noticeable feature is that on the parallel portion, once one is well away from the head, the pressure distribution is symmetrical athwart ships as well as fore and aft. It is believed that this is supported by (unpublished) calculations carried out during the

‡ *Rep. Engng. Div. Nat. Phys. Lab.* (unpublished).

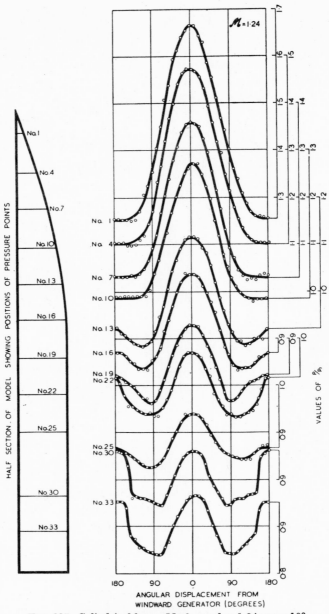

HALF SECTION OF MODEL SHOWING POSITIONS OF PRESSURE POINTS

VALUES OF $p/p_t$

ANGULAR DISPLACEMENT FROM
WINDWARD GENERATOR (DEGREES)

FIG. 237. Cylindrical base. Mach number 1·24; yaw 10°.

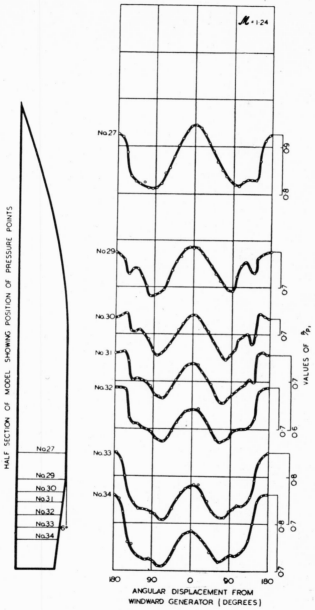

FIG. 238. Streamlined base.  Mach number 1·24; yaw 10°.

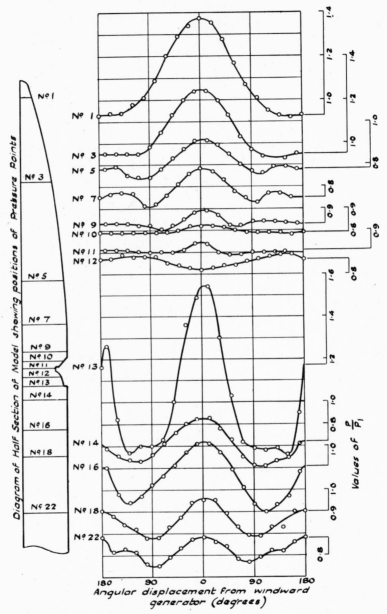

FIG. 239. Effect of notch. Mach number 1·25; yaw 10°.

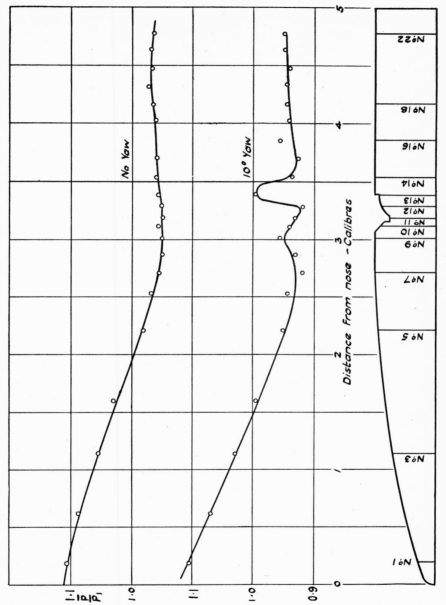

Fig. 240. Effect of notch. Mach number 1·25.

war. Fig. 239 has been included because it shows how very local
is the effect of a notch or other discontinuity; this is shown in another
way in Fig. 240, in which the average pressure round a section is
plotted in terms of the free-stream static pressure. It will be seen
that the effect is negligible at no yaw, and very small at the comparatively large yaw of 10°.

*Base pressure at yaw.* No systematic measurements appear to
exist. The base pressure was measured at two points, at about $\frac{1}{2}$
and $\frac{3}{4}$ radius, in the N.P.L. tests.† The two readings were approximately the same and the base pressure decreased markedly with
increasing yaw. Calculations on the same lines as the no yaw case
are presumably possible but would be much more complicated
because one effect of yaw is to cause the boundary layer to thicken,
or even to break away, on the leeward side. Plate 24 (*b*) illustrates
this phenomenon.

*Skin friction at yaw.* Here again detailed predictions must await
the unravelling of the complications induced in the boundary-layer
flow by the yaw.

*Effect of yaw on head shock.* The yaw will have some effect on the
head shock; the first-order effect for a cone at small yaw has been
calculated by Stone.‡ No systematic check of his predictions seems
to exist; they are apparently verified in certain respects by firing
trials at the B.R.L., Aberdeen; some preliminary measurements at
the N.P.L. range suggest that in detail the phenomena are more complicated than might be thought from the American results.

*Comparison with full scale.* The only full-scale pressure measurements appear to be by Bairstow *et al.*§ in which the effect of pressure
on the time of burning of a fuse was ingeniously used. These measurements, and those just discussed are plotted in Fig. 241 for comparison.
The agreement is as good as could be expected, if one bears in mind
that the heads are not quite similar, that the Mach numbers are somewhat different, and that the yaw in Bairstow's case is quite unknown.

## § 4. Pressure distribution in the wake

The application of the pitot transverse method to the measurement of drag in the case of transonic flow near the lower critical

† *Rep. Engng. Div. Nat. Phys. Lab.* (unpublished).
‡ 'Supersonic flow past a slightly yawing cone', *J. Math. Phys.* **27** (1948), 67.
§ Bairstow, Fowler, and Hartree, 'The pressure distribution on the head of a
shell moving at high velocities', *Proc. Roy. Soc.* A, **97** (1920), 202–18.

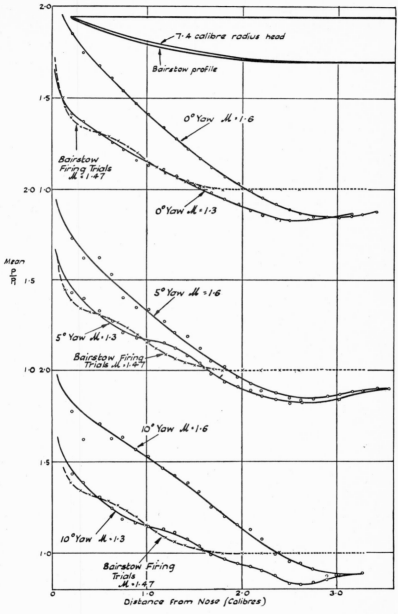

Fig. 241.

has been discussed in Chap. XI. Few measurements exist at higher Mach numbers, but Fig. 242 shows measurements made in the $4\frac{1}{2}$ in. induction type wind tunnel at a Mach number of about $1\frac{1}{3}$. The model was about 4 calibres long, 0·3 in. diameter, nose-supported, and the measurements had to be confined to the centre line of the wake. The total head measurements demonstrate the region of still air (§ 2) and that the rate of recovery of pressure in the later stages is very slow. Indeed, the wake is detectable in photographs of bullets in flight more than 50 calibres from the base.

## § 5. Drag, lift, and moment

The march of the drag coefficient for a sufficient variety of shapes to cover most cases arising in practice is shown in Fig. 243. The figure is designed to show broad trends, and comparatively small effects, such as those due to the presence of a driving band, have been ignored.

Curve $A$ has been included because measurements at the N.P.L. have shown that it applies, not only to circular cylinders 'end on', but also to cubes 'flat' and to many types of cylinder whose cross-section is not circular. Examples actually measured included cylinders whose cross-sections were rectangular, star-shaped, and triangular.

Curve $B$ is the well-known sphere curve and applies approximately to bodies of irregular shape of roughly spherical proportions.

There is very little evidence, save in a region near a Mach number of unity, of any scale effect for either of curves $A$ or $B$. This is due to the loss in the head shock, or wave-making resistance, swamping the effects of change of base pressure and of skin friction.

Curve $C$ is typical of the drag curves of projectiles at the beginning of the century, and curve $D$ represents about the best that can be achieved, in a practical design, by using both a very fine head and a streamlined base.

Taken as a family the curves show that as the head gets finer both the initial rise of drag and the position of maximum drag move nearer to a Mach number of unity.

Fig. 244 shows for the moment coefficient what Fig. 243 shows for the drag coefficient. Projectiles $A$ and $B$ of Fig. 244 are approximately equivalent to projectiles $C$ and $D$ of Fig. 243. Linearized theory predicts that $f_M$ is independent of Mach number and this is substantially confirmed by the slow variation which is found in practice.

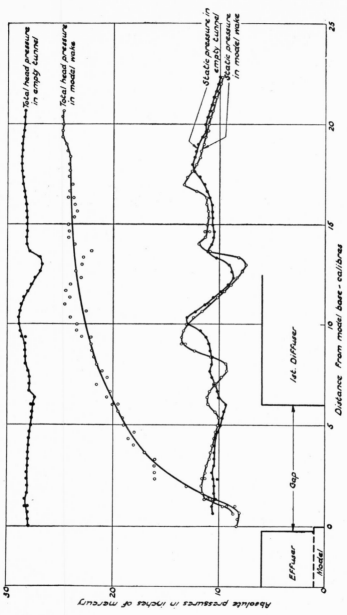

Fig. 242. Pressure distribution in wake.

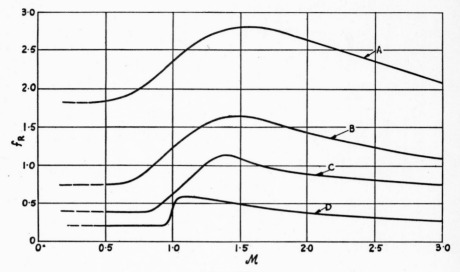

FIG. 243.

A. Disk.                                   B. Sphere.
C. Shell with blunt head.      D. Shell with fine head and boat tail.

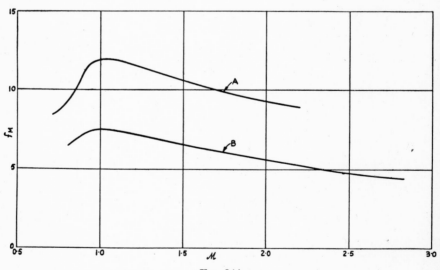

FIG. 244.

A. Shell with blunt head.          B. Shell with fine head.

The resultant of the several force distributions discussed earlier in this chapter is a force $F$ passing through the axis of the body and inclined at an angle $\Delta$ to it. The method of representing this force in the applications of external ballistics has been given earlier (§ 1) and is here repeated as Fig. 245, which also repeats the definitions of the coefficients arising from the method of treatment.

What has been written in § 2 will have made it clear that the results of wind-tunnel measurements, though primarily dependent on Mach number, are sufficiently dependent on Reynolds number for the possibilities of scale effect to be embarrassing; and, in fact, experience shows that a 10 per cent. difference of drag values between model and full scale is a very real possibility. The effects on lift and moment would seem *a priori* to be less serious. It so happens that most of the early supersonic wind tunnels, by reason of their dimensions and operating pressure, only just passed the million mark in their maximum attainable Reynolds number. In other words, most supersonic tunnels have worked in the laminar or at best part way into the transitional region; whereas, as Figs. 235 or 236 show, projectiles work well in the turbulent region. The importance of scale effect has only obtruded itself in the last decade and no systematic comparisons are known. The Germans made innumerable measurements of the drag, lift, and moment coefficients of various shapes in their tunnels during the war but most, if not all, seem to have been on an *ad hoc* basis and at one Reynolds number only.[†]

Table 2 has been prepared to show the kind of accord between calculation and measurement that exists. In it the values of $f_L$ and $f_M$ are compared for three very similar models. Model $A$ (Nos. 1, 2,

TABLE 2

| Number and Model | $M$ | $R$ millions | $f_L$ | $f_M$ | Remarks |
|---|---|---|---|---|---|
| 1. Model $A$ | 0·87 | 1·5 | 3·40 | 9·0 | N.P.L. ballistic range. |
| 2. Model $A$ | 1·03 | 1·8 | 3·12 | 10·8 | |
| 3. Model $B$ | 1·3 | 0·5 | 3·70 | 12·3 | $4\frac{1}{2}$ in. induction tunnel. |
| 4. Model $B$ | 1·6 | 0·5 | 3·90 | 11·5 | |
| 5. Model $A$ | 1·75 | 3 | 3·68 | 8·4 | As 1 and 2. |
| 6. Model $C$ | $> 1$ | Any | $\pi$ | 14·7 | Calculated from linearized theory (Chap. IX, § 10). |

[†] Owen, 'Apparatus and work of the W.V.A. supersonic institute', *Rep. Aero. Res. Coun.*, Nos. 9,281, 9,282, 9,361, 9,520 (1946).

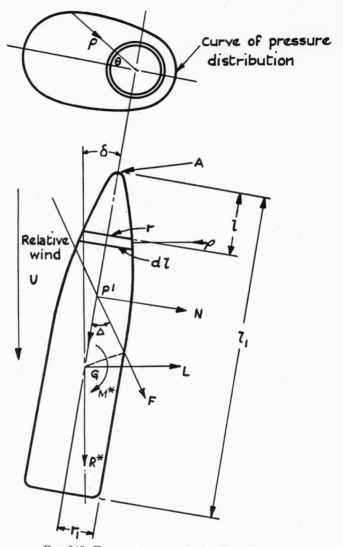

FIG. 245. Force system on a body of revolution.

Drag coefficient $f_R \equiv R^*/\rho U^2 r_1^2$.

Lift coefficient $f_L \equiv L/\rho U^2 r_1^2 \sin \delta$.

Moment coefficient $f_M \equiv M^*/\rho U^2 r_1^3 \sin \delta$.

and 5), fired in the ballistic range, was 4·6 calibres long, namely, 2·5 calibres of cylindrical portion and a 6-calibre radius head; model $B$ (Nos. 3 and 4), measured in the $4\frac{1}{2}$ in. induction tunnel, was 4·9 calibres long, namely, 2·5 calibres of cylindrical portion and a 7·4 calibre radius head; model $C$ (No. 6) is a hypothetical body again with 2·5 calibres of cylindrical portion and a prolate spheroidal head of fineness ratio 4:1. Fig. 255 shows the heads of models $A$ and $C$ superposed and Fig. 241 shows the head of model $B$.

In most balance measurements the model is stationary; the effect of spin seems to have been very little investigated. The experimental difficulties are formidable and it is generally assumed that its effect is not large. A set of German measurements† gave an increase of about $3\frac{1}{2}$ per cent. of $f_R$ with a spin 57 per cent. of the normal, thus confirming so far as they go the usual assumption that the effect of spin on drag anyway is quite small. On the other hand, the problem of spinning models would have to be solved if it were necessary to measure stability derivatives in a wind tunnel.

## § 6. Firing trials

*Introduction.* Wind-tunnel techniques have been fully described in Chap. XI, but it seems more appropriate to deal here with ballistic range techniques. But because knowledge of external ballistics is not widely disseminated it seems best to begin by recalling very briefly and broadly the course of a shell in flight. It is convenient to divide it into two stages:

1. Initially the shell departs very little from the plane trajectory (the trajectory with drag and gravity operating but with no yaw). Both the C.G. and the axis of the shell oscillate helically about the plane trajectory. In time both these oscillations die away and the second stage begins.

2. Here the curvature of the trajectory has an appreciable effect and the plane trajectory becomes less and less of an adequate approximation. Drift ceases to be negligible and large yaws may develop.

Broadly speaking, stage 1 covers all firing at low elevation and stage 2 covers the second half of all trajectories at maximum range and all except the initial stages of high angle fire.

*Equations of motion.* The current theory‡ begins by deriving the equations of motion in very general terms in vector notation. But

† Owen, loc. cit. p. 725.
‡ Fowler, Gallop, Lock, and Richmond, 'The aerodynamics of a spinning shell', *Philos. Trans.* A, **221** (1921), 295; *Textbook of Anti-Aircraft Gunnery*, H.M.S.O., 1925; Nielsen and Synge, 'On the motion of a spinning shell', *Quart. Appl. Math.* **4** (1946), 201; Kelly, McShane, and Reno, *External Ballistics*.

the two stages are handled both analytically and numerically, by different systems of equations with different axes and to some extent different approximations. The equations appropriate to stage 1 are designated 'type $\alpha$' and those appropriate to stage 2 'type $\beta$'.

The ballistic range technique is concerned only with the type $\alpha$ motion, which has been very thoroughly checked in the past twenty-five years and can be accepted as an accurate first approximation to the actual motion.

*Top analogy.* The following treatment does not pretend to derive the type-$\alpha$ equations of motion either of a top or of a shell; rather it is an attempt to write down, as simply as possible, the main steps of such a derivation. The underlying idea is to bring out such analogy as may exist between the two motions and so facilitate discussion of the value of model experiments.

For the top let the axial spin and moment of inertia be $N$ and $A$ respectively, and the longitudinal moment of inertia $B$. Take axes through the point of support $O$ as shown in Fig. 246 (*a*). If $\delta$ be the angle of inclination of the top to the vertical, then the weight of the top ($F$) causes a couple $\mu \sin \delta$ in the plane $XOA$; let this plane initially make an angle $\phi_0$ with the plane $XOY$. $\delta$ (the angle of yaw) is assumed to be such that $\cos \delta \approx 1$, $\sin \delta \approx \delta$. If $l$, $m$, $n$ be the direction cosines of $OA$, then the equations of motion are

$$B\ddot{m} + AN\dot{n} - \mu m = 0,$$
$$B\ddot{n} - AN\dot{m} - \mu n = 0.$$

That is

$$\ddot{m} + \Omega \dot{n} - \frac{\Omega^2}{4s} m = 0,$$

$$\ddot{n} - \Omega \dot{m} - \frac{\Omega^2}{4s} n = 0,$$

where

$$\Omega \equiv AN/B, \qquad s \equiv A^2 N^2/4B\mu;$$

$l \approx 1$, and $m$ and $n$ are small.

Writing $\eta \equiv \delta \exp(i\phi) \equiv m + in$ the equations can be combined to give

$$\ddot{\eta} - i\Omega\dot{\eta} - \frac{\Omega^2}{4s} \eta = 0.$$

The solution can be exhibited in many forms; the one most appropriate to the present discussion is

$$\eta = K_1 \eta_1 + K_2 \eta_2,$$

where $K_1$ and $K_2$ are (possibly complex) constants $Q_1 \exp i\phi_1$, $Q_2 \exp i\phi_2$,

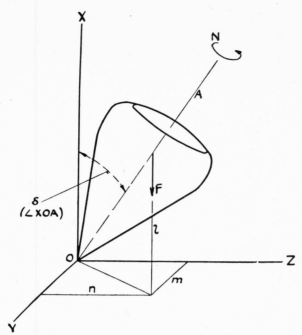

(a) Top.   $F$ causes a couple $\mu \sin \delta$ in plane $XOA$.

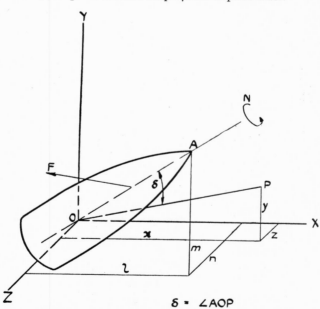

$\delta = \angle AOP$

(b) Shell.   $F$ causes a couple $\mu \sin \delta$ in plane $POA$.
Fig. 246. Comparison of top and shell.

and $\eta_1$, $\eta_2$ are given respectively by

$$\exp(iP_1) \quad \text{and} \quad \exp(iP_2)$$

with

$$\left.\begin{array}{ll} P_1 = p_1+p_2, & P_2 = p_1-p_2 \\ p_1 = \tfrac{1}{2}\Omega t, & p_2 = \tfrac{1}{2}\Omega\sigma t \end{array}\right\} \text{ where } \sigma^2 \equiv 1-\frac{1}{s},$$

The initial condition we require is $\delta_0 = 0$ $(\dot{\delta}_0 \neq 0)$.
This leads to

$$Q_1 = Q_2 = \dot{\delta}_0/\sigma\Omega,$$

$$\phi_1 = \phi_0-\tfrac{1}{2}\pi, \qquad \phi_2 = \phi_0+\tfrac{1}{2}\pi,$$

so that finally

$$\eta = \frac{\dot{\delta}_0}{\sigma\Omega}\{\exp i(p_1-p_2+\phi_0+\tfrac{1}{2}\pi)+\exp i(p_1+p_2+\phi_0-\tfrac{1}{2}\pi)\},$$

which can be reduced to the more familiar form

$$\delta = \delta_{\max}|(\sin \tfrac{1}{2}\Omega\sigma t)|,$$

$$\phi = \phi_0+\tfrac{1}{2}\Omega t.$$

For the shell a system of moving axes as shown in Fig. 246 (b) is used. The origin is the centre of gravity of the shell and $OX$ at any instant is tangential to the plane trajectory. The latter is defined as the trajectory the shell would follow if gravity and air resistance alone were operative with no yaw. $OX$ makes an angle $\theta_1$ with the horizontal and $\cos\theta_1$ will be abbreviated to $c$. $OP$ (direction cosines $x$, $y$, $z$) is the direction of motion of the C.G. and $OA$ (direction cosines $l$, $m$, $n$) the direction of the axis of the shell. The yaw $\delta$, being defined as the angle between the axis of the shell and the direction of motion, is the angle $POA$. The most important resultant of the aerodynamic forces is $F$, which acts through the centre of pressure and in the plane of yaw. This force is equivalent to a couple $(M^* = \mu\sin\delta)$ in the plane of yaw and two forces acting through $O$. They are the drag $(R^*)$ acting in the direction of motion reversed and the cross-wind force $(L)$ acting at right angles to the direction of motion. Two other couples have to be considered; they are caused respectively by the variation of yaw and the spin of the shell. The first $(H)$, analogous to the 'pitching couple due to pitching' of an aircraft, has its axis in the direction of the angular velocity of $OA$ reversed and is of magnitude $Bh\omega$, where $\omega$ is the angular velocity of $OA$. The second $(J)$, the Magnus couple, has its axis at right angles to $OA$ in the plane $POA$ and is of magnitude $AN\gamma \sin \delta$. In both cases forces associated with these couples are neglected.

Under this force system and referred to this system of axes the equations of motion are, approximately,

$$
\left.
\begin{aligned}
\ddot{m}+\Omega\dot{n}+h\dot{m}-\frac{\Omega^2}{4s}(m-y)-\Omega\gamma(n-z) &= 0 \\
\ddot{n}-\Omega\dot{m}+h\dot{n}-\frac{\Omega^2}{4s}(n-z)+\Omega\gamma(m-y) &= 0
\end{aligned}
\right\}
$$

for the angular motion, and

$$
\left.
\begin{aligned}
\dot{y}-k(m-y) &= 0 \\
\dot{z}-k(n-z) &= 0
\end{aligned}
\right\}
$$

for the motion of the C.G., where $k \equiv L/m^*U \sin \delta$.

Writing $m+in = \eta+c\zeta$, $y+iz = c\zeta$ the equations reduce to

$$
\ddot{\eta}-(i\Omega-h-k)\dot{\eta}-\left\{\frac{\Omega^2}{4s}+i\Omega(k-\gamma)-hk-\dot{k}-k\frac{\dot{c}}{c}\right\}\eta-
$$
$$
-(i\Omega\dot{c}-h\dot{c}-\ddot{c})\zeta = 0,
$$
$$
\zeta-\frac{k}{c}\eta = 0.
$$

The important part of the solution of these equations from the point of view of yaw is

$$
\eta = K_1\eta_1+K_2\eta_2,
$$

where $K_1$ and $K_2$ have the same meanings as on p. 728 and $P_1$ and $P_2$ are now given by

$$
P_1 = p_1+p_2+i(q_1+q_2),
$$
$$
P_2 = p_1-p_2+i(q_1-q_2),
$$

where
$$
q_1 \equiv \tfrac{1}{2}(h+k)t, \qquad q_2 \equiv \frac{1}{2}\frac{h-k+2\gamma}{\sigma}t.
$$

It is convenient to write

$$
r_p \equiv Q_2\exp[-(q_1-q_2)],
$$
$$
r_n \equiv Q_1\exp[-(q_1+q_2)].
$$

Inserting the same initial conditions ($\delta_0 = 0$, $\dot{\delta}_0 \neq 0$) as before we get

$$
Q_1 = Q_2 = \dot{\delta}_0/\sigma\Omega.
$$

So

$$\eta = \frac{\dot{\delta_0}}{\sigma\Omega}\{\exp[-(q_1-q_2)]\exp i(p_1-p_2+\phi_0+\tfrac{1}{2}\pi)+$$

$$+\exp[-(q_1+q_2)]\exp i(p_1+p_2+\phi_0-\tfrac{1}{2}\pi)\},$$

$$r_p = \frac{\dot{\delta_0}}{\sigma\Omega}\exp[-(q_1-q_2)] \quad \text{and} \quad r_n = \frac{\dot{\delta_0}}{\sigma\Omega}\exp[-(q_1+q_2)].$$

This differs from the solution for the top only in that the two vectors $r_p$ and $r_n$ contain exponential terms representing the damping; in the case of the top the damping is provided by the friction at the toe. Introduced in this way the damping is difficult to control in amount, but Harding has shown that both the kinds of shell motion arising in practice, and which will be described later, can be imitated, qualitatively at any rate, by a gyroscopic model.

*Gyroscopic model.* A diagram of this model is shown in Fig. 247. It consists of a rod supported in gimbals ($d$) and free to rotate about a transverse axis through the centre $O$ representing the C.G. of a shell travelling vertically upwards in the direction $OZ$. The model does not rotate about its longitudinal axis, but the motor and flywheel ($e$) at its base do, and this supply of axial angular momentum is sufficient to give gyroscopic stability when the C.G. of the model is above the gimbals. The yaw is represented by the angle $ZOZ'$ when the axis of the model lies along $OZ'$ and the scale ($a$) enables this to be read when the plane of yaw coincides with the vertical plane through the scale.

The external couples acting on the model are:

The overturning moment due to gravity which can be adjusted by moving the jockey weight ($c$). This represents $M*$.

A couple opposing the transverse rotation of the model caused by the air resistance acting on the vanes ($b$). These vanes are four in number and are shaped to a shell profile for aesthetic reasons. This couple represents $H$.

A couple acting about the transverse axis in the plane of yaw due to the eddy-current drag on the copper disk ($f$) attached to the motor flywheel and rotating in the field of the permanent magnet ($g$). This couple is approximately proportional to the yaw and can be varied in amount by adjusting the distance between the magnet and the disk. This couple represents $J$.

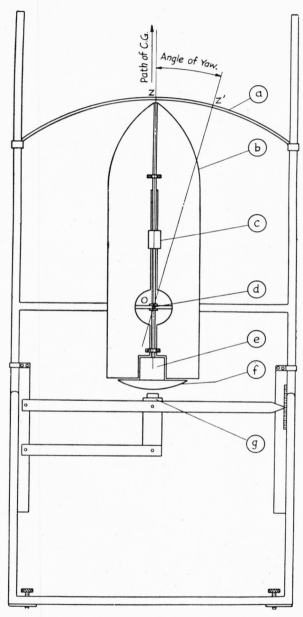

Fig. 247. Gyroscopic model showing the yawing motion of a spinning shell.

FLOW PAST BODIES OF REVOLUTION [XIII. 6

*Solution of the equations.* The full solution of the equations for a spinning shell is:

(1) the yawing motion

$$\eta \equiv \delta \exp(i\phi) = K_1 \exp(iP_1) + K_2 \exp(iP_2),$$

already given but repeated for convenience;

(2) the helical motion of the C.G.

$$\zeta_1 \equiv H_1 + iZ_1 \equiv r \exp(i\theta) = -\frac{4kU}{\Omega^2}\left\{\frac{K_1 \exp(iP_1)}{(1+\sigma)^2} + \frac{K_2 \exp(iP_2)}{(1-\sigma)^2}\right\};$$

(3) the transverse motion of the C.G.

$$\zeta_2 \equiv H_2 + iZ_2 = \frac{2k}{i\Omega}\left\{\frac{K_1}{1+\sigma} + \frac{K_2}{1-\sigma}\right\} \int U \, dt;$$

and the two cases which occur in practice are the ordinary case of firing from a gun with negligible initial yaw and broadside fire from an aircraft with considerable initial yaw.

In the first case $\delta_0 = 0$ but the shell receives an impulse (from muzzle blast, etc.) so $\dot{\delta}_0$ is not zero, and the equations become

$$\delta \exp(i\phi) = (\dot{\delta}_0/\sigma\Omega)\{\exp[-(q_1-q_2)]\exp i(p_1-p_2+\phi_0+\tfrac{1}{2}\pi) +$$
$$+ \exp[-(q_1+q_2)]\exp i(p_1+p_2+\phi_0-\tfrac{1}{2}\pi)\},$$

$$r \exp(i\theta) = \frac{4kU\dot{\delta}_0}{\sigma\Omega^3(1-\sigma)^2}\left\{\exp[-(q_1-q_2)]\exp i(p_1-p_2+\phi_0-\tfrac{1}{2}\pi) + \right.$$
$$\left. + \left(\frac{1-\sigma}{1+\sigma}\right)^2 \exp[-(q_1+q_2)]\exp i(p_1+p_2-\phi_0+\tfrac{1}{2}\pi)\right\},$$

$$H_2 + iZ_2 = \frac{2k\dot{\delta}_0}{\sigma\Omega^2(1-\sigma)}\left\{\exp i(\phi_0+\pi) + \frac{1-\sigma}{1+\sigma}\exp i\phi_0\right\} \int U \, dt.$$

In the second case $\delta_0 = \arctan(\text{aircraft speed/projectile speed})$, but it is assumed that the initial rate of change of yaw can be neglected; the appropriate form of the equations then is:

$$\delta \exp(i\phi) = \frac{\delta_0(1+\sigma)}{2\sigma}\left\{\exp[-(q_1-q_2)]\exp i(p_1-p_2+\phi_0) + \right.$$
$$\left. + \frac{1-\sigma}{1+\sigma}\exp[-(q_1+q_2)]\exp i(p_1+p_2+\phi_0+\pi)\right\},$$

$$r \exp(i\theta) = \frac{2kU\delta_0(1+\sigma)}{\sigma\Omega^2(1-\sigma)^2}\left\{\exp[-(q_1-q_2)]\exp i(p_1-p_2+\phi_0+\pi) + \right.$$
$$\left. + \left(\frac{1-\sigma}{1+\sigma}\right)^2 \exp[-(q_1+q_2)]\exp i(p_1+p_2+\phi_0)\right\},$$

$$H_2 + iZ_2 = \frac{k\delta_0(1+\sigma)}{\Omega\sigma(1-\sigma)} \left\{ \exp i(\phi_0 + \tfrac{1}{2}\pi) + \right.$$

$$\left. + \frac{1-\sigma}{1+\sigma} \exp i\left(\phi_0 + \frac{3\pi}{2}\right) \right\} \int U \, dt.$$

To get an idea of the effect of broadside fire put $\Omega = 2{,}000$, $k = 5$, $\sigma = \tfrac{2}{3}$, $\delta_0 = 10°$, which correspond in round numbers to a 0·303 bullet fired broadside from an aircraft flying at 300 m.p.h. It will be found that the multiplier of the { } in the last equation is about 0·004, that is the trajectory deviates by about $\tfrac{1}{4}°$ from the line of aim. The initial radius of the helical motion of the C.G. is about $\tfrac{1}{5}$ in.

It is sometimes convenient to represent the yawing motion by a polar diagram in which the scalar of the radius vector represents $\delta$ and its argument $\phi$; this curve is called the 'rosette'. The equation for yaw shows that the 'rosette' is generated by the resultant of a vector $r_p$ rotating about a fixed centre with absolute angular velocity $p_1 - p_2 = \tfrac{1}{2}\Omega(1-\sigma)$ and another vector $r_n$ rotating about the moving end of $r_p$ with absolute angular velocity $p_1 + p_2 = \tfrac{1}{2}\Omega(1+\sigma)$. The relative angular velocity of the two vectors is $2p_2 \ (= \Omega\sigma)$ and

$$\delta^2 = r_p^2 + r_n^2 - 2r_p\,r_n \cos(\Omega\sigma t).$$

A motion of this type can be fitted to all the rounds so far fired in the ballistic range in spite of the fact that the theory was originally only claimed to be valid for $\sin\delta \approx \delta$ (say $\delta \leqslant 10°$) and rounds have been fired up to 25° maximum yaw.

Nielson and Synge have given an analytically more logical account of the theory leading to what is, for all practical purposes, the same set of equations; and McShane pointed out that the Fowler *et al.* solution is valid whatever the value of the spin. He has, in fact, given the equations in a form applicable whether there is spin or not, and has pointed out that if the independent variable in them be changed to arc length $s \left( = \int_0^t U \, dt \right)$ then the equation for the yawing motion becomes independent of velocity, except for a term which is in practice negligible and the possible variation of the aerodynamic force coefficients with Mach and Reynolds numbers. Thus the yawing motion of a projectile depends on the arc length along the trajectory and is essentially independent of the velocity.

Howarth has analysed the case where the mass distribution is eccentric and his conclusions have been verified at the N.P.L.

## § 7. Firing trials. Measuring techniques

The several aerodynamic force coefficients ($f_L$, etc.) occurring in the equations are determined by firing trials in a ballistic range. Plate 25 (a) is a general view of the N.P.L. ballistic range; Plate 25 (b) is a close-up of a measuring station, called for simplicity a frame.

In its essentials the method amounts to taking pairs of spark shadowgraphs of the projectile in its passage down the range, using these shadowgraphs to ascertain the motion of the projectile, and then substituting this ascertained motion in the classical theory of Fowler et al.,† thus determining the several aerodynamic force coefficients already mentioned. Each frame gives one pair of shadow-graphs mutually at right angles and in the plane approximately perpendicular to the line joining the gun to the target. The positions of the frames are known from a preliminary survey and thus the actual position of the projectile in space is known at a number of points of its trajectory. In the case of the N.P.L. range nineteen pairs of shadowgraphs are taken in a distance of about 100 ft. The shadow-graphs give complete spatial information. To measure drag the time-intervals between the several frames are also needed. These are obtained by feeding part of the voltage surge which occurs when a frame sparks to one pair of plates of a double-beam cathode-ray tube. The other pair of plates is supplied with a 10 kc./s. timing wave.

The details of the method‡ of taking the shadowgraphs can be followed from Plate 25 (b). The projectile on approaching the frame passes through a light screen which is illuminating a photo-electric cell. The pulse of dark thus obtained is amplified and applied to trigger a thyratron. This pulse is in turn passed through a delay circuit to a second large thyratron whose discharge initiates the spark. The spark is obtained in the usual 'Boys' manner from a large capacitance and the purpose of the time-delay circuit is to enable the projectile to move from the light screen to a point between the plate and the spark gap when the latter sparks. In practice it is possible to measure distances to about 0·01 in. and times to about 1 microsecond.

† Loc. cit. on p. 727.
‡ Harding and Saunders, Rep. Engng. Div. Nat. Phys. Lab. (unpublished).

PLATE 25

(*a*) General view of ballistic range

(*b*) View of a frame

The yawing motion desired is induced by the 'cross-wind jet' apparatus. In principle this consists of a jet of air directed at right angles to the trajectory, and its operation is best understood by reference to Fig. 248. It is customary to represent the yawing motion of a projectile by a polar diagram in which the scalar of the radius vector represents magnitude of the yaw and the argument the

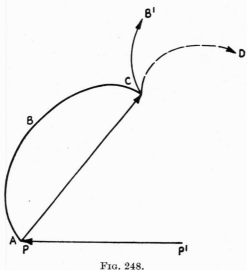

Fig. 248.

ABC  Yawing motion in jet.        CD  Yawing motion in range.
P  Pole for motion in range.      P'  Pole for motion in jet.
PP'  Yaw immediately after entering jet.
PC  Yaw immediately after emerging from jet and entering range.

orientation. As we have already seen (p. 735) this representation has been found to be adequate for all yaws likely to be encountered in practice (say 25° or less). It follows that a sudden change in head wind can be represented, within the same approximation, by a change of pole. In Fig. 248 the projectile is supposed to enter the jet with negligible yaw; it immediately acquires a yaw $P'P$, where $P'P = $ arctan(jet speed/projectile speed) to a suitable scale, and thereafter precesses along some path $ABC$ with $P'$ as pole. At the end of the jet (say at $C$) it emerges with yaw $PC$ into the still air of the range, and precession continues about $P$ as pole. In practice $PC > P'C$, so that the jet gives a magnification; in other words, for a given jet velocity yaws can be induced which are larger than the ratio of jet speed to projectile speed. The diagram has been drawn for the case of most practical importance, namely, beam firing from aircraft, which can only be accurately simulated by so adjusting the jet length that the projectile emerges at a cusp in the polar diagram. In the N.P.L. apparatus the length can be varied up to a maximum of 16 ft. and the velocity up to a maximum of 500 ft./sec. This velocity, coupled to a magnification of about 30 per cent., enables beam firing up to 450 m.p.h. to be imitated.

It can also be shown that the transverse velocity of the C.G. arising from the yaw, or aerodynamic throw-off as it is called, over the whole trajectory is very small for this particular case, the throw-off in the jet and on emergence cancelling to a first approximation. This can be best understood by reference to Fig. 249. Omitting the small term due to the nutational vector, the throw-off velocity $(v)$ can be written

$$v = wr_p$$

oriented at $\phi_0 + \frac{1}{2}\pi$ and the C.G. radius $R_0$ at $\phi_0 + \pi$, where

$$w = \frac{2kU}{\Omega(1-\sigma)} \quad \text{and} \quad r_p = \delta_0 \frac{1+\sigma}{2\sigma}.$$

On emerging from the jet after a complete number of nutational periods at $B$

$$\delta'_0 = 2\delta_0 \sin(\tfrac{1}{2}\phi) \quad \text{and} \quad r'_p = 2r_p \sin(\tfrac{1}{2}\phi),$$

and the throw-off velocity corresponding to this yaw is

$$v' = 2wr_p \sin(\tfrac{1}{2}\phi) \tag{1}$$

oriented at $\qquad\qquad \phi_0 + \pi + \tfrac{1}{2}\phi.$

$oa$ is the initial C.G. radius and $\overline{ae}$ represents $v$; on emerging $oa$ has rotated to $ob$, and $\Delta bcd$ represents the velocities of the C.G., $bd$ being the resultant of $bc$, the velocity about the spiral centre, and $\overline{cd} = \overline{ae} = v$.

Now $\qquad\qquad ob = \dfrac{4kU}{\Omega^2(1-\sigma)^2} r_p,$

and its angular velocity is

$$\tfrac{1}{2}\Omega(1-\sigma).$$

Hence $\qquad\qquad bc = \dfrac{2kU}{\Omega(1-\sigma)} r_p = wr_p = cd$

and $\qquad bd = 2wr_p \sin(\tfrac{1}{2}\phi)$ oriented at $\phi_0 + \tfrac{1}{2}\phi.$ $\qquad$ (2)

Comparison of eqns. (1) and (2) shows that

$$\overline{bd} = -v',$$

and the throw-off cancels.

This simple result is only true under the conditions stated, but under all practical conditions of emergence there is a considerable reduction of throw-off. As a result the presence or absence of the jet has little effect on the aiming point.

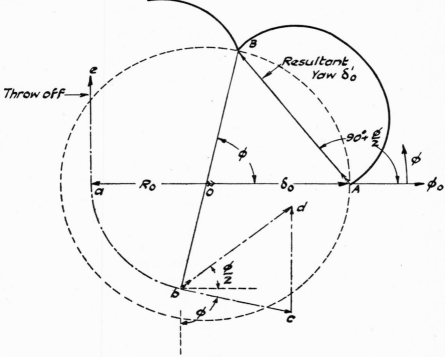

FIG. 249. Resultant yaw and C.G. velocity just after leaving cross-wind jet at a yaw minimum.

The reduction of the shadowgraphs is lengthy and will not be given in detail; broadly it amounts to finding the curves (Figs. 250, 251, and 252) which are the 'best fit' to the nineteen (or less) known elements of the motion of the body in its passage down the range. In outline it is as follows: the periodic time $T$ of the yaw gives $\Omega T$ and hence $\sigma$, $s$, and $f_M$; $\Omega$ can be calculated from the spin and the dynamical properties of the body and a check obtained from the fit of the rosette and $(\phi, \Omega t)$ curves; the initial radius of the C.G. spiral gives $k$ and $f_L$; the slope of the $(\log_e r, \Omega t)$ curve gives $q_1 - q_2$, $h$, and $f_H$ which can be checked from the yaw curves; finally, $\gamma$ and $f_J$ are obtained from $q_1 + q_2$. The slope of the velocity time curve

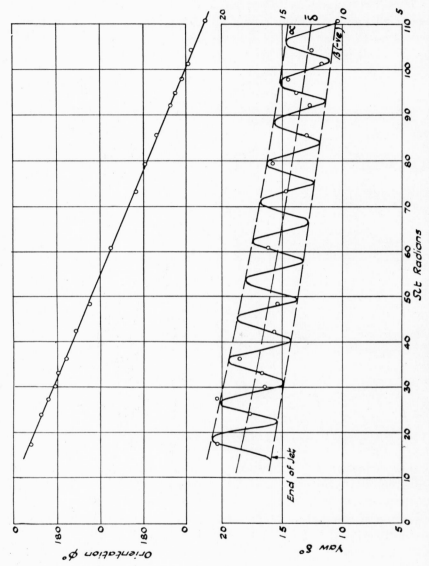

Fig. 250. Orientation and yaw of Mark VIIIz bullet fired across a jet. Nominal muzzle velocity 2,400 ft./sec.

does not in general justify attempting to take variation of acceleration down the range into account; its presence can usually be

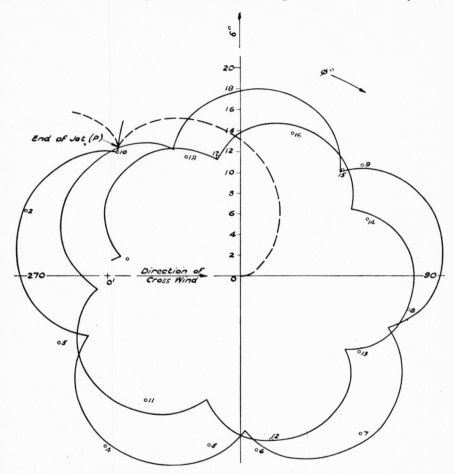

FIG. 251. Orientation and yaw of bullet axis from direction of motion of C.G.
        In jet                        ———— direction of head wind $O'$.
        Subsequently in range ————     ,,     ,,    ,,    ,,     $O$.

detected, but quantitative results have only been practicable with
an especially clearly defined record and a large heavily damped yaw.
    Figs. 250, 251, and 252 illustrate a typical case with cross wind
firing and a large yaw. The spin is left-handed and the numbers
against the points are the numbers of the frames. The small inset

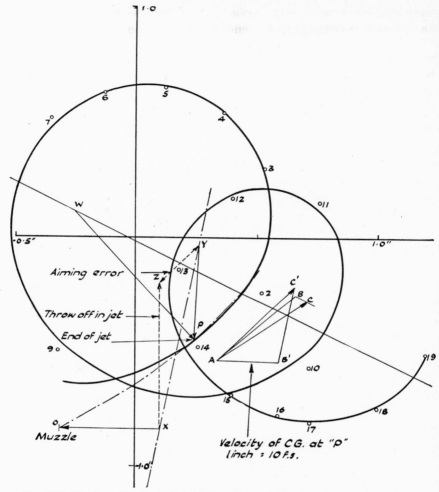

FIG. 252. Motion of C.G. of Mark VIIIz. Nominal muzzle velocity 2,400 ft./sec.
C.G. motion in jet — . — . —          Subsequently in range ————

diagram $AB'CBC'$ of Fig. 252 shows how nearly the throw-off cancels in practice:

$$\overline{AC'} = \overline{AB'} \text{ the velocity about the spiral centre in the jet}$$
$$+ \overline{B'C'} \text{ the throw-off,}$$
$$\overline{AC} = \overline{AB} \text{ the resultant velocity at } P \text{ from the analysis}$$
$$+ \overline{BC} \text{ residual throw-off,}$$

and          $\overline{BC}$ is very small.

Table 3 summarizes the results that have been obtained; the values of the aerodynamic force coefficients tabulated are the average of several rounds fired at the same nominal M.V., that is, at about the same Mach number. As regards accuracy $f_R$ and $f_M$ can be determined to 1 or 2 per cent. and $f_L$ to 5 per cent.; the accuracy of $f_H$ and $f_J$ varies widely with the amount of damping but is very unlikely to be better than 10 per cent. and in some cases may be wrong by a factor of 2. In particular $f_J$ is determined last and is thus liable to considerable scatter due to accumulation of errors. Except for $f_H$,

## TABLE 3

| No. | $M$ | $f_L$ | $f_M$ | $f_H$ | $f_J$ | Remarks |
|-----|-----|-------|-------|-------|-------|---------|
| 1 | 0·8 | 3·9 | 9·1 | .. | .. | |
|   | 1·0 | 4·6 | 11·6 | 70 | .. | |
|   | 1·2 | 2·6 | 11·1 | 70 | .. | Original firing trials by |
|   | 1·4 | 3·1 | 10·6 | 70 | .. | Fowler *et al.* Form A. |
|   | 1·6 | 3·4 | 10·1 | .. | .. | |
|   | 1·8 | 3·8 | 9·7 | 60 | .. | |
| 2 | 0·7 | .. | 9·1 | .. | .. | |
|   | 0·9 | .. | 11·2 | 55 | .. | |
|   | 1·1 | .. | 11·6 | 55 | .. | |
|   | 1·3 | .. | 11·2 | 75 | .. | As (1). Form B. |
|   | 1·5 | .. | 11·0 | 75 | .. | |
|   | 1·7 | .. | 11·0 | 80 | .. | |
|   | 1·9 | .. | 10·9 | 80 | .. | |
| 3 | 0·82 | 3·01 | 6·83 | −8 | 1·4 | |
|   | 0·93 | 3·21 | 7·46 | 19 | −0·3 | Ballistic range. |
|   | 1·14 | 3·00 | 6·90 | 21 | 0·5 | 3¼ cals. long. |
|   | 1·36 | 3·08 | 6·51 | 54 | −2·9 | 3 C.R.H. |
|   | 1·55 | 3·03 | 6·99 | 93 | −3·5 | ¼ cal. nose. |
|   | 1·89 | 3·61 | 5·77 | 33 | −1·5 | Flat base. |
|   | 2·28 | 3·14 | 5·03 | 28 | −1·5 | |
|   | 2·70 | 2·88 | 4·50 | 21 | 0·0 | |
| 4 | 0·83 | 2·2 | 7·52 | 6 | −0·1 | 3¼ cals. long. |
|   | 1·57 | 3·3 | 5·51 | 41 | −2·2 | 3¾ C.R.H. |
|   | 2·63 | 3·0 | 4·44 | 38 | −3·0 | 0·07 cal. nose. 0·5/10° base. |
| 5 | 0·79 | 2·1 | 8·23 | † | 16 | 4·6 cal. long. |
|   | 0·87 | 2·4 | 8·94 | † | 14 | 6 C.R.H. |
|   | 1·03 | 3·1 | 10·81 | 58 | 1·5 | 0·1 cal. nose. |
|   | 1·75 | 3·7 | 8·35 | −1 | 1·5 | Flat base. |
| 6 | 2·07 | 4·8 | 10·7 | 53 | −1·0 | Mk. VII Rifle bullet. |
|   | 2·07 | 4·4 | 8·9 | 42 | −1·7 | Mk. VIII Rifle bullet. |
| 7 | Small | .. | .. | 22 | .. | Lock model oscillating in horizontal plane in tunnel. |
| 8 | > 1 | .. | .. | 30 | .. | Calculated from Stewartson's formula, Chap. IX. |

† Scatter so great that averaging is a meaningless process.

which seems to increase with yaw, no dependence on yaw of the coefficients has been detected.

## § 8. Stability and damping

The stability conditions can be derived in many ways. Of course, there is the 'top' condition

$$s > 1,$$

but in addition instability is possible unless both components of the yaw are damped. This means that both $q_1 - q_2$ and $q_1 + q_2$ must be positive.

This leads to: $\qquad h + k > 0,$

$$4s(h+\gamma)(k-\gamma) > (h+k)^2.$$

An equivalent form is that there is instability unless

$$\frac{2(k-\gamma)}{1-\sigma} > h+k > \frac{2(k-\gamma)}{1+\sigma}.$$

A complete discussion of the stability of both fin and spin stabilized projectiles will be found in Rankin's paper.[†]

An analysis of the individual measurements from which Table 3 was compiled shows that all the rounds fired at Mach numbers below about 0·9 are unstable. This shows itself in an augmentation of the (slower) precessional component of the yaw and of the C.G. spiral. The (faster) nutational component usually remains constant or decreases. The physical mechanism that brings about these conditions is not fully understood, but there is little doubt that it is connected with the violent pressure changes that occur about the lower critical.

In Chap. IX, § 10 linearized theory is applied to derive the pressure distribution on a solid of revolution oscillating through a small angle.[‡] In the notation of this chapter the formula for the pressure difference is most conveniently written:

$$\Delta p = \frac{\rho \cos \theta}{\pi r_1} \left[ S(2U\dot{\delta}+\ddot{\beta}+x\ddot{\delta}) + \frac{dS}{dx}(U^2\delta+U\dot{\beta}+Ux\dot{\delta}) \right],$$

wherein $\dot{\beta}$ is the vertical velocity of the origin of coordinates, in this case the nose, and $S(x)$ is the cross-sectional area at $x$.

From this the moment about the C.G. distant $l_g$ from the nose can be calculated; and since it is permissible to write with consistent approximation $\qquad \dot{\beta} = -l_g \dot{\delta},$

[†] Loc. cit. on p. 688.                    [‡] Stewartson (unpublished).

the result is:

$$M^* = \rho S(l)\left\{\left(l - l_g - \frac{V_1}{S(l)}\right) U^2\delta + (l - l_g)^2 U\dot{\delta} + \frac{V_1}{S(l)}(K^2 - l_g^2)\ddot{\delta}\right\},$$

where $V_1$ is the volume occupied by the shell and $K$ the radius of gyration of this volume about a transverse axis through the nose of the shell.

In any motion of the shell the term in $\ddot{\delta}$ which represents a virtual mass effect will be unimportant compared with the corresponding terms introduced by the inertia of the shell. The term in $\delta$ leads immediately to the expression for $f_M$ given in Chap. IX, eqn. (57); the term in $\dot{\delta}$ gives the value

$$h = \frac{\rho U S(l)(l - l_g)^2}{B}$$

for the damping factor $h$, and this in turn gives

$$f_H = \frac{Bh}{\rho U r_1^4} = \frac{S(l)(l - l_g)^2}{r_1^4}.$$

The theoretical value 30 for $f_H$ (quoted in Table 3) which was derived from this formula, taking $l = 4\frac{1}{2}$ calibres $= 9r_1$ and $l_g = 3$ calibres $= 6r_1$, appears to be rather low but the diversity of shapes used in the firings should not be overlooked in making comparisons nor should Lock's† wind-tunnel measurements of $f_H$ for an oscillating shell which gave a value of 22.

Moreover in making these comparisons in Table 3 and also in Table 2 it must be remembered that the position of the C.G. is necessarily taken as datum in ballistics. Its position, however, as Synge has pointed out, is quite irrelevant to the values of the aerodynamic force coefficients as such. In making the calculations the C.G. has been taken one-third of the length from the base as a representative average value. A fairer method is to compare the calculated and measured values of $f_L$ and the position of the C.P.; on this basis linearized theory‡ underestimates the force somewhat but places the centre of pressure much too near the nose.

Nevertheless perhaps the most important cause of the discrepancy between the theoretical and experimental results is the neglect in the theory of contributions from base pressure which cannot be assessed with any confidence.

† *Textbook of Anti-Aircraft Gunnery*, p. 667.
‡ Lighthill, 'Supersonic flow past bodies of revolution', *Rep. Memor. Aero. Res. Coun.*, No. 2,003 (1945).

## § 9. Miscellaneous comments

*Effect of yaw on drag.* Again no systematic measurements have been made: indeed none are possible until the question of scale effect has been more thoroughly investigated. But some idea of the nature of the effect and a rough comparison between tunnel and firing trials can be obtained from Fig. 253. The agreement is satisfactory when it is remembered that the several projectiles involved had somewhat different shapes of head and that the Mach numbers are not precisely the same. The results, broadly speaking, confirm the empirical formula used in ballistics,

$$f_R = f_{R_0}\left(1 + \frac{\delta^2}{200}\right),$$

with $\delta$ in degrees; but more work is needed before this or any other formula can be placed on a firm basis.

*Temperature effects.* The rise of temperature on approaching the projectile is important in ballistics. Measurements made on the models[†] shown in Fig. 254 showed that the ratio $T_w/T_1$ as measured was always within 2 per cent. of its calculated value (Chap. XIV, § 15).

## § 10. The transonic region

Both calculation and measurement are much more difficult in the transonic region. Calculation because the existence of local shocks implies free boundary conditions and measurement, in wind tunnels at any rate, because blockage conditions soon demand an impossibly large ratio of tunnel to model area. In fact, the ballistic technique is at present the only one usable close to the speed of sound. A glance at Plate 21 (*b*) will show the sort of flow that occurs in this region.

The lower critical Mach number $M_c$ can be calculated reasonably simply by the device of replacing the head of the projectile by a prolate spheroid of about the same mean curvature near the shoulder.[‡] The justification for this is that experience shows that sonic velocities are first attained in this region. The formula is

$$q/U_1 = A_1 \cos\delta(1 + A_2^2\tan^2\delta)^{\frac{1}{2}},$$

† Hankins and Cope, 'The flow of gases at sonic and supersonic speeds', *Proc. Instn. Mech. Engrs.* **155** (1946), 401; Cope, 'Heat transfer at high speeds', *Proc. 7th Int. Congr. Appl. Mech. Lond.* **3** (1948), 120.

‡ *Rep. Engng. Div. Nat. Phys. Lab.* (unpublished).

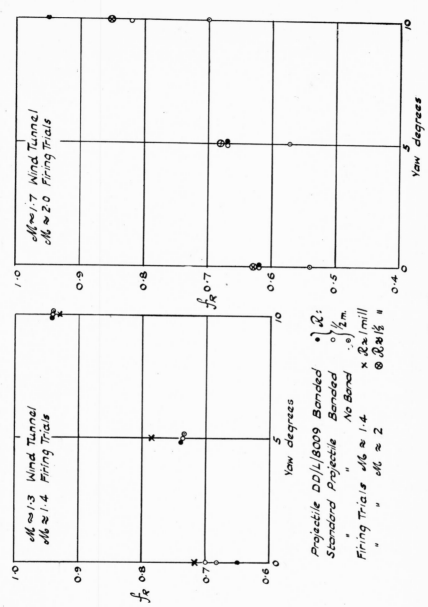

FIG. 253.

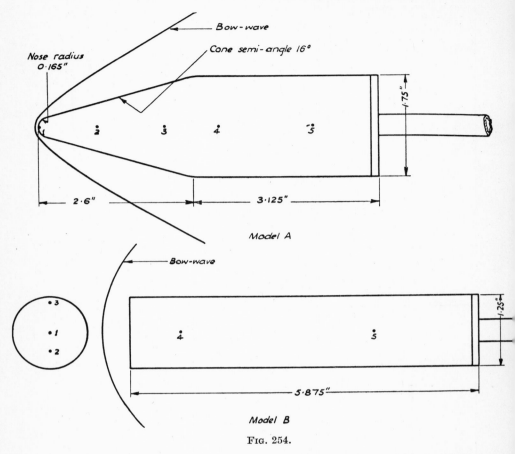

FIG. 254.

where $q$ is the *maximum* velocity, $U_1$ and $\delta$ have their usual meanings,
and
$$A_1 \equiv e^2/A_3,$$
$$A_2 \equiv 2A_3/(2e^2 - A_3),$$
$$A_3 \equiv 1 - \frac{1-e^2}{2e}\log_e\frac{1+e}{1-e},$$

$e$ being the eccentricity $= [1-(\text{fineness ratio})^2]$; once $q/U_1$ is known
then $M_c$ follows.

With no yaw ($\delta = 0$) the formula simplifies, and values of $M_c$ were
given by Lock.† Table 4 gives some results obtained in this way;

† 'The problem of high speed flight as affected by compressibility', *J. Roy. Aero.
Soc.* **42** (1938), 193–228.

Fig. 255 shows a 4:1 spheroid superposed on a 6 C.R.H. head and Fig. 256 enables $M_c$ at no yaw to be read off if the fineness ratio be known.

TABLE 4

| Fineness ratio | δ (degrees) | $q/U_1$ | $M_c$ |
|---|---|---|---|
| $\frac{1}{4}$ | 0 | 1·08 | 0·85 |
|  | 10 | 1·14 | 0·78 |
| $\frac{1}{10}$ | 0 | 1·02 | 0·93 |
|  | 10 | 1·08 | 0·85 |
| $\frac{1}{15}$ | 0 | 1·00₅ | 0·96 |
|  | 10 | 1·06 | 0·88 |

These calculations suggest that the effect of yaw with heads of the proportion used in practice is to decrease $M_c$ by a roughly constant amount for a given yaw. This, of course, means that a fine head is spoilt more by yaw than a blunt head, which is borne out, qualitatively, in practice. The quantitative accuracy of the formula is tested in Fig. 257. The points are drag balance measurements† at zero and at 10° yaw, of two models with rather similar heads, either of which can reasonably be replaced by a 4:1 spheroid. The line is the drag coefficient as determined from firing trials. And the calculated values for $M_c$ for zero and 10° yaw for such a spheroid are also shown. The agreement for 10° yaw is as good as could be expected. The agreement for no yaw is more debatable, but there are good grounds for thinking that the hump in the curve, which begins at $M \approx 0\cdot7$ and ends just before the sharp rise at $M \approx 0\cdot9$, is due to base pressure and boundary-layer changes akin to those observed by Knowler.‡ On this basis the agreement for no yaw is also reasonable and it seems that this method of calculating the shock stall is of practical value as a reliable first approximation.

As a matter of interest the base pressure changes have been plotted in Fig. 258; the Reynolds number in these measurements is about $\frac{1}{4}$ million for $M \approx \frac{1}{2}$, increasing to about $\frac{1}{2}$ million for Mach numbers near unity and thereafter decreasing slightly.

Maccoll§ has attempted the calculation of transonic flow and

† Cope, *Rep. Engng. Divn. Nat. Phys. Lab.* (unpublished).
‡ Loc. cit. on p. 686.
§ Maccoll, 'Investigation of compressible flow at sonic speeds.' Paper presented at 6th Int. Congr. Appl. Mech. Paris (1946).

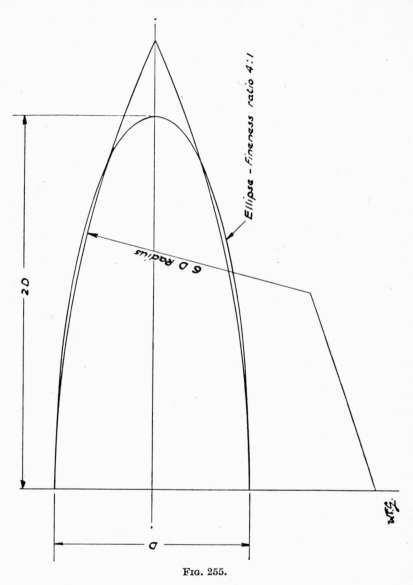

FIG. 255.

measurements have been made at the N.P.L. for comparison. The
essential assumptions are shown in Fig. 259 for the two cases when
the main stream flow is subsonic and supersonic, called by him the
lower and upper sonic régimes respectively.

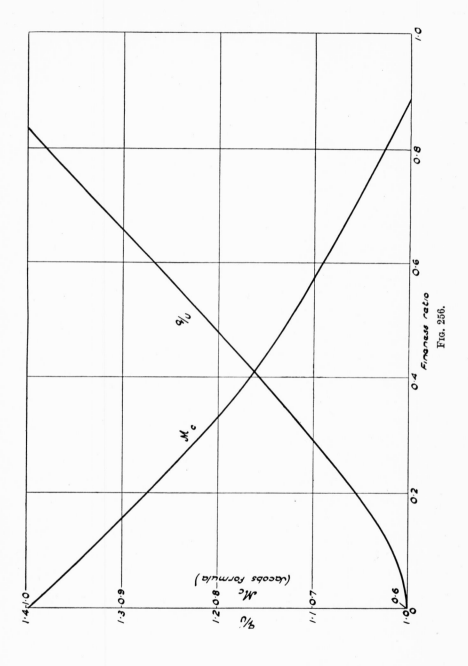

Fineness ratio

$M_c$
(Jacobs formula)

$q/u$

FIG. 256.

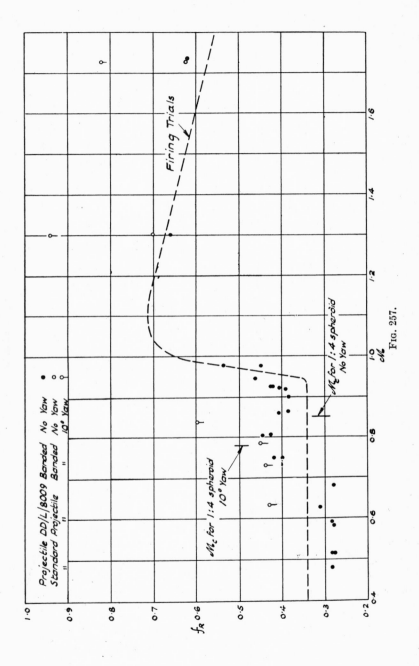

FIG. 257.

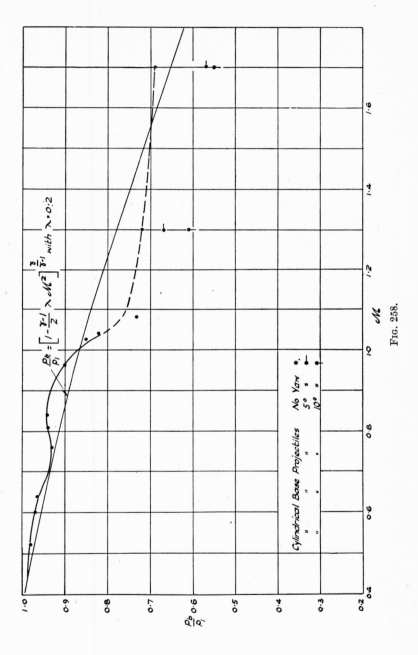

$$\frac{p_b}{p_1} = \left[1 - \frac{\gamma-1}{2} \lambda \mathcal{M}^2\right]^{\frac{\gamma}{\gamma-1}} \text{ with } \lambda = 0.2$$

Cylindrical Base Projectiles   No Yaw   •

        "       "       5°   "

        "       "      10°   "

$\mathcal{M}$

$\frac{p_b}{p_1}$

FIG. 258.

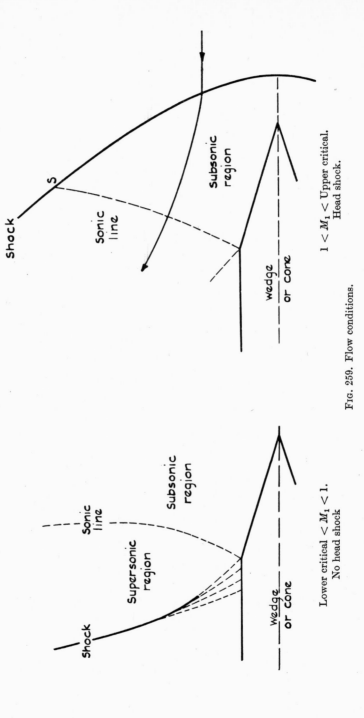

Fig. 259. Flow conditions.

$1 < M_1 <$ Upper critical.
Head shock.

Lower critical $< M_1 < 1.$
No head shock

The assumptions are:

1. That the sonic line begins at the shoulder $S$ of the body.
2. That the direction of flow across the sonic line is normal to it.

If these are true it follows:

That the sonic line is normal to the wedge or cone surface at $S$.

These conditions were originally formulated on evidence from the measured wavelet angle immediately behind the shoulder in shadow

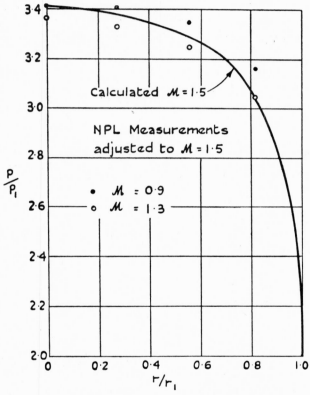

FIG. 260. Pressure on the head of a circular cylinder end-on to the flow.

photographs of projectiles with conical heads of various angles. This angle had a value which implied free expansion round the shoulder from a speed along the conical surface just ahead of the corner equal to the local speed of sound; and this was true even for the extreme case of a flat-headed body (a cylinder end-on).

The actual calculations are carried out by an iterative process, such as the method of squares, applied to a net of suitable mesh. The length of the sonic line and (in the case of upper sonic problems) the position of the shock is assumed and adjusted as the iteration converges. Calculations on the same shape in both lower and upper sonic régimes showed that the pressure distribution curve was similar in shape. From this Maccoll concluded that for all practical purposes the pressure field varied in unison with the stagnation pressure. Using this he was able to adjust N.P.L. measurements† of the pressure on the end of a cylinder to the Mach number of his calculations. The result is shown in Fig. 260 and the comparison is fairly satisfactory, the observations following the shape of the calculated curve. Holder's measurements‡ of the bow-wave position also confirm the calculations. So that, although the method is laborious and more checks are desirable, all the evidence available supports the view that the main assumptions are an exceedingly useful first approximation to the condition existing in a very complicated flow régime.

† Cope, *Rep. Engng. Div. Nat. Phys. Lab.* (unpublished).

‡ Holder and Chinneck, 'Observations of the flow past elliptic-nosed two-dimensional cylinders and bodies of revolution in supersonic airstreams', *Rep. Aero. Res. Coun.*, No. 14,216 (1951).

# HEAT TRANSFER

## § 1. Introduction

HEAT is transferred by conduction, convection, and radiation, but here we shall not discuss transfer by radiation or *pure* conduction. This restricted field of study can be divided into cases of laminar or turbulent flow and alternatively into cases of forced or free convection. By forced convection we mean that the motion is caused by an external agency. By free or natural convection we mean that the motion is caused by the action of gravity on the fluid of variable density and temperature. The velocities occurring in free convection are small, so that forced convection, if present, will generally dominate the picture. In industrial applications of heat transfer forced convection with turbulent flow is the most frequent type encountered; in aeronautical applications forced convection for laminar and turbulent flow are both important. Free convection is important in many domestic matters such as the generation of chimney draughts for fires and in the operation of room radiators; the flow associated with this free convection may be laminar or turbulent according to circumstances.

Except at high speeds the calculation of temperature distribution and heat transfer in laminar flow with forced convection presents no special mathematical difficulties and is normally simpler than the corresponding calculation of velocity distribution and skin friction, because the equation for the temperature is linear. But a knowledge of the velocity distribution is required for the calculation of the temperature distribution, and thus the calculation of temperature distribution is restricted to cases where the velocity distribution can be determined.

If the speed is high it is no longer possible to separate the calculation of velocity distribution from the calculation of the temperature distribution. Only the case of the flat plate with laminar boundary layer has been solved for these conditions, and this work is described in Chap. X.

The accurate calculation of velocity and temperature distribution for free convection with laminar flow presents considerable mathematical difficulties which have only been overcome in a few cases. Little progress has been made with the study of free convection with turbulent flow.

The analysis of heat transfer for forced convection in turbulent flow is dependent on a knowledge of the distributions of mean velocity and of the velocity fluctuations, which is still far from complete. Prior to the developments in the understanding of turbulent flow which have taken place since 1925, the only important step in the analysis of heat transfer in turbulent flow was due to Osborne Reynolds, who suggested that heat and momentum were transferred by the same exchange mechanism, and deduced that heat transfer was proportional to skin friction. Discussion of the validity of this concept and its improvement is one of the main subjects of the section on turbulent flow.

For gases increase of speed brings with it an increase in importance of kinetic temperature effects, which are proportional to the square of the velocity. It will be shown that this emphasizes the significance of the concept of total temperature in heat transfer. (The total temperature is the temperature attained when the stream is brought to rest without change of energy.) The reason for this is that the total temperature is often constant when no heat transfer is occurring, whereas large variations of static temperature may occur. In this way we are led to the substitution of the concept of energy transfer for that of heat transfer in studying the flow of gases, and attention is drawn to the real situation, which is that heat transfer is a special case of energy transfer, and can only be treated in isolation if the speeds, and hence the kinetic temperature effects, are not too large.

The spread of heat in jets and wakes is not considered in the section on turbulent flow as it is thought that this subject may be treated more conveniently together with the corresponding analysis of velocity distributions in jets and wakes. The second edition of *Modern Developments in Fluid Dynamics* will cover these two aspects of flow in jets and wakes.

On the other hand, the growing importance of the analogy between heat transfer and diffusion justifies the inclusion of an account of this topic, which appears as an appendix to this chapter.

# Section I

## Laminar Flow

### § 2. The equations of state and of motion

The equation of state of a fluid relates the pressure $p$ to the density $\rho$ and the absolute temperature $T$. Gases are assumed to obey the perfect gas law:

$$\frac{p}{\rho T} = \frac{p_0}{\rho_0 T_0} = \frac{\bar{R}}{m}, \tag{1}$$

where $p_0$, $\rho_0$, $T_0$ are the pressure, density, and absolute temperature in some standard condition, $\bar{R}$ is the gas constant, and $m$ is the molecular weight of the gas. For the present study it is in the main permissible to regard liquids as incompressible, when the equation of state has the form

$$\rho = \rho_0, \tag{2}$$

but for the derivation of the energy equation and for the calculation of the buoyancy force in free convection problems the equation of state of liquids is taken to be

$$\rho - \rho_0 = -\beta \rho_0 (T - T_0), \tag{3}$$

where $\beta$ is the coefficient of expansion of the liquid with temperature.

The equation of continuity is

$$\frac{\partial \rho}{\partial t} + \frac{\partial}{\partial x}(\rho u) + \frac{\partial}{\partial y}(\rho v) + \frac{\partial}{\partial z}(\rho w) = 0, \tag{4}$$

which may also be written

$$\frac{1}{\rho}\frac{D\rho}{Dt} + \frac{\partial u}{\partial x} + \frac{\partial v}{\partial y} + \frac{\partial w}{\partial z} = 0. \tag{5}$$

The equations of motion are given in Chap. II. For problems of free convection we assume (1) that the pressure is the same as the hydrostatic pressure in the fluid when at rest, and (2) that the only external force is that of gravity. Hence the external force $\mathbf{F}$ per unit mass (Chap. II, eqn. (60)) is given by

$$\mathbf{F} = \mathbf{\acute{g}},$$

where $\mathbf{\acute{g}}$ is the vector of the earth's acceleration; also

$$\operatorname{grad} p = \rho_0 \mathbf{\acute{g}},$$

where $\rho_0$ is the density of the unheated fluid which may usually be taken to be constant. We write

$$\rho \mathbf{F}' = \rho \mathbf{F} - \operatorname{grad} p,$$

so that

$$\mathbf{F}' = \left(\frac{\rho - \rho_0}{\rho}\right) \mathbf{g};$$

$\mathbf{F}'$ can be regarded as the buoyancy force per unit mass in problems of free convection and the pressure may now be treated as constant. For gases, from (1) with $p$ constant, we obtain

$$\mathbf{F}' = -\mathbf{g}\left(\frac{T - T_0}{T_0}\right).$$

For liquids we get from (3)

$$\mathbf{F}' = -\beta \mathbf{g}(T - T_0). \tag{6}$$

In general we can take this expression (6) for the buoyancy force as applying to both gases and liquids with the coefficient of expansion $\beta$ equal to $1/T_0$ for gases.

## § 3. The energy equation†

For liquids we shall take the energy equation in the form (92) of Chap. II. From (3) we get

$$-\frac{1}{\rho}\left(\frac{\partial \rho}{\partial T}\right)_p = \beta$$

approximately, so that equation (92) of Chap. II becomes

$$\rho c_p \frac{DT}{Dt} = \Phi + \beta T \frac{Dp}{Dt} + \left[\frac{\partial}{\partial x}\left(k\frac{\partial T}{\partial x}\right) + \frac{\partial}{\partial y}\left(k\frac{\partial T}{\partial y}\right) + \frac{\partial}{\partial z}\left(k\frac{\partial T}{\partial z}\right)\right].$$

Now $\beta$ is a small quantity, e.g. $\beta = 1 \cdot 5 \times 10^{-4}$ per degree C. for water at $15°$ C., and as a consequence of this the second term on the right-hand side is negligible. In addition the speeds of motion in liquids are normally so small that the dissipation can be ignored. Hence the energy equation for liquids can be simplified to

$$\rho c_p \frac{DT}{Dt} = \frac{\partial}{\partial x}\left(k\frac{\partial T}{\partial x}\right) + \frac{\partial}{\partial y}\left(k\frac{\partial T}{\partial y}\right) + \frac{\partial}{\partial z}\left(k\frac{\partial T}{\partial z}\right), \tag{7}$$

or, if the thermal conductivity $k$ is independent of temperature,

$$\frac{DT}{Dt} = \kappa \nabla^2 T, \tag{8}$$

† It may be permissible to remind the reader that mechanical units are used for the expression of quantities of heat and all other dependent concepts.

where $\kappa = k/\rho c_p$; $\kappa$ is called the thermometric conductivity or the thermal diffusivity of the liquid.

The energy equation for a perfect gas is taken in the form [eqn. (93) of Chap. II]:

$$\rho c_p \frac{DT}{Dt} - \frac{Dp}{Dt} = \Phi + \left[ \frac{\partial}{\partial x} \left( k \frac{\partial T}{\partial x} \right) + \frac{\partial}{\partial y} \left( k \frac{\partial T}{\partial y} \right) + \frac{\partial}{\partial z} \left( k \frac{\partial T}{\partial z} \right) \right]. \qquad (9)$$

It is convenient also to express the energy equation for perfect gases in terms of the total temperature (or total head temperature) $T_H$ which is defined as

$$T_H = T + \frac{q^2}{2c_p}.$$

In terms of $T_H$ it is shown in Appendix I that the energy equation can be written in the form

$$\rho c_p \frac{DT_H}{Dt} - \frac{\partial p}{\partial t} = \left[ \frac{\partial}{\partial x} \left( k \frac{\partial}{\partial x} \right) + \frac{\partial}{\partial y} \left( k \frac{\partial}{\partial y} \right) + \frac{\partial}{\partial z} \left( k \frac{\partial}{\partial z} \right) \right] \left[ T_H + \frac{(\sigma - 1)}{2c_p} q^2 \right],$$
$$(10)$$

where $\sigma = \mu c_p / k$, provided that the body forces can be ignored and that another small term can be neglected.

We may here anticipate a little by noting that, if the motion is slow, the term $Dp/Dt$ and the dissipation function $\Phi$ may be neglected, when (9) reduces to

$$\rho c_p \frac{DT}{Dt} = \frac{\partial}{\partial x} \left( k \frac{\partial T}{\partial x} \right) + \frac{\partial}{\partial y} \left( k \frac{\partial T}{\partial y} \right) + \frac{\partial}{\partial z} \left( k \frac{\partial T}{\partial z} \right),$$

or, if the thermal conductivity is independent of temperature, to eqn. (8), which is the form for liquids.

## § 4. Dynamical similarity. Forced convection

At low speeds when no heat transfer is occurring the flow of a viscous fluid depends only on the Reynolds number, and the flow pattern is identical for two experiments made at the same Reynolds number. At high speeds the Mach number becomes significant as well as the Reynolds number. Furthermore, thermal effects are always present to some extent in high-speed flow and this requires the introduction of the Prandtl number $\sigma = \mu c_p / k$ as a significant parameter. The Prandtl number is nearly constant for gases and is equal to 0·72 for air. This value is calculated from the values (1) $\mu = 1·709 \times 10^{-4}$ g./(cm. sec.) at 0° C. from the International Critical Tables, (2) $c_p = 1·012$ joule/g. deg. C. [0·2417 calories/g. deg.

C.], and (3) $k = 2 \cdot 39 \times 10^{-4}$ joule/cm. deg. (C.) sec. $[5 \cdot 72 \times 10^{-5}$ cal./cm. deg. (C.) sec.] at $0°$ C. given by Hercus and Sutherland.[†] Measurements of the thermal conductivity of air over a range of temperatures by Sherratt and Griffiths[‡] indicate that $\mu c_p/k$ may fall to $0 \cdot 70$ at $120°$ C.

For liquids the Prandtl number $\sigma = \mu c_p/k$ varies with temperature, owing mainly to the variation of the viscosity; a table of values of $\sigma$ for water is given in Table 1.[§] The dependence of viscosity and thermal conductivity on temperature are additional complications.

TABLE 1

*Values of $\sigma = \mu c_p/k$ for Water*

| Temperature, °C. | 0 | 5 | 10 | 15 | 20 | 25 | 30 |
|---|---|---|---|---|---|---|---|
| $\sigma$ | 12·45 | 10·46 | 8·93 | 7·73 | 6·75 | 5·96 | 5·30 |
| Temperature, °C. | 40 | 50 | 60 | 70 | 80 | 90 | 100 |
| $\sigma$ | 4·29 | 3·55 | 2·99 | 2·56 | 2·22 | 1·95 | 1·74 |

Our main concern in the present chapter is the calculation of the quantity of heat transferred from a body which is kept at a temperature $T_1$, and immersed in a fluid which is kept at a temperature $T_0$ at a large distance from the body. In the case of flow in a pipe the temperature of the walls of the pipe and of the fluid at the entry may be supposed to be specified. The rate of transfer of heat from the surface of a body can be expressed in terms of the non-dimensional Nusselt heat transfer coefficient $K_N$ which is defined by the relation

$$Q = K_N kS(T_1 - T_0)/d, \tag{11}$$

where $Q$ is the quantity of heat transferred in unit time across an area $S$, $(T_1 - T_0)$ is a representative temperature difference, and $d$ is a representative length. We shall also use $Q$ to denote the quantity of heat transferred in unit time across unit area.

The significance of the Nusselt number is most easily grasped by considering some simple problems in heat conduction. We start with the case of two large plates each of area $S$ and distance $d$ apart which

† *Proc. Roy. Soc.* A, **145** (1934), 599–611.
‡ *Phil. Mag.* **27** (1939), 68–75.
§ Taken from Eagle and Ferguson, *Proc. Roy. Soc.* A, **127** (1930), 540–66, who calculated it from Bingham and Jackson's table of viscosities in *Bull. Nat. Bur. Stand.* **14** (1919), 75, Callendar's tables of specific heats, and Kaye and Higgins's data on thermal conductivity in *Proc. Roy. Soc.* A, **117** (1928), 459–70.

are maintained at different temperatures $T_1$ and $T_0$ with fluid at rest between them. Then the rate of heat transfer between the plates is
$$Q = k(T_1 - T_0)S/d,$$
if end effects may be ignored. From the definition of the Nusselt number in (11) we obtain the result for this example:
$$K_N = 1.$$

As a second example consider a sphere of diameter $d$ maintained at temperature $T_1$ at rest in a fluid which has a temperature $T_0$ at infinity. From the theory of heat conduction or from (8) we obtain the equation
$$\nabla^2 T = 0$$
for the temperature distribution in the fluid, and the relevant solution satisfying the boundary conditions is
$$\frac{T - T_0}{T_1 - T_0} = \frac{d}{2r},$$
where $r$ is the radial distance from the centre of the sphere. The radial temperature gradient at the surface of the sphere is then
$$\left(\frac{dT}{dr}\right)_{r=\frac{1}{2}d} = -\frac{2(T_1 - T_0)}{d}.$$
The rate of heat transfer from the surface of area $S$ is
$$Q = -kS\left(\frac{dT}{dr}\right)_{r=\frac{1}{2}d} = +\frac{2kS(T_1 - T_0)}{d},$$
and the corresponding value of the Nusselt number is
$$K_N = 2,$$
if the sphere diameter is taken as the representative length.

The above examples show that the Nusselt heat-transfer coefficient is basically a heat-conduction coefficient. But for many problems of forced convection there is a close analogy between heat transfer and skin friction, and the Nusselt number is then not the most significant heat-transfer coefficient. To bring out this analogy we shall introduce the Stanton heat-transfer coefficient $K_S$ defined by the equation
$$Q = K_S \rho c_p SU(T_1 - T_0), \tag{12}$$
where $U$ is a representative velocity. The two heat-transfer coefficients $K_N$ and $K_S$ are simply related by the equation
$$K_S = K_N/(\sigma R),$$
where $R$ is the Reynolds number $Ud/\nu$ and $\sigma$ is the Prandtl number.

The solution of problems of forced convection can generally be expressed in the form†
$$K_N = f(R, M, \sigma),$$
or
$$K_S = F(R, M, \sigma),$$
where $M$ is the Mach number.

When the speed is low the dependence of the heat transfer on the Mach number is absent. If the temperature differences present in the field are large it may be necessary to take into account the variation with temperature of the physical properties of the fluid, such as viscosity. In such cases the heat transfer will depend on the quantity $(T_1 - T_0)/T_0$; this dependence is absent if $(T_1 - T_0)/T_0$ is small or if the physical properties of the fluid vary only slowly with temperature, and it will generally be ignored in developing the theory.

The effect of high speed on heat transfer and skin friction has been discussed in Chap. X. It is there shown that in gases temperature variations of order
$$\frac{U^2}{2c_p} = \left(\frac{\gamma-1}{2}\right)M_0^2 T_0$$
arise from the variation of pressure and from the dissipation due to viscosity, where $M_0$ is the stream Mach number. These temperature variations depend on the Mach number and it is not necessary to introduce another non-dimensional parameter on account of them. But it must be remembered that, on the one hand, if the temperature $U^2/(2c_p)$ is appreciable in relation to the imposed temperature difference $(T_1 - T_0)$, then the heat-transfer coefficients $K_N$ and $K_S$ will be functions of the Mach number; on the other hand, large values of $(T_1 - T_0)$ may introduce effects due to the variation of the physical properties of the fluid with temperature, as has been explained above.

## § 5. Dynamical similarity. Free convection

In free convection the motion is caused by the effect of gravity on the fluid and hence neither the Reynolds number nor the Mach number is significant, since no representative velocity exists. We shall express the dependence of the heat transfer on the physical conditions in terms of the quantity
$$Ra = d^3\beta g(T_1 - T_0)/\nu\kappa, \tag{13}$$

† The product $\sigma R = Ud/\kappa$ is called the Péclet number and is sometimes used to express the solutions of problems in place of $R$ or $\sigma$.

which will be referred to as the 'Rayleigh number' as it was first introduced by Rayleigh[†] in an investigation of the stability of a fluid heated from below. As above, in this expression $\beta$ is the coefficient of expansion of the fluid with temperature, $(T_1-T_0)$ is a representative temperature difference, and $d$ is a representative length. The Rayleigh number is related to the Grashof number $Gr$, defined as

$$Gr = d^3\beta g(T_1-T_0)/\nu^2,$$

by the equation

$$Ra = \sigma Gr,$$

where $\sigma = \nu/\kappa$; it will appear later that the Rayleigh number has some advantages over the Grashof number. The solution of problems in free convection is then expressed in the form

$$K_N = f(Ra, \sigma).$$

In addition the heat transfer coefficient may depend on $(T_1-T_0)/T_0$, which is associated, as explained above, with the variation of the physical properties of the fluid with temperature.

## § 6. The convection of heat in potential flow

The theory of the convection of heat in potential flow has been developed by Boussinesq[‡] and by King.[§] Let $\phi$ and $\psi$ be the velocity potential and the stream-function for the steady potential flow of an incompressible fluid in two dimensions. Then the velocities are given by

$$\left.\begin{aligned} u = \frac{\partial\phi}{\partial x} = \frac{\partial\psi}{\partial y} \\ v = \frac{\partial\phi}{\partial y} = -\frac{\partial\psi}{\partial x} \end{aligned}\right\} \tag{14}$$

while the temperature distribution is given by (8):

$$u\frac{\partial T}{\partial x} + v\frac{\partial T}{\partial y} = \kappa\nabla^2 T. \tag{15}$$

Substituting from (14) for $u$ and $v$ and changing coordinates from $(x, y)$ to $(\phi, \psi)$, we find from eqn. (15) that

$$\frac{\partial T}{\partial\phi} = \kappa\left(\frac{\partial^2 T}{\partial\phi^2} + \frac{\partial^2 T}{\partial\psi^2}\right). \tag{16}$$

Boussinesq neglects the term $\partial^2 T/\partial\phi^2$ in (16) and builds up solutions

† *Phil. Mag.* **32** (1916), 529–46; *Sci. Pap.* **6**, 432–46.
‡ *J. Math.* **1** (1905), 285–332.
§ *Philos. Trans.* A, **214** (1914), 373–432.

of the simplified equation based on the 'point-source solution'

$$T = \frac{1}{\phi^{\frac{1}{2}}}\exp\left(-\frac{\psi^2}{4\kappa\phi}\right),$$

while King retains the complete equation and builds up solutions from the solution

$$T = \exp\left(\frac{\phi}{2\kappa}\right)K_0\left[\frac{(\phi^2+\psi^2)^{\frac{1}{2}}}{2\kappa}\right],$$

where $K_0$ is the modified Bessel function of the second kind.

For the circular cylinder, which King considered in detail, he chose a distribution of heat flux from the surface which gave results for the total heat flux in agreement with his experimental results. This distribution involves discontinuities of temperature between the surface and the fluid flowing over it; the theory is unsatisfactory, and it is clear that the effects of viscosity are of great importance.

## § 7. Boundary-layer equations

When the Reynolds number is large, the conditions with respect to the temperature distribution near the surface of a heated body past which fluid is flowing resemble those with respect to the velocity distribution.[†] A boundary layer of small thickness exists near the surface, in which the temperature falls rapidly from its value at the surface to the value in the main body of the fluid, and the approximation of Vol. I (1938), chap. iv may be applied to the equations for the velocity and temperature. The equations for the thermal layer will be developed on the assumption that the Prandtl number $\sigma$ is of order unity, in which case the thickness of the thermal layer is of the same order of magnitude as that of the viscous layer.

Consider the flow near a cylindrical body held normal to a stream of undisturbed velocity $U$. The motion is two-dimensional, and if $x$ is measured along the surface, $y$ normal to it, and $z$ along the generators of the cylinder, the terms depending on $z$ disappear. Thus the equations of motion are (eqns. (11) and (22) of Chap. X):

$$\left.\begin{aligned}\rho\left(\frac{\partial u}{\partial t}+u\frac{\partial u}{\partial x}+v\frac{\partial u}{\partial y}\right) &= -\frac{\partial p}{\partial x}+\rho X+\frac{\partial}{\partial y}\left(\mu\frac{\partial u}{\partial y}\right)\\ -\rho K u^2 &= -\frac{\partial p}{\partial y}+\rho Y\end{aligned}\right\}, \qquad (17)$$

---

† This may not be true if the Prandtl number is small compared with unity. For mercury $\sigma = 0\cdot03$, but for most fluids $\sigma$ is either of the order unity or is appreciably in excess of it.

where $K$ is the curvature of the surface. The components of $\mathbf{g}$ at the point $(x, y)$ are $(lg, mg)$, where $(l, m)$ are the direction cosines of the downward-drawn vertical and $g$ is the magnitude of the earth's acceleration. Hence for the components of the buoyancy force arising from the variable density, we have, from (6),

$$\left.\begin{array}{l} X' = -\beta lg(T - T_0) \\ Y' = -\beta mg(T - T_0) \end{array}\right\}. \tag{18}$$

For problems of free convection we may take the pressure as constant and the body forces as given by (18) (see § 2). The equation of continuity is

$$\frac{\partial u}{\partial x} + \frac{\partial v}{\partial y} + \frac{1}{\rho}\frac{D\rho}{Dt} = 0. \tag{19}$$

Now suppose that $\delta_u$ and $\delta_T$ are the thicknesses of the viscous and thermal layers respectively and further that $\delta_u$ and $\delta_T$ are of the same order of magnitude. Let $U$, the velocity at infinity, and $d$, a characteristic length of the body, be of standard order; then $\partial u/\partial x$ and $\partial v/\partial y$ are both $O(1)$. If the density variations in the field are small compared with $\rho_0$, the density in the undisturbed stream, then the term $\rho^{-1}D\rho/Dt$ in eqn. (19) is small compared with unity and the equation of continuity reduces to the form

$$\frac{\partial u}{\partial x} + \frac{\partial v}{\partial y} = 0, \tag{20}$$

which is the equation of continuity for incompressible fluids; this is only valid if the Mach number is not large, less than 0·5, say, and if the temperature difference between the surface and the main stream is small compared with the standard absolute temperature $T_0$. In many of the examples given later in this chapter it will be assumed that both these conditions are satisfied, and this imposes a limit on the range of validity of the solutions.

We now consider the approximations which can be introduced into the energy equations. For liquids (7) is

$$\rho c_p\left(\frac{\partial T}{\partial t} + u\frac{\partial T}{\partial x} + v\frac{\partial T}{\partial y}\right) = k\left(\frac{\partial^2 T}{\partial x^2} + \frac{\partial^2 T}{\partial y^2}\right),$$

if the thermal conductivity is constant. The velocity $u$ varies from zero at $y = 0$ to $u_1$ (say) at $y = \delta_u$, while the temperature $T$ varies from $T_1$, the surface temperature, at $y = 0$ to $T_0$, the temperature in the body of the fluid, at $y = \delta_T$. Taking $u_1$ and $(T_1 - T_0)$ as quantities of standard order, $u$ is $O(1)$, $v$ is $O(\delta_u)$, $u\,\partial T/\partial x$ is $O(1)$, and $v\,\partial T/\partial y$ is $O(\delta_u/\delta_T)$ which is $O(1)$. Also $\partial^2 T/\partial x^2$ is $O(1)$ and $\partial^2 T/\partial y^2$ is $O(\delta_T^{-2})$, and hence $\partial^2 T/\partial x^2$ may be neglected in comparison with $\partial^2 T/\partial y^2$.

The energy equation for liquids then becomes

$$\rho c_p\left(\frac{\partial T}{\partial t}+u\frac{\partial T}{\partial x}+v\frac{\partial T}{\partial y}\right)=k\frac{\partial^2 T}{\partial y^2}. \tag{21}$$

If $k$ is variable the right-hand side is replaced by the expression

$$\frac{\partial}{\partial y}\left(k\frac{\partial T}{\partial y}\right).$$

The energy equation (9) for gases becomes

$$\rho c_p\left(\frac{\partial T}{\partial t}+u\frac{\partial T}{\partial x}+v\frac{\partial T}{\partial y}\right)-\left(\frac{\partial p}{\partial t}+u\frac{\partial p}{\partial x}+v\frac{\partial p}{\partial y}\right)=k\left(\frac{\partial^2 T}{\partial x^2}+\frac{\partial^2 T}{\partial y^2}\right)+\Phi,$$

if the thermal conductivity is constant. The dissipation function is, from (85) of Chap. II,

$$\Phi=\mu\left[-\frac{2}{3}\left(\frac{\partial u}{\partial x}+\frac{\partial v}{\partial y}\right)^2+2\left(\frac{\partial u}{\partial x}\right)^2+2\left(\frac{\partial v}{\partial y}\right)^2+\left(\frac{\partial v}{\partial x}+\frac{\partial u}{\partial y}\right)^2\right].$$

Now $\partial u/\partial x$ and $\partial v/\partial y$ are $O(1)$, $\partial v/\partial x$ is $O(\delta_u)$, and $\partial u/\partial y$ is $O(\delta_u^{-1})$. Hence, ignoring terms of lower order, the dissipation function becomes

$$\Phi=\mu\left(\frac{\partial u}{\partial y}\right)^2. \tag{22}$$

From (17) it follows that $\partial p/\partial y$ is at most $O(1)$ and hence $v\,\partial p/\partial y$ is $O(\delta_u)$, so that $v\,\partial p/\partial y$ can be neglected in comparison with $u\,\partial p/\partial x$ which is $O(1)$. Also $\partial^2 T/\partial x^2$ can be neglected in comparison with $\partial^2 T/\partial y^2$, as for liquids.

Introducing these approximations the energy equation for gases becomes

$$\rho c_p\left(\frac{\partial T}{\partial t}+u\frac{\partial T}{\partial x}+v\frac{\partial T}{\partial y}\right)-\left(\frac{\partial p}{\partial t}+u\frac{\partial p}{\partial x}\right)=k\frac{\partial^2 T}{\partial y^2}+\mu\left(\frac{\partial u}{\partial y}\right)^2. \tag{23}$$

If the thermal conductivity is variable, the first term on the right-hand side is replaced by the expression $\dfrac{\partial}{\partial y}\left(k\dfrac{\partial T}{\partial y}\right)$.

Introducing similar approximations into the equivalent form (10) of the energy equation for gases leads to the equation

$$\rho c_p\left(\frac{\partial T_H}{\partial t}+u\frac{\partial T_H}{\partial x}+v\frac{\partial T_H}{\partial y}\right)-\frac{\partial p}{\partial t}=k\frac{\partial^2}{\partial y^2}\left[T_H+\left(\frac{\sigma-1}{2}\right)\frac{u^2}{c_p}\right], \tag{24}$$

where $T_H$ is the total temperature; if $k$ is variable the operator $k(\partial^2/\partial y^2)$ is replaced by $\partial/\partial y\{k(\partial/\partial y)\}$. If the motion is steady the term $\partial p/\partial t$ in this equation is zero; if $\sigma$ is not very different from unity and the velocity variations in the field are not too large, so that

$$\frac{(\sigma-1)U^2}{2c_p(T_1-T_0)}$$

is small compared with unity, where $U$ is the stream velocity and $(T_1-T_0)$ is the imposed temperature difference, then the last term on the right-hand side can be neglected and the equation reduces to

$$\frac{\partial T_H}{\partial t}+u\frac{\partial T_H}{\partial x}+v\frac{\partial T_H}{\partial y} = \kappa\frac{\partial^2 T_H}{\partial y^2}, \tag{25}$$

where $\kappa = k/\rho c_p$. This equation is of the same form as the equation for liquids with substitution of the total temperature $T_H$ for the temperature $T$. If the velocity variations in the field are such that $U^2/(2c_p)$ is small compared with $(T_1-T_0)$, i.e. if

$$\frac{(\gamma-1)M_0^2 T_0}{2(T_1-T_0)} \ll 1,$$

then $T_H$ may be replaced by $T$ and the equations become identical.

## § 8. Boundary conditions

The conditions satisfied by the temperature usually require (i) that it shall have given values at the surface of the body or alternatively that there shall be no heat transferred from the surface, in which case the temperature gradient normal to the surface must vanish; and (ii) that the temperature shall have a given value at a large distance from the body. For flow through a pipe the condition at infinity is replaced by a corresponding condition at the entry.

It is convenient to replace the condition at infinity by a condition which is satisfied at the outer edge of the boundary layer. Outside this layer the terms on the right-hand side of (7), (9), and (10) which arise from conductivity and dissipation are negligible. For liquids (7) becomes

$$\rho c_p \frac{DT}{Dt} = 0,$$

and hence                          $T = T_0.$

For the flow of liquids the temperature is therefore constant except in the regions in which conductivity and viscosity are important and the condition at infinity may be replaced by an identical condition at the edge of the boundary layer.

To obtain the corresponding condition for gases we use (10) which, for steady flow outside the boundary layer with body forces neglected, becomes

$$c_p \frac{DT_H}{Dt} = 0.$$

Hence

$$T_H = T_{H_0},$$

where $T_{H_0}$ is the total temperature at infinity. Thus for gases the temperature distribution is such that the total temperature is constant, except in the boundary layer where conduction and viscosity are important. Since the total temperature is proportional to the total energy per unit mass $c_p T + \frac{1}{2}q^2$, this is equivalent to the statement that the total energy is constant outside the boundary layer (which is Bernoulli's equation).

## § 9. The momentum and energy integral equations for the boundary layer

We repeat here the momentum integral equation derived in Chap. X including the term arising from the gravity forces. In general, for gases and liquids,

$$\frac{\partial}{\partial t} \int_0^h (\rho_1 u_1 - \rho u) \, dy - u_1 \frac{\partial}{\partial t} \int_0^h (\rho_1 - \rho) \, dy +$$

$$+ \frac{\partial}{\partial x} \int_0^h \rho u (u_1 - u) \, dy + \frac{\partial u_1}{\partial x} \int_0^h (\rho_1 u_1 - \rho u) \, dy$$

$$= lg \int_0^h \beta \rho (T - T_0) \, dy + \tau_0, \quad (26)$$

where $h$ is a length which is greater than the boundary-layer thickness, $\rho_1$ and $u_1$ are the density and velocity at the edge of the boundary layer, and $\tau_0$ is the wall shear stress which is equal to $\mu(\partial u/\partial y)_{y=0}$ for laminar flow.

The corresponding energy integral equation† for the boundary layer may be derived either by integration of the energy equation

† The energy integral equation for gases was originally derived by Frankl (*Trans. Cen. Aero-Hydrodyn. Inst. Moscow*, No. 176 (1934), 3–18), who applied it to calculate the effect of compressibility and dissipation on the drag of a flat plate.

or by considering the energy balance in an element of the layer. Only the former method will be given here.

We begin by considering liquids. Integrating (21) across the boundary layer in a direction normal to the surface of the body from $y = 0$ to $y = h$, where $h$ is a length which is greater than the thickness of either the viscous or the thermal boundary layer, we obtain

$$\rho c_p \int_0^h \left(\frac{\partial T}{\partial t} + u\frac{\partial T}{\partial x} + v\frac{\partial T}{\partial y}\right) dy = -k\left(\frac{\partial T}{\partial y}\right)_{y=0}, \qquad (27)$$

since $\partial T/\partial y$ vanishes for $y = h$. Now

$$\int_0^h \frac{\partial T}{\partial t}\, dy = \int_0^h \frac{\partial}{\partial t}(T-T_0)\, dy = \frac{\partial}{\partial t}\int_0^h (T-T_0)\, dy,$$

$$\int_0^h u\frac{\partial T}{\partial x}\, dy = \int_0^h u\frac{\partial}{\partial x}(T-T_0)\, dy$$

$$= \frac{\partial}{\partial x}\int_0^h u(T-T_0)\, dy - \int_0^h (T-T_0)\frac{\partial u}{\partial x}\, dy,$$

and

$$\int_0^h v\frac{\partial T}{\partial y}\, dy = \int_0^h v\frac{\partial}{\partial y}(T-T_0)\, dy = [v(T-T_0)]_0^h - \int_0^h (T-T_0)\frac{\partial v}{\partial y}\, dy,$$

where $T_0$ is the temperature outside the boundary layer.

Also $v$ vanishes for $y = 0$ and $T = T_0$ for $y = h$, so that $[v(T-T_0)]_0^h$ is equal to zero. Hence, substituting in (27) and making use of the equation of continuity (20), we obtain

$$\rho c_p \left[\frac{\partial}{\partial t}\int_0^h (T-T_0)\, dy + \frac{\partial}{\partial x}\int_0^h u(T-T_0)\, dy\right] = -k\left[\frac{\partial}{\partial y}(T-T_0)\right]_{y=0}. \qquad (28)$$

This equation has been deduced for laminar flow, but it can be shown that a similar equation holds for turbulent flow if the right-hand side is replaced by $Q_0$, which is the rate of transfer of heat per unit area into the fluid at the surface $y = 0$.

For the calculation of the corresponding equation for the steady motion of gases we take the energy equation for the boundary layer in the form (24), which is

$$\rho c_p\left(u\frac{\partial T_H}{\partial x}+v\frac{\partial T_H}{\partial y}\right) = k\frac{\partial^2}{\partial y^2}\left[T_H+\frac{(\sigma-1)u^2}{2c_p}\right].$$

Integrating as above from $y = 0$ to $y = h$ we obtain

$$c_p\int_0^h\left(\rho u\frac{\partial T_H}{\partial x}+\rho v\frac{\partial T_H}{\partial y}\right)dy = -k\left(\frac{\partial T_H}{\partial y}\right)_{y=0}, \qquad (29)$$

since $\partial T_H/\partial y$ vanishes for $y = h$ and $\partial(u^2)/\partial y = 2u\,\partial u/\partial y$ vanishes both for $y = 0$ and $y = h$.

Now

$$\int_0^h\rho u\frac{\partial T_H}{\partial x}\,dy = \frac{\partial}{\partial x}\int_0^h\rho u(T_H-T_{H_0})\,dy - \int_0^h(T_H-T_{H_0})\frac{\partial}{\partial x}(\rho u)\,dy,$$

and

$$\int_0^h\rho v\frac{\partial T_H}{\partial y}\,dy = \int_0^h\rho v\frac{\partial}{\partial y}(T_H-T_{H_0})\,dy$$

$$= [\rho v(T_H-T_{H_0})]_0^h - \int_0^h(T_H-T_{H_0})\frac{\partial}{\partial y}(\rho v)\,dy.$$

Also $v$ vanishes for $y = 0$ and $T_H-T_{H_0}$ vanishes for $y = h$. The equation of continuity (4) becomes for steady motion

$$\frac{\partial}{\partial x}(\rho u)+\frac{\partial}{\partial y}(\rho v) = 0,$$

and substituting in (29) we obtain

$$c_p\frac{\partial}{\partial x}\int_0^h\rho u(T_H-T_{H_0})\,dy = -k\left(\frac{\partial T_H}{\partial y}\right)_{y=0}. \qquad (30)$$

This is a simple and convenient form of the energy integral equation for the steady motion of gases. The equation has been calculated for laminar flow but, as above, a similar equation holds for turbulent flow with the right-hand side replaced by $Q_0$, the rate of heat transfer per unit area into the fluid at the surface $y = 0$.

When the motion is slow enough for the difference between $T_H$

and $T$ and for the density variations to be ignored, (30) may be reduced to the form

$$\rho c_p \frac{\partial}{\partial x} \int_0^h u(T-T_0)\, dy = -k\left(\frac{\partial T}{\partial y}\right)_{y=0}, \tag{31}$$

which is the same as for liquids in steady motion.

## § 10. A solution for thermal entry length

A simple solution for the case when heat is supplied from a station on a plate or in a pipe, when the viscous boundary layer is already established, was given by Lévêque.† We assume that the velocity component parallel to the wall is given by $u = Ay$, where $y$ is the distance from the wall and $A$ is a constant, and that the velocity component normal to the wall vanishes. Then neglecting dissipation and pressure effects, eqns. (21) or (23) for the temperature become

$$u \frac{\partial T}{\partial x} = \kappa \frac{\partial^2 T}{\partial y^2}. \tag{32}$$

If the wall is maintained at a constant temperature $T_1$ for $x > 0$ and the stream temperature is $T_0$ the boundary conditions are:

$$T = T_1 \quad \text{for} \quad y = 0 \quad (x > 0),$$
$$T = T_0 \quad \text{for} \quad y \to \infty,$$

and $\qquad\qquad T = T_0 \quad \text{for} \quad x = 0.$

Putting $\qquad u = Ay, \quad \theta = \dfrac{T-T_0}{T_1-T_0}, \quad \text{and} \quad \eta = y\left(\dfrac{A}{9\kappa x}\right)^{\frac{1}{3}},$

and assuming that $\theta$ is a function of $\eta$ only, eqn. (32) becomes

$$\theta''(\eta) + 3\eta^2 \theta'(\eta) = 0.$$

The solution of this equation, which satisfies the boundary conditions $\theta = 1$ for $\eta = 0$ and $\theta = 0$ for $\eta \to \infty$, is

$$\theta(\eta) = 1 - 1 \cdot 120 \int_0^\eta \exp(-t^3)\, dt;$$

this function is plotted in Fig. 261. The surface temperature gradient, which determines the rate of heat transfer from the surface, is

$$\left(\frac{\partial T}{\partial y}\right)_{y=0} = -1 \cdot 120(T_1 - T_0)\left(\frac{A}{9\kappa x}\right)^{\frac{1}{3}}.$$

† *Comptes Rendus*, **185** (1927), 1190–2.

This solution was adapted by Lévêque to calculate the heat transfer to fluids in laminar flow in tubes just after the beginning of the heated section. It thus supplements the solution of Graetz and Nusselt, which is inaccurate in this region.

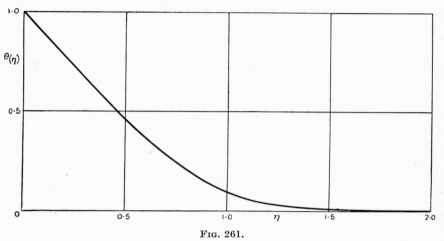

FIG. 261.

## § 11. Laminar flow in a circular pipe. Wall at constant temperature

The solution of the problem of heat transfer to a fluid flowing with the Poiseuille velocity distribution through a circular pipe of radius $a$, at a section of which the temperature of the surface changes discontinuously, has been obtained by Graetz† and Nusselt.‡ Take cylindrical coordinates $r$, $\phi$, $z$, with the origin at the centre of the section at which the wall temperature changes from $T_0$ to $T_1$, and the axis of $z$ along the axis of the pipe. The motion is steady, and eqn. (8) for the temperature is

$$\frac{D\theta}{Dt} = \kappa \nabla^2 \theta, \tag{33}$$

where

$$\theta = \frac{T - T_1}{T_0 - T_1},$$

and $\kappa$ is the thermometric conductivity; in this equation the terms due to the pressure gradient and the dissipation have been neglected.

† *Ann. Phys.* **18** (1883), 79–94; **25** (1885), 337–57.
‡ *Z. Ver. dtsch. Ing.* **54** (1910), 1154–8.

The boundary conditions are

$$\theta = 0 \quad \text{for} \quad z > 0 \quad \text{and} \quad r = a, \tag{34}$$

$$\theta = 1 \quad \text{for} \quad z = 0 \quad \text{and} \quad r < a. \tag{35}$$

For the Poiseuille flow

$$\left.\begin{array}{l} u_r = 0, \qquad u_\phi = 0 \\ u_z = 2u_m[1 - (r/a)^2] \end{array}\right\}, \tag{36}$$

where $u_m$ is the mean velocity. With these values for the velocity components eqn. (33) becomes

$$2u_m\left[1 - \left(\frac{r}{a}\right)^2\right]\frac{\partial\theta}{\partial z} = \kappa\left[\frac{\partial^2\theta}{\partial r^2} + \frac{1}{r}\frac{\partial\theta}{\partial r} + \frac{\partial^2\theta}{\partial z^2}\right]; \tag{37}$$

the term $\partial^2\theta/\partial\phi^2$ vanishes since there is symmetry about the axis of the pipe. It is assumed that $\partial^2\theta/\partial z^2$ may be neglected in comparison with $\partial^2\theta/\partial r^2 + r^{-1}\,\partial\theta/\partial r$. Solutions are then obtained by putting

$$\theta = A\exp\left(-\beta^2\frac{\kappa z}{2u_m a^2}\right)\psi(r),$$

where $\beta$ is an undetermined constant, so that eqn. (37) becomes

$$\frac{d^2\psi}{dr^2} + \frac{1}{r}\frac{d\psi}{dr} + \frac{\beta^2}{a^2}\left[1 - \left(\frac{r}{a}\right)^2\right]\psi = 0.$$

If we write $\qquad\qquad \beta r/a = r',$

this equation is $\qquad \dfrac{d^2\psi}{dr'^2} + \dfrac{1}{r'}\dfrac{d\psi}{dr'} + \left[1 - \left(\dfrac{r'}{\beta}\right)^2\right]\psi = 0.$

The series solution of this equation which is free from singularities at the origin is

$$\psi(r', \beta) = 1 - \frac{r'^2}{4} + \frac{3r'^4}{2.4!}\left(\frac{1}{4} + \frac{1}{\beta^2}\right) + \dots.$$

The boundary condition (34) requires that $\psi$ shall satisfy

$$\psi(\beta, \beta) = 0.$$

This equation has an infinite number of roots, of which the first three are $\qquad \beta_0 = 2.705, \qquad \beta_1 = 6.66, \qquad \beta_2 = 10.6.$

Hence there are an infinite number of partial solutions of the form

$$A_n\exp\left(-\beta_n^2\frac{\kappa z}{2u_m a^2}\right)\chi_n\left(\frac{r}{a}\right),$$

where $\chi_n(r/a)$ stands for $\psi(\beta_n r/a, \beta_n)$. The constants $A_n$ are determined from the boundary condition (35), and Nusselt gives for the first three

$$A_0 = +1\cdot477, \qquad A_1 = -0\cdot810, \qquad A_2 = +0\cdot385.$$

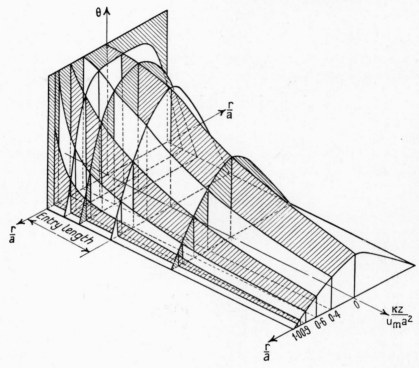

FIG. 262.

The temperature distribution is

$$\theta = A_0 \exp\left(-\beta_0^2 \frac{\kappa z}{2u_m a^2}\right)\chi_0\left(\frac{r}{a}\right) + A_1 \exp\left(-\beta_1^2 \frac{\kappa z}{2u_m a^2}\right)\chi_1\left(\frac{r}{a}\right) +$$

$$+ A_2 \exp\left(-\beta_2^2 \frac{\kappa z}{2u_m a^2}\right)\chi_2\left(\frac{r}{a}\right) + \dots,$$

or
$$\theta = f\left(\frac{\kappa z}{u_m d^2}, \frac{r}{a}\right), \qquad (38)$$

where $d = 2a$ is the diameter of the pipe. Fig. 262 shows the temperature distribution given by (38). The outer layers of fluid take up the temperature of the walls very quickly and the radial temperature distribution soon becomes steady.

To obtain a comparison with experimental results it is necessary to calculate the mean temperature weighted with respect to the velocity, since this is the temperature which is measured when fluid which has passed through the pipe is mixed. This mean temperature $\theta_M$ is given by

$$\theta_M = \frac{\int_0^a \theta u_m[1-(r/a)^2]\pi r\, dr}{\int_0^a u_m[1-(r/a)^2]\pi r\, dr},$$

which becomes
$$\theta_M = \frac{\int_0^1 \theta(1-\xi^2)\xi\, d\xi}{\int_0^1 (1-\xi^2)\xi\, d\xi}$$

on putting $\xi = r/a$. The value of the integral in the denominator is 0·25, while the value of the numerator has been calculated from (38) by Gröber[†] and by Jacob and Eck.[‡] They obtain

$$\theta_M = 0\cdot819\exp\left(-14\cdot6272\frac{\kappa z}{u_m d^2}\right) + 0\cdot0976\exp\left(-89\cdot22\frac{\kappa z}{u_m d^2}\right) +$$
$$+0\cdot01896\exp\left(-212\frac{\kappa z}{u_m d^2}\right)+...,$$

or
$$\theta_M = f_1\left(\frac{\kappa z}{u_m d^2}\right).$$

Putting
$$\theta_M = \frac{T_M - T_1}{T_0 - T_1},$$

we have for the mean absolute temperature $T_M$

$$T_M = T_1 + (T_0 - T_1)f_1.$$

The heat transfer to the wall in unit time for a length $l$ is given by the difference between the heat content of the fluid entering at $z = 0$ and leaving at $z = l$. Hence we obtain

$$Q = \tfrac{1}{4}d^2\rho c_p\, u_m(T_0-T_1)[1-f_1(\kappa l/u_m d^2)].$$

[†] *Die Grundgesetze der Wärmeleitung und des Wärmeüberganges*, Berlin (1933), p. 181.
[‡] *Forsch. Ing-Wes.* 3 (1932), 121–6.

The Nusselt number depends on the choice of a mean temperature difference, which is taken to be the arithmetic mean of the mean temperature differences between the fluid and the wall at entry and exit—i.e. $\frac{1}{2}(1+\theta_M)(T_0-T_1)$.  Hence (eqn. (11))

$$K_N = \frac{u_m d^2}{2\kappa l}\left(\frac{1-f_1}{1+f_1}\right),$$

with $\kappa l/(u_m d^2)$ as the variable in the function $f_1$ and taking $d$ as the representative length. A comparison between this formula and experimental results for oil is given in Figs. 263 and 264, for which the experimental results are taken from McAdams's book.[†] (We abbreviate $\log_{10}$ to log; all other bases are explicitly stated.) Fig. 263 gives the results for heating oils and Fig. 264 for cooling oils. It will be seen that different results are obtained in the two cases, and this is partly due to the variation of viscosity with temperature which causes a distortion of the velocity distribution from the parabolic form.

## § 12. Laminar flow in a circular pipe with constant temperature gradient

A related problem which has a simple solution is that of finding the temperature distribution in a circular pipe whose walls are kept at a uniform temperature gradient, and in which fluid is flowing with the Poiseuille velocity distribution.[‡] The conditions will be similar at each section of the pipe, and we may put

$$T = Az+g(r),$$

where $A$ is the temperature gradient. Substituting this form together with the velocity distribution given by (36) in eqn. (8), we obtain the equation

$$2u_m\left[1-\left(\frac{r}{a}\right)^2\right]A = \kappa\left(\frac{d^2g}{dr^2}+\frac{1}{r}\frac{dg}{dr}\right).$$

The solution which is free from singularities and satisfies the condition $g = 0$ at the surface of the pipe, $r = a$, is

$$g(r) = -\frac{2u_m Aa^2}{\kappa}\left[\frac{3}{16}-\frac{1}{4}\left(\frac{r}{a}\right)^2+\frac{1}{16}\left(\frac{r}{a}\right)^4\right]. \tag{39}$$

This gives $\qquad\qquad T_{\max} = Az-\dfrac{3u_m Aa^2}{8\kappa}$

† *Heat Transmission*, New York (1942), p. 189.
‡ Cf. Wilson, *Proc. Camb. Phil. Soc.* **12** (1902–4), 406–23; Nusselt, loc. cit. on p. 774; Eagle and Ferguson, *Proc. Roy. Soc.* A, **127** (1930), 540–66.

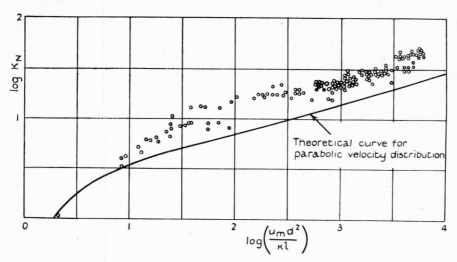

FIG. 263. Laminar flow in pipes. Liquid heated by wall.

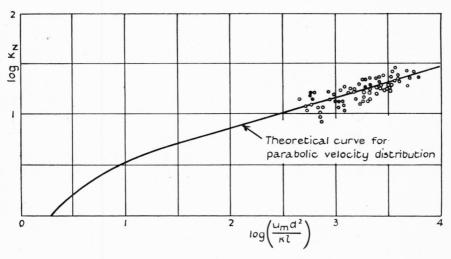

FIG. 264. Laminar flow in pipes. Liquid cooled by wall.

as the temperature at the centre of the pipe; for the mean temperatures $T_m$ and $T_M$ we obtain

$$T_m = \frac{2}{a^2}\int_0^a Tr\,dr = Az - \frac{1}{6}\frac{u_m A a^2}{\kappa},$$

and
$$T_M = \frac{2}{a^2 u_m} \int_0^a T u_z r \, dr = Az - \frac{11}{48} \frac{u_m A a^2}{\kappa},$$

where $T_m$ is the unweighted mean and $T_M$ the mean weighted with respect to the velocity—i.e. the temperature which is measured in fluid which is mixed after passing through the pipe. The rate of heat transfer per unit area, $Q$, is equal to $k(\partial T/\partial r)_{r=a}$, which from (39) is $k u_m A a/2\kappa$; and the value of the Nusselt number $K_N$ (eqn. (11) with $d$ as the pipe diameter) is, when based on the mean temperature $T_m$,

$$K_N = -\frac{2aQ}{k(T_m - Az)} = 6,$$

but when based on $T_M$ it is

$$K_N = 48/11.$$

## § 13. Forced convection in a laminar boundary layer at a flat plate along the stream

For steady flow of a gas past a flat plate, at temperature $T_1$ and parallel to a stream of velocity $U$ and temperature $T_0$, the pressure $p$ is constant, so that eqn. (23) governing the temperature distribution is

$$\rho c_p \left( u \frac{\partial T}{\partial x} + v \frac{\partial T}{\partial y} \right) = k \frac{\partial^2 T}{\partial y^2} + \mu \left( \frac{\partial u}{\partial y} \right)^2. \tag{40}$$

When the heat generated by dissipation is neglected, this becomes

$$u \frac{\partial T}{\partial x} + v \frac{\partial T}{\partial y} = \kappa \frac{\partial^2 T}{\partial y^2}, \tag{41}$$

and the boundary conditions are

$$T = T_1 \quad \text{at} \quad y = 0, \qquad T = T_0 \quad \text{at} \quad y = \infty.$$

(The same equation holds for liquids.)

For small temperature differences the velocity distribution is the same as for isothermal flow. The velocity $u_1$ outside the boundary layer is taken equal to the undisturbed velocity $U$, and the solution in Vol. I (1938), chap. iv, § 53, shows that, if

$$\eta = \tfrac{1}{2}(U/\nu x)^{\frac{1}{2}} y$$

and $\psi$ is the stream-function, then

$$\psi = (\nu U x)^{\frac{1}{2}} f(\eta), \qquad u = \tfrac{1}{2} U f', \qquad v = \tfrac{1}{2}(U\nu/x)^{\frac{1}{2}}(\eta f' - f),$$

where $f(\eta)$ satisfies the equation

$$f'''+ff'' = 0.$$

With these values of $u$ and $v$ eqn. (41) can be satisfied if the temperature is a function of $\eta$ only. If we put

$$T = T_1-(T_1-T_0)\theta(\eta),$$

(41) becomes

$$\theta''+\sigma f\theta' = 0, \tag{42}$$

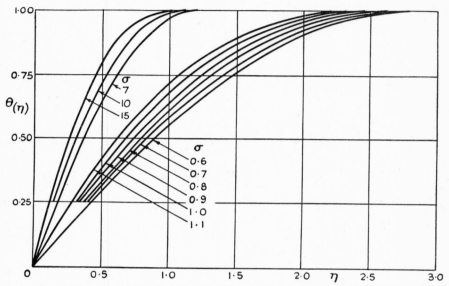

FIG. 265. Temperature distribution in the boundary layer of a heated plate.

where $\sigma = \nu/\kappa$, and the boundary conditions satisfied by $\theta$ are $\theta = 0$ at $\eta = 0$, $\theta = 1$ at $\eta = \infty$. The solution of (42) with these boundary conditions is

$$\theta(\eta) = \alpha_1(\sigma) \int_0^\eta \exp\left\{-\sigma \int_0^\eta f\,d\eta\right\} d\eta,$$

where

$$\frac{1}{\alpha_1(\sigma)} = \int_0^\infty \exp\left\{-\sigma \int_0^\eta f\,d\eta\right\} d\eta.$$

Substituting $f = -f'''/f''$, we obtain the alternative form

$$\theta(\eta) = \alpha_1(\sigma) \int_0^\eta \left[\frac{f''(\eta)}{f''(0)}\right]^\sigma d\eta.$$

Fig. 265 shows the variation of $\theta$ with $\eta$ for a number of values of $\sigma$.

Pohlhausen† tabulates $\alpha_1(\sigma)$, and remarks that

$$\alpha_1(\sigma) \doteqdot 0 \cdot 664 \sigma^{\frac{1}{3}},$$

which is shown for comparison in Table 2.

### TABLE 2

| $\sigma$ | $\alpha_1(\sigma)$ | $0 \cdot 664 \sigma^{\frac{1}{3}}$ |
|----------|-------------------|-----------------------------------|
| 0·6  | 0·552 | 0·560 |
| 0·7  | 0·585 | 0·589 |
| 0·8  | 0·614 | 0·616 |
| 0·9  | 0·640 | 0·641 |
| 1·0  | 0·664 | 0·664 |
| 1·1  | 0·687 | 0·685 |
| 7·0  | 1·29  | 1·26  |
| 10·0 | 1·46  | 1·43  |
| 15·0 | 1·67  | 1·64  |

The heat transfer in unit time from one side of a plate of length $l$ and breadth $b$ is

$$Q = -kb \int_0^l \left(\frac{\partial T}{\partial y}\right)_{y=0} dx$$

$$= \alpha_1(\sigma) kb (T_1 - T_0)(Ul/\nu)^{\frac{1}{2}},$$

and the corresponding value of the Nusselt number is

$$K_N = \alpha_1(\sigma)\sqrt{(Ul/\nu)} = \alpha_1(\sigma) R^{\frac{1}{2}}.$$

Also the Stanton number is

$$K_S = \frac{K_N}{\sigma R} = \frac{\alpha_1(\sigma)}{\sigma R^{\frac{1}{2}}} \doteqdot \tfrac{1}{2}\sigma^{-\frac{2}{3}} C_f,$$

where $C_f (= 1 \cdot 328 R^{-\frac{1}{2}})$ is the coefficient of mean friction of the surface.

The local value of $K_N$ is one-half of the total value. Measurements to determine the heat transfer from a heated flat plate have been made by Elias.‡ The results in the laminar region for the local heat transfer are scanty and scattered; the theoretical formula seems to represent them as well as could be expected.

The energy eqns. (28) and (30) can also be used to obtain an expression for the heat transfer. For brevity we shall consider only the case of an incompressible fluid, though the result for a com-

† *Z. angew. Math. Mech.* **1** (1921), 115–20.
‡ Ibid. **9** (1929), 434–53; **10** (1930), 1–14.

pressible fluid is substantially the same. An approximate expression for the velocity distribution (Vol. I (1938), chap. iv, § 60) is

$$\frac{u}{U} = \frac{2y}{\delta_u} - \frac{2y^3}{\delta_u^3} + \frac{y^4}{\delta_u^4},$$

where $\delta_u = 5 \cdot 83(\nu x/U)^{\frac{1}{2}}$ and is the thickness of the viscous layer. The energy integral eqn. (28) becomes

$$\frac{d}{dx} \int_0^h u(T-T_0)\,dy = -\kappa \left(\frac{\partial T}{\partial y}\right)_{y=0}. \tag{43}$$

Assuming that the temperature distribution is similar to the velocity distribution, so that

$$\frac{T-T_0}{T_1-T_0} = 1 - \frac{2y}{\delta_T} + \frac{2y^3}{\delta_T^3} - \frac{y^4}{\delta_T^4},$$

for $y < \delta_T$ and $T = T_0$ for $y > \delta_T$, where $\delta_T$ is the thickness of the thermal layer, and substituting in (43) we obtain

$$\int^h u(T-T_0)\,dy = U(T_1-T_0)\delta_T(\tfrac{2}{15}\chi - \tfrac{3}{140}\chi^3 + \tfrac{1}{180}\chi^4),$$

where $\chi = \delta_T/\delta_u$ and is the ratio of the thicknesses of the thermal and viscous layers. Then (43) gives

$$U\delta_T^2(\tfrac{2}{15}\chi - \tfrac{3}{140}\chi^3 + \tfrac{1}{180}\chi^4) = 4\kappa x. \tag{44}$$

For the viscous layer

$$U\delta_u^2(\tfrac{2}{15} - \tfrac{3}{140} + \tfrac{1}{180}) = 4\nu x, \tag{45}$$

and dividing (44) by (45) we have

$$\chi^3[1 + 0 \cdot 182(1-\chi^2) - 0 \cdot 047(1-\chi^3)] = 1/\sigma. \tag{46}$$

An approximate solution of (46) which, for values of $\sigma$ greater than unity, differs by less than 5 per cent. from the accurate solution is

$$\chi = \sigma^{-\frac{1}{3}}. \tag{47}$$

From (45) and (47) we obtain for the heat transferred in unit time from one side of a plate of length $l$ and breadth $b$

$$Q = 0 \cdot 686\sigma^{\frac{1}{3}}kb(T_1-T_0)\sqrt{(Ul/\nu)},$$

and the corresponding value of the Nusselt number is[†]

$$K_N = 0 \cdot 686\sigma^{\frac{1}{3}}\sqrt{(Ul/\nu)}.$$

† Cf. Kroujiline, *J. Tech. Phys. U.S.S.R.* **3** (1936), 183–94.

This result is close to the more accurate result of Pohlhausen. It applies only for $\delta_T/\delta_u < 1$, that is for $\sigma > 1$, since the value of $u$ used in (43) holds only for $y < \delta_u$. For $\delta_T/\delta_u > 1$ the algebra is more complicated, because two different expressions have to be used for $u$; but it gives an identical expression for the rate of heat transfer for values of $\sigma$ greater than 0·5.

## § 14. The reading of a plate thermometer in a stream

Pohlhausen† has also obtained the solution of the problem of the plate thermometer—i.e. the temperature which a thermometer in the form of a flat plate placed parallel to the stream will read when no heat is being transmitted to or from it by the fluid. In this problem the heat generated by dissipation cannot be neglected, and the temperature distribution is now given by (40) together with the condition of zero heat transfer from the surface. The velocity distribution is the same as before, but the boundary conditions for the temperature are now $\partial T/\partial y = 0$ at $y = 0$, $T = T_0$ at $y = \infty$. Changing to the new variable $\eta$ as in § 13, and putting

$$T = T_0 + \frac{U^2}{2c_p}\theta(\eta),$$

we obtain
$$\theta'' + \sigma f\theta' + 0{\cdot}5\sigma f''^2 = 0, \tag{48}$$

where $f(\eta)$ has the same meaning as in § 13. The boundary conditions are $\theta' = 0$ at $\eta = 0$, and $\theta = 0$ at $\eta = \infty$. The solution of (48) satisfying these conditions is

$$\theta(\eta) = 0{\cdot}5\sigma \int\limits_{\eta}^{\infty} \exp\left(-\sigma \int\limits_{0}^{\eta} f\, d\eta\right)\left[\int\limits_{0}^{\eta} f''^2 \exp\left(\sigma \int\limits_{0}^{\eta} f\, d\eta\right) d\eta\right] d\eta. \tag{49}$$

Hence, if $\theta(0)$ is denoted by $\alpha_2(\sigma)$,

$$\alpha_2(\sigma) = 0{\cdot}5\sigma \int\limits_{0}^{\infty} \exp\left(-\sigma \int\limits_{0}^{\eta} f\, d\eta\right)\left[\int\limits_{0}^{\eta} f''^2 \exp\left(\sigma \int\limits_{0}^{\eta} f\, d\eta\right) d\eta\right] d\eta.$$

Since $f = -f'''/f''$, and therefore

$$\exp\left(\sigma \int\limits_{0}^{\eta} f\, d\eta\right) = [f''(\eta)/f''(0)]^{-\sigma},$$

(49) may be written

$$\theta(\eta) = 0{\cdot}5\sigma \int\limits_{\eta}^{\infty} (f'')^{\sigma}\left[\int\limits_{0}^{\eta} (f'')^{2-\sigma}\, d\eta\right] d\eta,$$

† *Z. angew. Math. Mech.* **1** (1921), 120, 121.

with a corresponding expression for $\alpha_2$. For $\sigma = 1$ the expression for $\theta$ reduces to

$$\theta(\eta) = 1 - \tfrac{1}{4}f'^2$$

since $f'(0) = 0, f'(\infty) = 2$, and hence

$$T = T_0 + \frac{1}{2c_p}(U^2 - u^2).$$

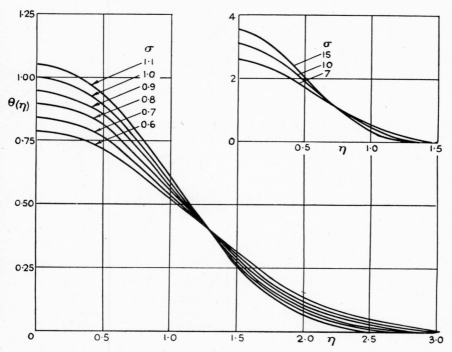

Fig. 266. Temperature distribution in the boundary layer of a plate thermometer.

This result, which is equivalent to the statement that the energy per unit mass $(c_p T + \tfrac{1}{2}u^2)$ is constant (or that the total temperature is constant) for $\sigma = 1$, may be verified directly from the original equation (40) (see also Chap. X, § 13).

Pohlhausen has tabulated the function (49) for a number of values of $\sigma$, and his results are reproduced in Fig. 266. He also gives values of $\alpha_2(\sigma)$, which are reproduced, together with the approximate form $\sigma^{\frac{1}{2}}$ for comparison, in Table 3.

TABLE 3

| $\sigma$ | $\alpha_2(\sigma)$ | $\sigma^{\frac{1}{2}}$ |
|---|---|---|
| 0·6 | 0·77 | 0·77 |
| 0·7 | 0·835 | 0·835 |
| 0·8 | 0·895 | 0·895 |
| 0·9 | 0·95 | 0·95 |
| 1·0 | 1·00 | 1·00 |
| 1·1 | 1·05 | 1·05 |
| 7·0 | 2·51 | 2·65 |
| 10·0 | 2·96 | 3·15 |
| 15·0 | 3·54 | 3·87 |

The difference between the reading $T_1$ of an insulated body and the temperature $T_0$ of the main stream will be referred to as the kinetic temperature and denoted by $\Delta T$, so that for the plate thermometer we have

$$T_1 - T_0 = \Delta T = \frac{U^2}{2c_p} \alpha_2(\sigma) \doteqdot \frac{U^2}{2c_p} \sigma^{\frac{1}{2}}. \qquad (50)$$

In terms of the total temperature this result can be written

$$T_{H_1} - T_{H_0} = \frac{U^2}{2c_p}(\sigma^{\frac{1}{2}} - 1), \qquad (51)$$

since $T_{H_1} = T_1$ as $u$ vanishes at the plate and $T_{H_0} = T_0 + (U^2/2c_p)$.

Hilton[†] has measured the temperature of some thin tufnol cylinders and obtained results in good agreement with the above formula. The results of temperature measurements by Eckert and Weise[‡] at a long cylinder with its axis along the stream and on a flat plate are shown plotted against Reynolds number in Fig. 267. At low values of $R$ good agreement with Pohlhausen's formula is obtained and the deviation from it for $R > 5 \times 10^5$ is due to transition to turbulent flow. The surface temperature when the boundary layer is turbulent is considered later.

## § 15. Kinetic temperature of a body in a stream

Solutions of the equation for the temperature read by thermometers of shapes other than the flat plate have not been obtained in a general form. We shall consider here the information available to determine the kinetic temperature of bodies of any shape. The

† Proc. Roy. Soc. A, 168 (1938), 43–56.
‡ Jb. dtsch. Luftfahrtforsch. 2 (1940), 25–31.

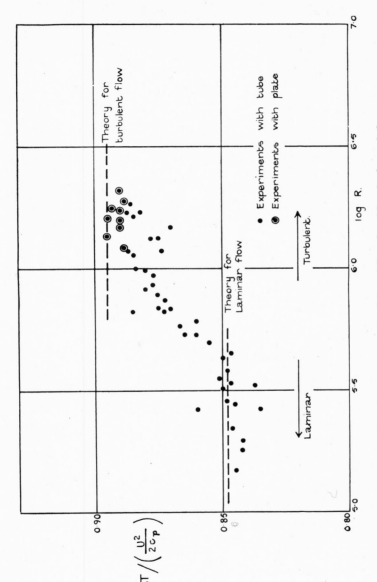

Fig. 267. Kinetic temperature for plate and for tube with axis along wind.

eqn. (24) for the total temperature distribution in the boundary layer for steady flow of a gas, for the special case $\sigma = 1$, becomes

$$u\frac{\partial T_H}{\partial x} + v\frac{\partial T_H}{\partial y} = \kappa\frac{\partial^2 T_H}{\partial y^2}.$$

This has an integral $\qquad T_H = T_{H_0},$

i.e. $\qquad\qquad T + \frac{u^2}{2c_p} = T_0 + \frac{U^2}{2c_p},$

which satisfies the condition of zero heat transfer from the surface, and hence determines the temperature of the body. At the surface of a body in the gas the velocity is zero so that the total temperature at the surface $T_{H_1}$ is equal to the surface temperature $T_1$ and hence†

$$\Delta T = T_1 - T_0 = \frac{U^2}{2c_p},$$

which determines the kinetic temperature in this special case ($\sigma = 1$). The result will apply for bodies of all shapes with laminar boundary layers up to the separation point but not necessarily behind this point. It is useful to remember that for air $U^2/2c_p$ is almost exactly equal to $1°$ C. for $U = 100$ m.p.h.

A simple approximate form for the temperature distribution on a body for which $\sigma$ is not equal to unity can be derived from Pohlhausen's solution for the plate thermometer in combination of the energy integral equation. The latter eqn. (30) becomes

$$\frac{d}{dx}\int_0^h \rho u(T_H - T_{H_0})\,dy = 0,$$

when the surface is insulated so that the surface temperature gradient vanishes and hence

$$\int^h \rho u(T_H - T_{H_0})\,dy = 0, \qquad\qquad (52)$$

since the left-hand side vanishes at the leading edge or at the forward stagnation point. This equation implies that there is no net energy transfer along the stream direction within the boundary layer and it follows that the temperature at a point on the surface is mainly determined by the local conditions. Thus, apart from the variation of the velocity distribution across the boundary layer, the temperature at a station on the body can be determined as though

† Busemann, *Handb. Exp. Phys.* **4**, Pt. I (1931), 366; see also Chap. X above.

it were part of a flat plate in a stream of velocity equal to the local velocity outside the boundary layer at the station under considera-tion. From (51) the total temperature at the surface would then be given by

$$T_{H_1} - T_{H_0} = \frac{u_1^2}{2c_p}(\sigma^{\frac{1}{2}} - 1),$$

where $u_1$ is the local velocity outside the boundary layer. Then the temperature at the surface $T_1$, which is equal to $T_{H_1}$, since the velocity is zero at the surface, is given by this solution and by the definition for the total temperature $T_{H_0}$, which is

$$T_{H_0} = T_0 + \frac{U^2}{2c_p}.$$

Hence the surface temperature $T_1$ and the kinetic temperature $\Delta T$ are given by†

$$\Delta T = T_1 - T_0 = \frac{U^2}{2c_p}\left[1 + \frac{u_1^2}{U^2}(\sigma^{\frac{1}{2}} - 1)\right]. \qquad (53)$$

The principal assumption made in deriving this approximate formula is that the difference between the actual velocity distribu-tion across the boundary layer at the station considered and the flat plate velocity distribution may be ignored in the process of calculation. The effect of the variation of boundary-layer velocity distribution has been studied by Eckert and Drewitz; they have calculated the kinetic temperature for $\sigma = 0.7$ when the velocity outside the boundary layer is of the form $u_1 = cx^m$, where $m$ is a constant which lies between $-0.0654$ and $+4$ and $x$ is the distance measured from the stagnation point. If the kinetic temperature $\Delta T$ is represented by the equation

$$\Delta T = T_1 - T_0 = \frac{U^2}{2c_p}\left[1 + \frac{u_1^2}{U^2}(f(\sigma) - 1)\right],$$

where the approximate form for the function $f(\sigma)$, given above, is $\sigma^{\frac{1}{2}}$, then the more accurate values obtained by Eckert and Drewitz for $\sigma = 0.7$ are shown in Table 4.

### TABLE 4

| $\beta = \dfrac{2m}{m+1}$ . | $-0.14$ | $0$ | $0.2$ | $0.5$ | $1.0$ | $1.6$ |
|---|---|---|---|---|---|---|
| $m$ . . | $-0.0654$ | $0$ | $0.111$ | $0.333$ | $1.0$ | $4.0$ |
| $f(0.7)$ . | $0.838$ | $0.833$ | $0.818$ | $0.782$ | $0.791$ | $0.768$ |

† Eckert and Drewitz, *Luftfahrtforsch.* **19** (1942), 189–96; Squire, *Rep. Memor. Aero. Res. Coun.*, No. 1,986 (1942).

The results of measurements by Eckert and Weise[†] of the pressure distribution and surface temperature over a non-conducting circular cylinder in an air stream ($\sigma = 0\cdot72$) for $M = 0\cdot685$, $R = 1\cdot4 \times 10^4$, are compared with the calculated results in Fig. 268 and good agreement with eqn. (53) is obtained. The values of $f(0\cdot72)$ deduced from the measurements, are also shown; these rise gradually from $0\cdot82$ near the stagnation point to $0\cdot84$ at the separation point, which is in fair accordance with the results for $\sigma = 0\cdot7$ given in Table 4 in which $\beta = 1$ corresponds to the stagnation point region and $\beta = -0\cdot14$ is close to separation. The value for $f(\sigma)$ given by the approximate form (53) is $\sigma^{\frac{1}{3}} = 0\cdot845$. The small variation of both theoretical and experimental results from the values given by (53) indicates that it may be used in all practical cases for the region ahead of the laminar separation point. There is no method of calculation available for the rear part of a bluff body.

When the boundary layer is turbulent the stagnation temperature distribution across it still satisfies eqn. (52), but the lack of information about the dissipation of energy in turbulent flow makes it difficult to develop a satisfactory theory.

Ackermann[‡] and the present author[§] have derived the formula

$$\Delta T = \frac{U^2}{2c_p}\sigma^{\frac{1}{3}} \tag{54}$$

for a flat plate with turbulent boundary layer. This is shown in Fig. 267 and is in fair accordance with the trend of the experimental results for $R > 10^6$. For the case of a cylinder with turbulent boundary layer the formula for the kinetic temperature corresponding to (53) and (54) is

$$\Delta T = \frac{U^2}{2c_p}\left[1 + \frac{u_1^2}{U^2}(\sigma^{\frac{1}{3}} - 1)\right].$$

## § 16. Forced convection from a cylinder near the forward stagnation point[||]

Near the forward stagnation point of a cylinder immersed in a moving fluid, the velocity $u_1$ outside the boundary layer increases linearly with distance from that point, so that $u_1 = \beta_1 x$. The velocities in the boundary layer are given in Vol. I (1938), chap. iv, § 54.

[†] *Forsch. Ing-Wes.* **13** (1942), 246–54.

[‡] Ibid. 226–34.                                                    [§] Loc. cit. on p. 789.

[||] This solution was originally given in Vol. II (1938), chap. xiv, § 270.

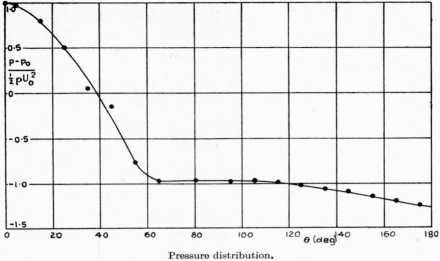

Pressure distribution.

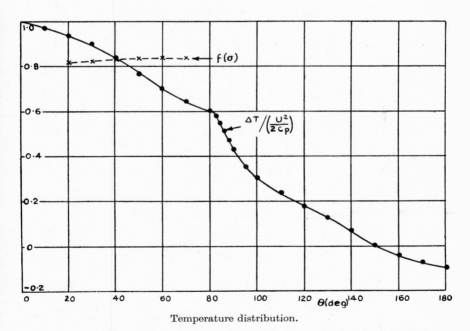

Temperature distribution.

FIG. 268. Pressure and kinetic temperature distributions round a circular cylinder.

If the body is heated to temperature $T_1$ eqns. (21) and (23) for the temperature distribution give

$$u\frac{\partial T}{\partial x}+v\frac{\partial T}{\partial y} = \kappa\frac{\partial^2 T}{\partial y^2}, \tag{55}$$

if we neglect the term $u\,\partial p/\partial x$ and the dissipation function $\Phi$. The boundary conditions are $T = T_1$ at $y = 0$, $T = T_0$ at $y = \infty$.

The equation has a solution which is a function of $y$ only. Putting

$$\eta = (\beta_1/\nu)^{\frac{1}{2}}y, \qquad u = \beta_1 xf'(\eta), \qquad v = -(\nu\beta_1)^{\frac{1}{2}}f(\eta),$$

as in Vol. I (1938), chap. iv, § 54, and further,

$$T = T_1-(T_1-T_0)\theta(\eta),$$

we find that (55) becomes

$$\theta''+\sigma f\theta' = 0. \tag{56}$$

The boundary conditions for $\theta$ are $\theta(0) = 0$, $\theta(\infty) = 1$, and the relevant solution of (56) is

$$\theta(\eta) = \alpha_3(\sigma)\int\limits_0^{\eta}\left[\exp\!\left(-\sigma\int\limits_0^{\eta} f\,d\eta\right)\right]d\eta,$$

where

$$\frac{1}{\alpha_3(\sigma)} = \int\limits_0^{\infty}\left[\exp\!\left(-\sigma\int\limits_0^{\eta} f\,d\eta\right)\right]d\eta.$$

The rate of heat transfer from a section of the cylinder of breadth $b$ and length $x$, measured from the stagnation point, is

$$Q = \alpha_3(\sigma)kbx(T_1-T_0)(\beta_1/\nu)^{\frac{1}{2}},$$

and the corresponding value of the Nusselt number is

$$K_N = \alpha_3(\sigma)(\beta_1 d^2/\nu)^{\frac{1}{2}}, \tag{57}$$

where $d$ is a representative length. A set of values of $\alpha_3(\sigma)$, together with the values of an approximate form $0 \cdot 570\sigma^{0 \cdot 4}$ for comparison, is given in Table 5.

## TABLE 5

| $\sigma$ | $\alpha_3(\sigma)$ | $0 \cdot 570\sigma^{0 \cdot 4}$ |
|---|---|---|
| 0·6 | 0·466 | 0·465 |
| 0·7 | 0·495 | 0·495 |
| 0·8 | 0·521 | 0·521 |
| 0·9 | 0·546 | 0·546 |
| 1·0 | 0·570 | 0·570 |
| 1·1 | 0·592 | 0·592 |
| 7·0 | 1·18 | 1·24 |
| 10·0 | 1·34 | 1·43 |
| 15·0 | 1·54 | 1·68 |

These results may be compared with measurements of the heat transfer from a circular cylinder near the forward stagnation point. In this region the theoretical value for the velocity outside the boundary layer is

$$u_1 = 4Ux/d,$$

where $U$ is the velocity of the main stream and $d$ is the diameter of the cylinder. For Reynolds numbers below the critical the experimental values are about 5 per cent. less than the theoretical value, so that we take

$$u_1 = 3{\cdot}8Ux/d.$$

Hence $\beta_1 = 3{\cdot}8U/d$ and, taking $\sigma$ for air as $0{\cdot}72$, we obtain from (57)

$$K_N = 0{\cdot}95(Ud/\nu)^{\frac{1}{2}}.$$

This is in fair agreement with measurements over a range of Reynolds number by Schmidt and Wenner† (see § 18 and Fig. 272), and is also in agreement with measurements by Small‡ and others.§

## § 17. Further solutions for forced convection

The solution given in § 16 and Pohlhausen's solution for the flat plate are particular cases of a more general solution‖ of (55) which is obtained by taking

$$u_1 = cx^m,$$

where $c$ and $m$ are constants, for the velocity distribution at the outer edge of the boundary layer. Then (Vol. I (1938), chap. iv, § 54) the stream function is $(u_1\nu x)^{\frac{1}{2}}f(\eta)$, where

$$\eta = (u_1/\nu x)^{\frac{1}{2}}y,$$

so that

$$u = u_1 f'(\eta),$$

$$v = -\tfrac{1}{2}(u_1\nu/x)^{\frac{1}{2}}[(m+1)f(\eta)+(m-1)\eta f'(\eta)].$$

It can be verified that, with these values for $u$ and $v$, (55) has a solution which is a function of $\eta$ only, so that, with

$$\frac{T_1-T}{T_1-T_0} = \theta(\eta),$$

we obtain

$$\theta'' + \tfrac{1}{2}\sigma(m+1)f\theta' = 0,$$

---

† *Forsch. Ing-Wes.* **12** (1941), 65–73.

‡ *Phil. Mag.* **19** (1935), 251–60.

§ Lohrisch, *Forschungsheft Ver. dtsch. Ing.*, No. 322 (1929), 46–67; Klein, *Arch. Wärmew.* **15** (1934), 150; Drew and Ryan, *Trans. Amer. Inst. Chem. Engrs.* **26** (1931), 118–47. Kroujiline's results (*J. Tech. Phys. U.S.S.R.* **51** (1938), 289–97) are appreciably higher.

‖ Fage and Falkner, *Rep. Memor. Aero. Res. Coun.*, No. 1,408 (1931); Eckert and Drewitz, loc. cit.

with the boundary conditions $\theta(0) = 0$, $\theta(\infty) = 1$. The relevant solution is

$$\theta(\eta) = \alpha_4(\sigma) \int_0^\eta \left[ \exp\left( -\frac{(m+1)\sigma}{2} \int_0^\eta f \, d\eta \right) \right] d\eta,$$

where

$$\frac{1}{\alpha_4(\sigma)} = \int_0^\infty \left[ \exp\left( -\frac{(m+1)\sigma}{2} \int_0^\eta f \, d\eta \right) \right] d\eta.$$

Eckert and Drewitz have calculated the values of $\theta(\eta)$ and $\alpha_4(\sigma)$ given by the above formula for $\sigma = 0{\cdot}7$ and for a range of values of $m$ using Hartree's tables of the function $f(\eta)$; the values of $\alpha_4(0{\cdot}7)$ are given in Table 6.

TABLE 6

| $\beta = \dfrac{2m}{m+1}$ . . | 0 | 0·2 | 0·5 | 1·0 | 1·6 |
|---|---|---|---|---|---|
| $m$ . . . | 0 | 0·111 | 0·333 | 1·0 | 4·0 |
| $\alpha_4(0{\cdot}7)$ . . | 0·413 | 0·444 | 0·470 | 0·496 | 0·514 |

The rate of heat transfer per unit area at the point $x$ can then be found from the formula

$$Q = -k(\partial T/\partial y)_{y=0} = \alpha_4(\sigma)k(T_1 - T_0)(u_1/\nu x)^{\frac{1}{2}}.$$

Eckert and Drewitz have applied this solution to the calculation of heat transfer from cylinders on the lines of Falkner and Skan's method for the boundary layer (see § 18).

Fage and Falkner have made calculations and experiments on heat transfer when the temperature differences between the surface and the free stream and the velocity outside the boundary layer vary as powers of the distance measured along the surface. The calculated results were compared with experimental results in air obtained by measuring the heat transfer (1) from a piece of platinum foil in the form of a flat plate and (2) from a nickel strip embedded in a circular cylinder, which were heated by passing an electric current through them. The results of the tests of the platinum foil are shown in Fig. 269 in the form of $K_N$ plotted against $R^{\frac{1}{2}}$, where $R$ is the Reynolds number based on the chord length of the foil; the theoretical results are also shown in the figure. The difference between theory and experiment is partly due to simplifying assumptions introduced to facilitate the calculations.

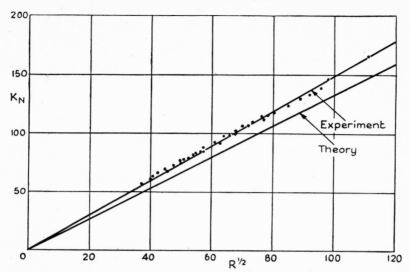

Fig. 269. Comparison between theory and experiment for heat transfer from plate.

## § 18. Forced convection from a circular cylinder

Many experimental investigations have been made to measure the total heat transfer from a circular cylinder at right angles to a stream. These have been analysed by McAdams[†] and his recommended mean experimental curves for air and for liquids are shown in Figs. 270 and 271, where $K_N$ is the Nusselt number and $R$ is the Reynolds number, both based on the cylinder diameter. For air the results can be expressed by the semi-empirical equation

$$K_N = 0{\cdot}36 + 0{\cdot}48 R^{\frac{1}{2}} \tag{58}$$

for the range $0{\cdot}1 < R < 10^3$. The results for liquids are mainly taken from tests by Davis,[‡] and McAdams's empirical curve has the equation

$$K_N = 0{\cdot}86 R^{0{\cdot}43} \sigma^{0{\cdot}3}.$$

Hilpert[§] has investigated the effect of varying the temperature difference between the tube and the air and found that it can be represented by replacing $R$ in eqn. (58) by $R(T_1/T_0)^{\frac{1}{2}}$, where $T_1$ and $T_0$ are the absolute temperatures of the tube and the air respectively.

† *Heat Transmission*, New York (1942); see also Schmidt, *Proc. 4th Int. Congr. Appl. Mech. Camb.* (1934), 97, 98.
‡ *Phil. Mag.* (6), **44** (1922), 920–40.
§ *Forsch. Ing-Wes.* **4** (1933), 215–44; *Forschungsh. Ver. dtsch. Ing.*, No. 355 (1932).

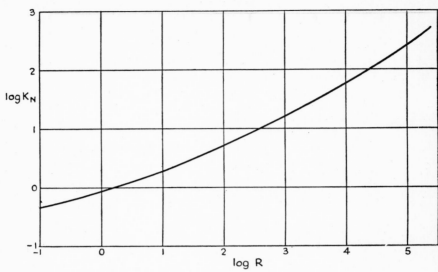

Fig. 270. Heat transfer from circular cylinders in air.

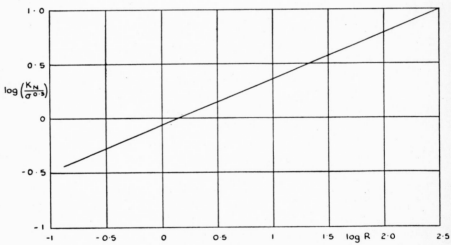

Fig. 271. Heat transfer from circular cylinders in liquids.

Measurements of the distribution of the heat transfer round the circumference of the cylinder have been made by a number of authors.† The results of Schmidt and Wenner are shown in Figs. 272, 273. Fig. 272 also gives calculated results for the front part of the

† See references given in § 16.

cylinder due to Eckert and Drewitz† and to Squire.‡ The effect of
the critical change in flow pattern at about $R = 2 \times 10^5$ on the heat
transfer is shown in Fig. 273, which illustrates the change in character
of the heat-transfer distribution with passage through the critical
Reynolds number.

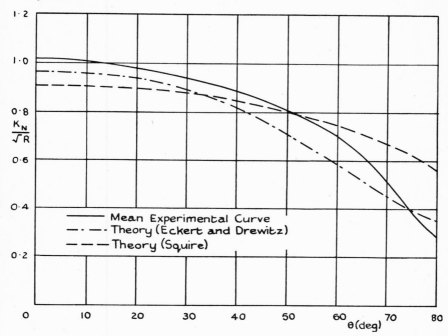

FIG. 272. Heat transfer from the front of a circular cylinder.

## § 19. Calculation of heat transfer for cylinders and aerofoils

The solutions given in §§ 13 to 17 apply to specially simple cases
and cannot be used directly for the calculation of heat transfer from
bodies of complicated shape such as aerofoils. In such cases it is
best to use a method analogous to the Pohlhausen method for the
frictional boundary layer, by assuming a temperature distribution
across the boundary layer, and using the energy integral eqn. (28)
or (31) to calculate the thickness of the thermal boundary layer.
A simple illustration of this method as applied to the flat plate has
been given in § 13 above and the application to aerofoils has been

† Loc. cit. See also Eckert, *Forschungsh. Ver. dtsch. Ing.*, No. 416 (1942).
‡ *Rep. Memor. Aero. Res. Coun.*, No. 1,986 (1942).

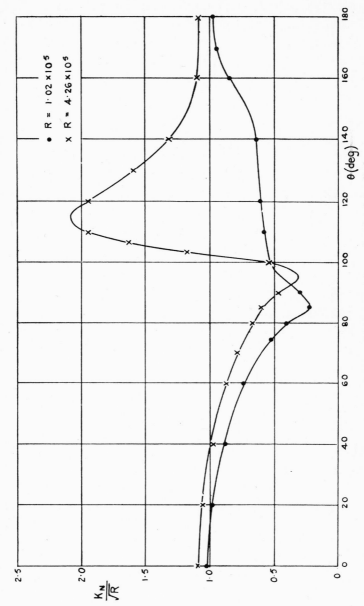

Fig. 273. Distribution of heat transfer round a circular cylinder.

given in a paper by the author,† which will be briefly described here.‡

It is assumed that the velocity and temperature distribution across the boundary layer can be represented by the Blasius velocity distribution but that the thickness of the frictional and thermal boundary layers are different. The displacement thickness of the frictional boundary layer is denoted by $\delta_1$, and this is calculated from the equation§

$$\delta_1^2 = \frac{2 \cdot 960 \nu}{u_1^6} \int_0^x u_1^5 \, dx, \tag{59}$$

where $x$ is measured along the surface from the forward stagnation point and $u_1$ is the velocity outside the boundary layer. The thermal displacement thickness $\delta_2$ is defined by the equation

$$\delta_2 = \int_0^h \left(\frac{T - T_0}{T_1 - T_0}\right) dy,$$

where $y$ is measured normal to the surface, $h$ is a length which is greater than the boundary-layer thickness, and $T_1$, $T_0$ are the temperatures of the surface and of the main stream respectively. Substitution of the assumed velocity and temperature distributions in the energy integral equation in the form (31) and integration leads to the relation

$$\lambda^2 \phi(\lambda) = \frac{0 \cdot 3861}{\sigma} \frac{u_1^4 \int_0^x u_1 \phi(\lambda) \, dx}{\phi(\lambda) \int_0^x u_1^5 \, dx}, \tag{60}$$

where $\lambda = \delta_2/\delta_1$ and $\phi(\lambda)$ is a function which together with $\lambda^2 \phi(\lambda)$ is given in Table 7.

TABLE 7

| $\lambda$ . . . | 0·5 | 0·625 | 0·667 | 0·833 | 1·0 |
|---|---|---|---|---|---|
| $\phi(\lambda)$ . . . | 0·2075 | 0·257 | 0·272 | 0·332 | 0·386 |
| $\lambda^2 \phi(\lambda)$ . . | 0·052 | 0·100 | 0·121 | 0·230 | 0·386 |
| $\lambda$ . . . | 1·25 | 1·429 | 1·667 | 1·818 | 2·0 |
| $\phi(\lambda)$ . . . | 0·456 | 0·499 | 0·548 | 0·575 | 0·599 |
| $\lambda^2 \phi(\lambda)$ . . | 0·713 | 1·018 | 1·522 | 1·901 | 2·398 |

† Loc. cit. on p. 797.

‡ Analogous methods of solution have been developed in Germany by Schuh, *M.A.P. Völkenrode Rep. R. & T.*, No. 1007 (1948).

§ Young and Winterbottom, *Rep. Memor. Aero. Res. Coun.*, No. 2,068 (1942); Thwaites, *Aero. Quart.* **1** (1949) 245–80.

The quantity $\lambda = \delta_2/\delta_1$ is determined from (60) by successive approximation, the first approximation being derived by omitting $\phi$ from the right-hand side. Also $\delta_1$ is given by (59), hence $\delta_2$ can be calculated. Finally the rate of heat transfer is calculated from the surface temperature gradient which is equal to $-0.5715(T_1-T_0)/\delta_2$ for the assumed variation of temperature across the boundary layer.

The above methods have all been developed for constant wall temperature. Solutions in certain cases of non-uniform wall temperature have been calculated by Fage and Falkner,[†] by Schuh,[‡] and by Chapman and Rubesin.[§] But if the variation of wall temperature is moderate it will often be sufficiently accurate to calculate the overall heat transfer on the assumption that the local heat-transfer coefficient is the same as for constant wall temperature.

To allow for the effect of kinetic heating on the heat transfer we note first that, if kinetic heating can be ignored, the rate of heat transfer can be calculated from the formula

$$Q = K_S \rho c_p \, SU(T_1-T_0),$$

where $T_1$ is the temperature of the body, $T_0$ is the stream temperature, and the other symbols have their usual significance. Also the heat transfer will vanish if the surface temperature exceeds the stream temperature by the kinetic temperature $\Delta T$. Since the equation satisfied by the temperature is linear, the effect of kinetic heating can therefore be represented by calculating the heat transfer from the formula

$$Q = K_S \rho c_p \, SU(T_1-T_0-\Delta T)$$

and using the value of $K_S$ obtained previously.[||] Thus for a heated body in a cooler stream we calculate the heat transfer by assuming that the effective temperature difference between body and stream is reduced by the kinetic temperature $\Delta T$. For the special case $\sigma = 1$ the above formula is equivalent to

$$Q = K_S \rho c_p \, SU(T_{H_1}-T_{H_0}),  \tag{61}$$

where $T_{H_1} = T_1$ is the total temperature at the surface and $T_{H_0}$ is the total temperature in the stream. Eqn. (61) may also be used as a rough guide in other cases.

In many cases the effect of radiation on heat transfer may be

† Loc. cit. on p. 793.                                    ‡ Loc. cit. on p. 799.
§ J. Aero. Sci. 16 (1949), 547–52.
|| See Tifford, ibid. 12 (1945), 241–51.

neglected. However, radiation becomes important if the surface temperature is high or if the density or speed are low, and allowance should be made for it in some free convection problems and for high-altitude flight.†

## § 20. Free convection from a heated vertical plate

We now leave the consideration of forced convection and turn to consider some of the important problems of free convection beginning with the case of the heated vertical plate in still air. This was considered by Lorenz‡ many years ago, on the assumption that the temperature and velocity at any point depend only on the distance from the plate. The experiments of Schmidt and Beckmann§ showed that this assumption is invalid, and indicated an alternative method of solution. The thickness of the layer in which the temperature and the velocity differed appreciably from the values at infinity was found to be small compared with the height of the plate: hence the approximations of the boundary-layer theory will be valid. The pressure $p$ is equal to the hydrostatic pressure, and with the origin at the lower edge of the plate, the axis of $x$ along the plate, and the axis of $y$ normal to it, the governing equations (§ 7) are

$$\frac{\partial u}{\partial x}+\frac{\partial v}{\partial y}=0,$$

$$u\frac{\partial u}{\partial x}+v\frac{\partial u}{\partial y}=\nu\frac{\partial^2 u}{\partial y^2}+g\beta(T-T_0),$$

$$u\frac{\partial T}{\partial x}+v\frac{\partial T}{\partial y}=\kappa\frac{\partial^2 T}{\partial y^2},$$

provided that the temperature difference between the wall and the air is small compared with the absolute temperature, so that the viscosity, density, and thermal conductivity can be assumed to be constant except for the effect of the density variation in producing the buoyancy force. The undisturbed air temperature is $T_0$; let $T_1$ be the temperature of the plate. Then with

$$\theta=\frac{T-T_0}{T_1-T_0},$$

† See Chap. X, § 13.
‡ *Ann. Phys.* **13** (1881), 582–606.
§ *Tech. Mech. Thermo-dynam. Berl.* **1** (1930), 341–9, 391–406. Cf. Schmidt, *Proc. 4th Int. Congr. Appl. Mech. Camb.* (1934), 98–102.

the last two equations become

$$u\frac{\partial u}{\partial x}+v\frac{\partial u}{\partial y} = \nu\frac{\partial^2 u}{\partial y^2}+g\beta(T_1-T_0)\theta,$$

$$u\frac{\partial \theta}{\partial x}+v\frac{\partial \theta}{\partial y} = \kappa\frac{\partial^2\theta}{\partial y^2}.$$

The boundary conditions are $u = v = 0$, $\theta = 1$ at $y = 0$, and $u = 0$, $\theta = 0$ at $y = \infty$. The partial differential equations can now (following Pohlhausen) be transformed into ordinary differential equations by the substitutions:

$$\eta = \left[\frac{g\beta(T_1-T_0)}{4\nu^2}\right]^{\frac{1}{4}}\frac{y}{x^{\frac{1}{4}}} = C\frac{y}{x^{\frac{1}{4}}} \quad \text{(say)},$$

$$\psi(x,y) = 4\nu Cx^{\frac{3}{4}}f(\eta),$$

$$\theta(x,y) = g(\eta),$$

where $\psi$ is the stream-function defined by

$$u = \frac{\partial\psi}{\partial y}, \qquad v = -\frac{\partial\psi}{\partial x},$$

so that $\quad u = 4\nu C^2 x^{\frac{1}{4}}f'(\eta), \qquad v = \nu C x^{-\frac{1}{4}}(\eta f'-3f).$

The equations for $f$ and $g$ are

$$\left.\begin{aligned} f'''+3ff''-2f'^2+g &= 0\\ g''+3\sigma fg' &= 0\end{aligned}\right\}, \tag{62}$$

and the boundary conditions are $f(0) = 0$, $f'(0) = 0$, $g(0) = 1$, $f'(\infty) = 0$, $g(\infty) = 0$. These boundary conditions also suffice to make $u = 0$, $v = 0$ at $x = 0$, and the transformations indicate that $\theta$ and the quantity $u/(4\nu C^2 x^{\frac{1}{4}})$ should be functions of $Cy/x^{\frac{1}{4}}$ only, where

$$C = \left[\frac{g\beta(T_1-T_0)}{4\nu^2}\right]^{\frac{1}{4}}.$$

The equations have been solved in series by Pohlhausen for air, assuming $\sigma = 0.733$, and the value of the surface temperature gradient at a point distant $x$ from the lower edge of the plate was found to be given by

$$\frac{-1}{(T_1-T_0)}\left(\frac{\partial T}{\partial y}\right)_{y=0} = 0.508\left[\frac{g\beta(T_1-T_0)}{4\nu^2 x}\right]^{\frac{1}{4}}.$$

The corresponding value of the Nusselt number for a plate of height $l$ is

$$K_N = 0.479\left[\frac{g\beta l^3(T_1-T_0)}{\nu^2}\right]^{\frac{1}{4}}.$$

We can also write this result as

$$K_N = 0 \cdot 517 (Ra)^{\frac{1}{4}}, \tag{63}$$

where $Ra = \dfrac{g \beta l^3 (T_1 - T_0)}{\nu \kappa}$ is the Rayleigh number, which is equal to the product of the Prandtl number and the Grashof number. Though the calculation described above is only valid for air ($\sigma$ taken to be equal to $0 \cdot 733$) the representation of the result by eqn. (63) is the

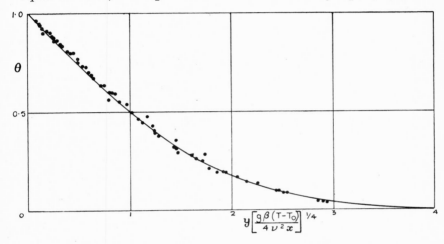

Fig. 274. Comparison between theory and experiment for the temperature distribution in the boundary layer of a heated vertical plate.

most convenient for generalization; this will appear later. Before proceeding further it may also be pointed out that the proportionality of $K_N$ to $(Ra)^{\frac{1}{4}}$ can be deduced from the form of the equations and that it applies for all cylindrical bodies if the boundary layer is laminar and of small thickness compared with the dimensions of the heated body.

Schmidt and Beckmann have made experiments on heat transfer from vertical plates in air in which the temperatures in the boundary layer were measured by thermocouples, and the velocities, which are only of order 1 ft./sec., were measured by an ingenious quartz-thread anemometer. The results obtained for a flat plate of height $12 \cdot 5$ cm. at a temperature of $65°$ C. in air at $15°$ C. are compared with the theoretical values in Figs. 274 and 275. They also measured the total heat transfer from the plate and the results obtained are shown in Fig. 276.

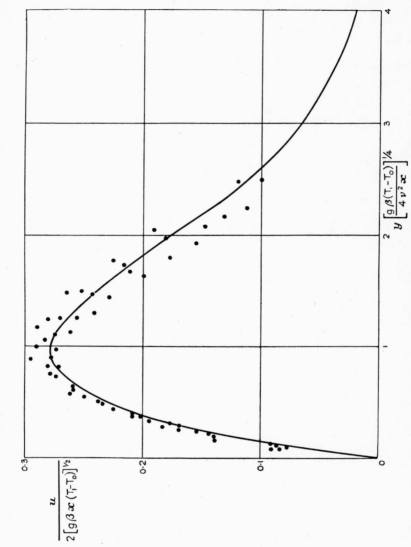

FIG. 275. Comparison between theory and experiment for the temperature distribution in the boundary layer of a heated vertical plate.

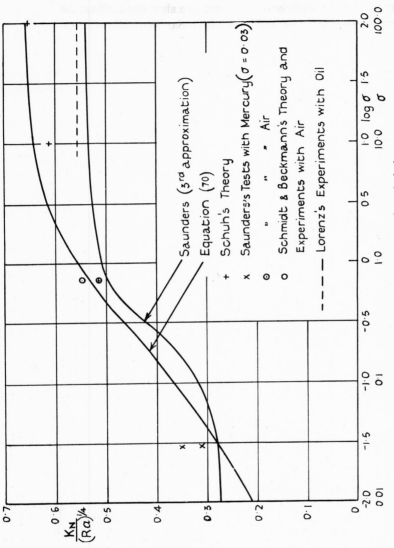

Fig. 276. Free convection from a heated vertical plate.

Before discussing the other data on heat transfer we shall describe three other approximate methods of calculation. Saunders† has solved eqns. (62), which he presented in a slightly different form, by taking suitable polynomial expressions for $g'$ in terms of $g$. These expressions satisfy some of the boundary conditions and include one or more constants which are determined so that the differential equations are satisfied at one or more stations. The temperature and velocity distributions obtained by Saunders's third approximation are compared with the distribution given by other methods in Figs. 277 and 278.

The third method, due to Schuh,‡ is a successive approximation method based on the formal solution of the differential equation

$$y'' + y'f(x,y) = g(x,y),$$

which may be written

$$y = \int_0^x \exp\left(-\int_0^{x_1} f(x_2,y)\,dx_2\right) dx_1 \left[\int_0^{x_1} g(x_2,y)\exp\left(\int_0^{x_2} f(x_3,y)\,dx_3\right) dx_2\right] +$$

$$+ C_1 \int_0^x \exp\left(-\int_0^{x_1} f(x_2,y)\,dx_2\right) dx_1 + C_2.$$

The procedure consists in estimating a first approximation to the solution and using the above formula to obtain successive approximations, where $C_1$ and $C_2$ are chosen to satisfy the boundary conditions. The method is equally applicable to equations of higher order which are linear in the two highest derivatives of $y$. By this method Schuh has obtained the solution of the eqns. (62) for free convection from a heated vertical plate for several values of $\sigma$ which are given in Table 8 and Fig. 276.

TABLE 8

| $\sigma$ . . . . | 0·733 | 10 | 100 | 1,000 |
|---|---|---|---|---|
| $K_N/(Ra)^{\frac{1}{4}}$ . . | 0·517 | 0·612 | 0·652 | 0·653 |

The calculated velocity and temperature distributions showed that as $\sigma$ increases greatly above unity the viscous boundary layer becomes progressively thicker than the thermal boundary layer.

The fourth method of solution, due to the present author, consists in inserting suitable polynomial expressions for the velocity and temperature into the momentum and energy integral eqns. (26) and

† *Proc. Roy. Soc.* A, **172** (1939), 55–71.          ‡ Loc. cit. on p. 799.

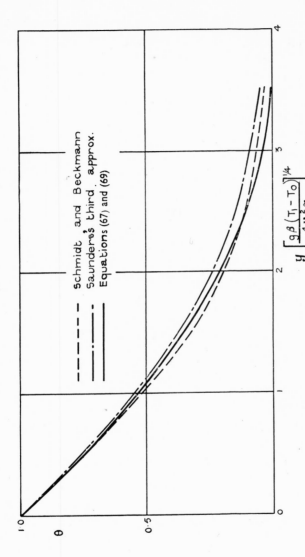

FIG. 277. Free convection from vertical plate. Calculated temperature distributions.

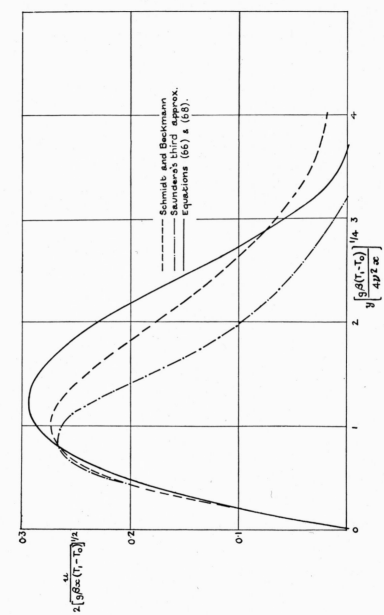

FIG. 278. Free convection from vertical plate. Calculated velocity distributions.

(31). For steady flow at a vertical plate, with constant pressure and dissipation neglected, these equations become

$$\frac{\partial}{\partial x}\int_0^h \rho u^2\, dy = g\int_0^h \beta\rho(T-T_0)\, dy - \mu\left(\frac{\partial u}{\partial y}\right)_{y=0}, \tag{64}$$

since the velocity $u_1$ at the edge of the boundary layer vanishes, and

$$\frac{\partial}{\partial x}\int_0^h \rho u(T-T_0)\, dy = -\rho\kappa\left(\frac{\partial T}{\partial y}\right)_{y=0}, \tag{65}$$

where $\kappa$ is equal to $k/\rho c_p$. For liquids we may put $\rho = \rho_0$ in (64) and (65), while for gases from the equation of state (1) we obtain $\rho T = \rho_0 T_0$.

The simplest suitable approximate expressions for $u$ and $T$ are

$$u = u_x \frac{y}{\delta}\left(1-\frac{y}{\delta}\right)^2, \tag{66}$$

and

$$\frac{T-T_0}{T_1-T_0} = \left(1-\frac{y}{\delta}\right)^2, \tag{67}$$

where $\delta$ is the boundary-layer thickness and $u_x$ is a velocity which is a function of $x$ and which is to be determined. The assumption that the boundary-layer thickness is the same for the viscous and the thermal boundary layer, which is implied by the form of these expressions, will not be valid for $\sigma$ large compared with unity; this is shown by Schuh's results for $\sigma = 10^2$ and $10^3$. Inserting (66) and (67) into (64) and (65) we obtain

$$\frac{d}{dx}\left(\frac{u_x^2\delta}{105}\right) = g\beta(T_1-T_0)\frac{\delta}{3} - \frac{\nu u_x}{\delta},$$

and

$$\frac{d}{dx}\left(\frac{u_x\delta}{30}\right) = \frac{2\kappa}{\delta};$$

in deriving these equations it has been assumed that the temperature difference $T_1-T_0$ between plate and fluid is small compared with the atmospheric temperature $T_0$, and in the first equation a term has been omitted which is of higher order in $(T_1-T_0)/T_0$ than those included. The solution of these equations is

$$u_x = 5{\cdot}17\kappa\left(1+\frac{20}{21\sigma}\right)^{-\frac{1}{2}}\left[\frac{\beta g(T_1-T_0)}{\nu\kappa}\right]^{\frac{1}{2}} x^{\frac{1}{2}}, \tag{68}$$

$$\delta = 3{\cdot}93\left(1+\frac{20}{21\sigma}\right)^{\frac{1}{4}}\left[\frac{\beta g(T_1-T_0)}{\nu\kappa}\right]^{-\frac{1}{4}} x^{\frac{1}{4}}. \tag{69}$$

The rate of heat transfer from one side of a plate of height $l$ and breadth $b$ is

$$Q = -kb \int_0^l \left(\frac{\partial T}{\partial y}\right)_{y=0} dx = 2kb(T_1 - T_0) \int_0^l \frac{dx}{\delta},$$

and the corresponding value of the Nusselt number is

$$K_N = 0 \cdot 678 \left(1 + \frac{20}{21\sigma}\right)^{-\frac{1}{4}} (Ra)^{\frac{1}{4}}, \tag{70}$$

where

$$Ra = \frac{gl^3\beta(T_1 - T_0)}{\nu\kappa}.$$

The velocity and temperature distributions given by the three methods are compared for $\sigma = 0 \cdot 73$ in Figs. 277 and 278 and the values of $K_N/(Ra)^{\frac{1}{4}}$ given by Saunders's third approximation and by (70) are plotted against $\sigma$ in Fig. 276, which also shows the value calculated by Schmidt and Beckmann for air. The experimental results of various authors[†] for vertical plates in air, mercury, and oil for $Ra < 10^9$ are shown in Fig. 276, and it will be seen that the agreement between the experiments and the various theories is satisfactory.

The experiments on free convection from vertical plates, particularly those made by Saunders, have verified that the Nusselt number is proportional to $(Ra)^{\frac{1}{4}}$, for $Ra < 10^9$. As an example of this, Saunders's results for air are shown in Fig. 279 for comparison with the theoretical formula (63).[‡]

## § 21. Free convection with turbulent boundary layer

It will be seen in Fig. 279 that the experimental results for air depart from the theory for $Ra > 2 \times 10^9$ and this is due to transition to turbulence in the boundary layer. For $Ra > 10^{10}$ Saunders's results for air can be represented by the equation

$$K_N = 0 \cdot 109(Ra)^{\frac{1}{3}}.$$

Saunders's experiments with water are also shown in Fig. 279, and they too indicate transition to turbulence at about $Ra = 2 \times 10^9$.

[†] Saunders, *Proc. Roy. Soc.* A, **157** (1936), 278–91; A, **172** (1939), 55–71; Lorenz, *Z. tech. Phys.* **15** (1934), 362–76.

[‡] In some cases the agreement between theory and experiment may be partly fortuitous, because of end-effects on the test plates, and also because the temperature differences used in the experiments are often larger than is strictly permissible for the application of the theory.

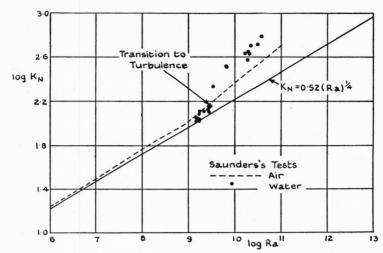

FIG. 279. Vertical plate. Transition to turbulence.

For $Ra > 10^{10}$ the measured values for water are somewhat lower than are given by the empirical formula

$$K_N = 0 \cdot 129(Ra)^{\frac{1}{3}},$$

which has been proposed by Lorenz,[†] as a result of his experiments with oils, for free convection for vertical plates in all liquids with turbulent boundary layers.

The measurements of Griffiths and Davis[‡] of velocity and temperature distributions for free convection with a turbulent layer have been recently analysed by Eckert and Jackson.[§]

Hermann[‖] has investigated the transition to turbulent flow both for vertical plates and for cylinders. It was found that $R_\delta$, the Reynolds number formed from the maximum velocity in the boundary layer and the boundary-layer thickness, was about 300 at the transition point for both plates and cylinders. This is associated with a value of about $10^9$ for the Rayleigh number for a vertical plate and of $3 \cdot 5 \times 10^8$ for a horizontal circular cylinder.

## § 22. Other problems of free convection

The results of tests on free convection from horizontal circular cylinders over a wide range of variables have been examined by

† Loc. cit. on p. 801.
‡ *Special Report No. 9 Food Investigation Board D.S.I.R.* 1922 (reprinted 1931).
§ *Nat. Adv. Comm. Aero. Tech. Notes*, No. 2,207 (1950).
‖ *Forschungsh. Ver. dtsch. Ing.* 379 (1936).

McAdams, who concluded that the Nusselt number is a function only of the Rayleigh number for all fluids. (Mercury is a probable exception to this because of its low Prandtl number.) The mean curve recommended by McAdams† is given in Fig. 280.

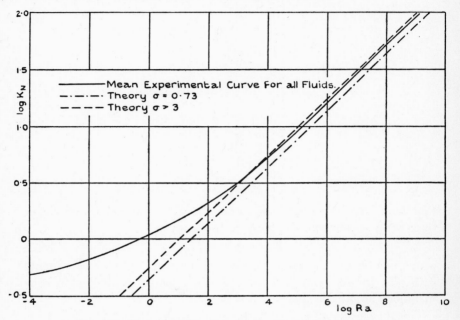

FIG. 280. Free convection from horizontal circular cylinders.

Hermann‡ has adapted the solution obtained by Pohlhausen for a vertical plate in air to derive a corresponding formula for circular cylinders (for $\sigma = 0.73$) and finds that

$$K_N = 0.40(Ra)^{\frac{1}{4}}.$$

A solution of the momentum and energy integral equations by the present author on similar lines to the solution for the flat plate given above led to the results

$$K_N = 0.44(Ra)^{\frac{1}{4}},$$

for air with $\sigma = 0.73$, and

$$K_N = 0.55(Ra)^{\frac{1}{4}},$$

for liquids for which $\sigma > 3$. The latter results are also shown in Fig. 280 and are in good agreement with the mean experimental

† Loc. cit. on p. 795.                          ‡ Loc. cit. on p. 811.

curve for $Ra > 10^4$, but for lower values of $Ra$ the measured heat transfer is higher than the calculated value; this is because the theory is based on the assumption that the boundary-layer thickness is small compared with the diameter of the cylinder, which is certainly not valid for $Ra < 10^4$.

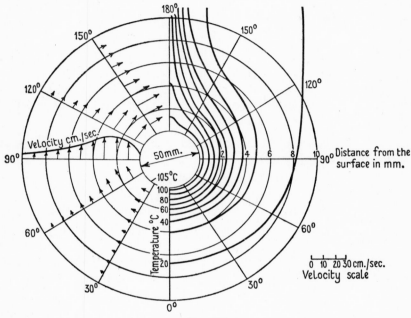

FIG. 281.

Schmidt and Jodlbauer[†] have measured the temperature and velocity distributions for free convection from a circular cylinder and their results for a cylinder of diameter 50 mm. with the surface at 105° C. in air at a temperature of 18° C. are shown in Fig. 281. (The radial distances outside the cylinder are enlarged 10 times in comparison with the scale for the cylinder diameter.)

Shell[‡] has adapted the theory of free convection from a vertical plate to the case of a sphere and obtained the result

$$K_N = 0 \cdot 463 (Ra)^{\frac{1}{4}}$$

for a heated sphere in air. Measurements gave results in agreement with the theory for $Ra > 10^6$.

[†] *Forsch. Ing-Wes.* **4** (1933), 157–72. See also Schmidt, *Proc. 4th Int. Congr. Appl. Mech. Camb.* (1934), 102, 103.

[‡] *Bull. Acad. Sci. Math. Nat. Belgrade*, No. 4 (1938), 189–94.

Hermann[†] has correlated the experimental data on the effect of absolute temperature difference on free convection from a horizontal circular cylinder in air. The values of the viscosity and conductivity at the surface temperature were used to calculate the coefficients, but the coefficient of expansion $\beta$ was taken equal to $1/T_0$, where $T_0$ is the absolute temperature of the air far from the cylinder. For $Ra > 10^4$ it was found that the Nusselt number $K_N$ was independent of $(T_1 - T_0)/T_0$, where $T_1$ is the absolute temperature at the surface, but that, for $Ra < 10^4$, $K_N$ fell slowly with increase of $(T_1 - T_0)/T_0$; for example, for $Ra = 1 \cdot 0$, $K_N$ was 11 per cent. less for $(T_1 - T_0)/T_0 = 0 \cdot 65$ than for $(T_1 - T_0)/T_0 = 0$. Thus the effect of absolute temperature difference on heat transfer is usually small.

## § 23. Measurement of heat transfer by the shadow method and by interferometer

The complete measurement of the temperature and velocity fields for free convection from a body is a lengthy process. The heat transfer from cylinders can, however, be measured by a direct shadow method which has been described by Schmidt.[‡] A beam of light is projected parallel to the axis of the cylinder and in its passage through the boundary layer the rays of light are deflected through an angle which is proportional to the temperature gradient. Thus the rays grazing the surface suffer a maximum deflexion, while rays on the edge of the boundary layer are not deflected at all. After passing along the cylinder the rays continue on their deflected paths and are recorded on a screen or photographic plate at a sufficient distance away from the specimen for the deflexions to have become easily measurable. (For the method to work satisfactorily the actual deflexion of the rays during their passage along the cylinder must be small.)

An example of the method as applied to a flat plate in air is given in Plate 26 (a) which is due to Schmidt. The dotted curve shows the actual size and position of the plate. The black shadow round the plate shows the extent of the boundary layer and the bright region beyond shows the region reached by the rays deflected by the heated air. The distance of the edge of the bright region from the surface of the plate, measured along the normal to the surface, is proportional to the temperature gradient at the surface of the plate at the

† Loc. cit. on p. 811.                    ‡ Loc. cit. on p. 813.

PLATE 26

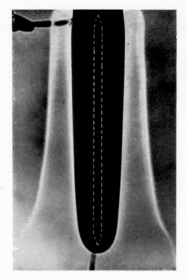

(*a*) Free convection from a vertical plate

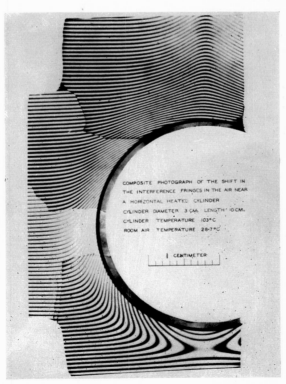

(*b*) Free convection from a circular cylinder

foot of this normal; this is a maximum at the bottom edge and diminishes gradually with distance from this edge.

The measurement of temperature distribution and heat transfer from cylinders using an interferometer has been described by R. B. Kennard.† An example of his work is shown in Plate 26 (b). The density of the gas at any point is determined from the fringe shift (see Chap. XI) and hence the temperature can be calculated from the equation of state since the pressure is everywhere atmospheric. The rate of heat transfer is determined from the temperature gradient at the surface.

## Section II

## Turbulent Flow

### § 24. The equation of eddy heat transfer

The energy equation for liquids will be taken to be (eqn. (7))

$$\rho c_p \frac{DT}{Dt} = \frac{\partial}{\partial x}\left(k\frac{\partial T}{\partial x}\right) + \frac{\partial}{\partial y}\left(k\frac{\partial T}{\partial y}\right) + \frac{\partial}{\partial z}\left(k\frac{\partial T}{\partial z}\right). \tag{71}$$

The energy equation for gases will be taken in the form (10), namely

$$\rho c_p \frac{DT_H}{Dt} - \frac{\partial p}{\partial t} = \left[\frac{\partial}{\partial x}\left(k\frac{\partial}{\partial x}\right) + \frac{\partial}{\partial y}\left(k\frac{\partial}{\partial y}\right) + \frac{\partial}{\partial z}\left(k\frac{\partial}{\partial z}\right)\right]\left[T_H + \frac{(\sigma-1)q^2}{2c_p}\right]. \tag{72}$$

In turbulent flow the effect of terms on the right-hand side of (71) and (72) which depend on viscosity and conductivity are for the most part of less importance than the convection terms. With this in mind we shall put $\sigma = 1$ in (72) so that the second term in the bracket on the right-hand side vanishes; this approximation is not valid in connexion with kinetic temperature effects (see § 15). With this further approximation eqn. (72) reduces to

$$\rho c_p \frac{DT_H}{Dt} - \frac{\partial p}{\partial t} = \left[\frac{\partial}{\partial x}\left(k\frac{\partial T_H}{\partial x}\right) + \frac{\partial}{\partial y}\left(k\frac{\partial T_H}{\partial y}\right) + \frac{\partial}{\partial z}\left(k\frac{\partial T_H}{\partial z}\right)\right]. \tag{73}$$

If the motion is slow we may replace the total temperature $T_H$ by $T$ and neglect the term $\partial p/\partial t$, when the equation reduces to the same form as for liquids.

The temperature at any point in a field of turbulent flow has a mean value denoted by $T$ and a fluctuation of magnitude $T''$, the

† *J. Res. Nat. Bur. Stand.* **8** (1932), 787–805; see also *Temperature, its Measurement and Control in Science and Industry*, New York (1941), pp. 685–706.

mean value of which is zero. The velocity has mean components
$U$, $V$, $W$ and fluctuating components $u$, $v$, $w$. Substituting $U+u$
for $u$, $V+v$ for $v$, $W+w$ for $w$, and $T+T'$ for $T$ in (71) and taking
mean values we obtain

$$\rho c_p\left(\frac{\partial T}{\partial t} + U\frac{\partial T}{\partial x} + V\frac{\partial T}{\partial y} + W\frac{\partial T}{\partial z}\right) = \frac{\partial}{\partial x}\left(k\frac{\partial T}{\partial x} - \rho c_p\,\overline{uT'}\right) +$$

$$+ \frac{\partial}{\partial y}\left(k\frac{\partial T}{\partial y} - \rho c_p\,\overline{vT'}\right) + \frac{\partial}{\partial z}\left(k\frac{\partial T}{\partial z} - \rho c_p\,\overline{wT'}\right), \quad (74)$$

where use has been made of the equation of continuity.

For gases the mean value of the total temperature is denoted by
$T_H$ and the fluctuation by $T'_H$, the mean value of which is zero.
Making corresponding substitutions in (73) and taking mean values
we obtain

$$\rho c_p\left(\frac{\partial T_H}{\partial t} + U\frac{\partial T_H}{\partial x} + V\frac{\partial T_H}{\partial y} + W\frac{\partial T_H}{\partial z}\right) = \frac{\partial}{\partial x}\left(k\frac{\partial T_H}{\partial x} - \rho c_p\,\overline{uT'_H}\right) +$$

$$+ \frac{\partial}{\partial y}\left(k\frac{\partial T_H}{\partial y} - \rho c_p\,\overline{vT'_H}\right) + \frac{\partial}{\partial z}\left(k\frac{\partial T_H}{\partial z} - \rho c_p\,\overline{wT'_H}\right), \quad (75)$$

assuming that the mean motion is steady, so that the mean value
of $\partial p/\partial t$ is zero, and where we have made use of the equation of
continuity for gases. In deriving this equation we have also assumed
that the fluctuations in density can be ignored; it is not certain that
this is always permissible, but the complication of trying to allow
for density fluctuations is so great that it is not practicable to try
to consider it here.

The rates of heat transfer by molecular conductivity across unit
areas normal to the coordinate axes are $-k\partial T/\partial x$, $-k\partial T/\partial y$, and
$-k\partial T/\partial z$ respectively. Eqn. (74) shows that, for liquids, the effect
of the fluctuations is to add to these rates of heat transfer the eddy
heat transfer terms $\rho c_p\,\overline{uT'}$, $\rho c_p\,\overline{vT'}$, $\rho c_p\,\overline{wT'}$ so that the resultant
rates of heat transfer are $(-k\partial T/\partial x + \rho c_p\,\overline{uT'})$, etc. Considerations
of the analogous eqn. (75) for gases shows that similar remarks apply
with the substitution of $T_H$ for $T$.†

The close correspondence between the heat transfer for liquids and
for gases indicated by the above analysis enables us in the main to
consider liquids from this point, as the corresponding results for
gases can be obtained by the replacement of $T$ by $T_H$, and $T'$ by

† Remembering that (75) is strictly valid only for $\sigma = 1$.

$T'_H$. If the motion of the gas is slow $T_H$ may be put equal to $T$ and there is then no difference between gases and liquids.

In turbulent flow the effect of the eddy transfer terms is large compared with the effect of the molecular conductivity terms except where the temperature gradient is very large; this is analogous to the result that the Reynolds stresses are large compared with the viscous stresses except where the rate of strain is large. If we neglect the molecular conductivity terms (74) reduces to

$$\frac{\partial T}{\partial t} + U\frac{\partial T}{\partial x} + V\frac{\partial T}{\partial y} + W\frac{\partial T}{\partial z} = -\frac{\partial}{\partial x}\overline{(uT')} - \frac{\partial}{\partial y}\overline{(vT')} - \frac{\partial}{\partial z}\overline{(wT')}.$$

(76)

In cylindrical polar coordinates $(r, \theta, z)$ (74) and (76) become

$$\rho c_p\left(\frac{\partial T}{\partial t} + V_r\frac{\partial T}{\partial r} + \frac{V_\theta}{r}\frac{\partial T}{\partial \theta} + V_z\frac{\partial T}{\partial z}\right) = \frac{1}{r}\frac{\partial}{\partial r}\left(rk\frac{\partial T}{\partial r} - \rho c_p\, \overline{r v_r\, T'}\right) +$$

$$+ \frac{1}{r}\frac{\partial}{\partial \theta}\left(\frac{k}{r}\frac{\partial T}{\partial \theta} - \rho c_p\, \overline{v_\theta\, T'}\right) + \frac{\partial}{\partial z}\left(k\frac{\partial T}{\partial z} - \rho c_p\, \overline{v_z\, T'}\right) \quad (77)$$

and

$$\frac{\partial T}{\partial t} + V_r\frac{\partial T}{\partial r} + \frac{V_\theta}{r}\frac{\partial T}{\partial \theta} + V_z\frac{\partial T}{\partial z} = -\frac{1}{r}\frac{\partial}{\partial r}\overline{(rv_r\, T')} - \frac{1}{r}\frac{\partial}{\partial \theta}\overline{(v_\theta\, T')} - \frac{\partial}{\partial z}\overline{(v_z\, T')}$$

(78)

respectively, where $V_r$, $V_\theta$, $V_z$ are the mean velocity components, and $v_r$, $v_\theta$, $v_z$ are the fluctuating velocity components.

## § 25. Example: flow between parallel walls with a constant temperature gradient in the direction of flow

Consider the heat transfer for steady flow between two parallel fixed walls each of which is kept at the same constant temperature gradient. The origin being taken midway between the walls, the axis of $x$ parallel to the mean flow and the axis of $y$ normal to it, the mean temperature may be written

$$T = Ax + \theta(y),$$

while for the mean velocity

$$U = U(y), \qquad V = 0, \qquad W = 0.$$

Of the eddy heat transfer terms $\overline{uT'}$ is independent of $x$ and $\overline{wT'}$ is zero, so that (74) becomes

$$\frac{\partial}{\partial y}\left(k\frac{\partial T}{\partial y} - \rho c_p\, \overline{vT'}\right) = \rho c_p\, UA,$$

and this may be integrated to give

$$\rho c_p \overline{vT'} = k \frac{\partial T}{\partial y} - \rho c_p A \int_0^y U \, dy, \tag{79}$$

the constant of integration vanishing since $\overline{vT'}$ and $\partial T/\partial y$ vanish by symmetry at the centre of the channel, $y = 0$.

For flow through a circular pipe with a constant temperature gradient in the direction of flow we put

$$T = Az + f(r).$$

The velocity components are

$$V_r = 0, \qquad V_\theta = 0, \qquad V_z = U(r).$$

Of the eddy heat transfer terms $\overline{v_z T'}$ is independent of $z$ and $\overline{v_\theta T'}$ is zero by symmetry, so that (77) becomes

$$\rho c_p U A = \frac{1}{r} \frac{\partial}{\partial r} \left( rk \frac{\partial T}{\partial r} - \rho c_p r \, \overline{v_r T'} \right).$$

This may be integrated to give

$$\rho c_p \overline{v_r T'} = k \frac{\partial T}{\partial r} - \frac{\rho c_p A}{r} \int_0^r U r \, dr. \tag{80}$$

## § 26. The mixture length theory

It has been shown (Vol. I (1938), chap. v, § 80) that, with the conception of mixture as in the kinetic theory of gases, the rate of transfer of a property $\theta$ across unit area normal to the $y$-axis and in the positive direction of the $x$-axis is

$$Q = -\overline{L_1 v} \, d\theta/dy, \tag{81}$$

where $L_1$ is written for $(h_2 - h_1)$. The two mixture length theories of turbulent flow, the momentum transfer theory and the vorticity transfer theory, differ in their respective assumptions that momentum and vorticity are transferable in this sense. However, heat (or energy) will certainly be transferable and we may therefore identify $Q$ with the rate of heat (or energy) transfer across unit area normal to the $y$-axis in the positive direction and therefore $Q = \rho c_p \overline{vT'}$. The property $\theta$ which is being transferred is the heat content per unit volume which is equal to $\rho c_p T$. Thus (81) becomes

$$\rho c_p \overline{vT'} = -\rho c_p \overline{L_1 v} \, dT/dy,$$

i.e.

$$\overline{vT'} = -\overline{L_1 v} \, dT/dy. \tag{82}$$

The result can also be derived by general dimensional considerations, but the above derivation shows up the physical significance of the exchange coefficient or eddy conductivity $\overline{L_1 v}$.

For the flow in a channel considered in § 25 we obtain from (79) and (82)

$$\frac{\partial T}{\partial y}(\kappa + \overline{L_1 v}) = A \int_0^y U \, dy, \tag{83}$$

where $\kappa = k/\rho c_p$; for the corresponding flow in a pipe, (80) gives

$$\frac{\partial T}{\partial r}(\kappa + \overline{L_{1r} v_r}) = \frac{A}{r} \int_0^r Ur \, dr, \tag{84}$$

where $L_{1r}$ is measured in the direction of $r$ increasing and $v_r$ is the turbulent velocity component in that direction.

## § 27. Reynolds's analogy between heat transfer and skin friction

Reynolds† suggested that in turbulent flow momentum and heat were transferred by the same mechanism. If we now consider flow parallel to the $x$-axis with heat transfer in the positive direction of the $y$-axis, this statement (which requires that the velocity fluctuations parallel to the mean flow should be proportional to the. temperature fluctuations) is represented analytically by the equation

$$\frac{\overline{vT'}}{(U_1 - U_0)(T_1 - T_0)} = \frac{\overline{uv}}{(U_1 - U_0)^2}, \tag{85}$$

where $U_0$, $U_1$, $T_0$, $T_1$ are the velocity and temperature respectively at a pair of corresponding reference planes. It follows that the rate of heat transfer $Q \; (= \rho c_p \overline{vT'})$ in the positive direction of the $y$-axis across unit area normal to this axis is correlated with the Reynolds shear stress $\tau \; (= -\rho \overline{uv})$ in such a way that

$$\frac{Q}{\rho c_p (U_1 - U_0)(T_1 - T_0)} = \frac{-\tau}{\rho (U_1 - U_0)^2}. \tag{86}$$

Between the heat transfer from a fixed wall at temperature $T_1$, for which $U_1 = 0$, and the skin friction at this wall we obtain from (86) the relation
$$K_S = \tfrac{1}{2} c_f, \tag{87}$$

where $K_S$ is the Stanton heat-transfer coefficient which is equal to

† *Proc. Manchester Lit. and Phil. Soc.* **14** (1874), 7–12; *Collected Papers* **1**, 81–5.

$Q_0/\rho c_p\, U_0(T_1-T_0)$ and $c_f$ is the skin-friction coefficient $\tau_0/(\tfrac{1}{2}\rho U_0^2)$, and where $Q_0$ and $\tau_0$ are the values of $Q$ and $\tau$ at the wall.

We consider below the conditions which must hold for Reynolds's analogy to be strictly valid. But we may anticipate this discussion by stating that these conditions are so restrictive that there are few cases in which it can be concluded on theoretical grounds that the analogy will hold. In every case some experimental support for its validity is required. But this does not destroy the value of the analogy, which lies in the link-up which it provides between the phenomena of heat transfer and skin friction. In spite of its limitations the analogy in its simple form often gives a surprisingly good guide to the experimental results.

## § 28. Further consideration of Reynolds's analogy

To examine more closely the conditions for which Reynolds's theory is applicable we shall consider the flow of a fluid in which the mean velocity in the $x$-direction is a function of $y$ only, or alternatively is large compared with the component in the $y$-direction (as for flow in channels, wakes, and boundary layers).

If the flow is laminar with the velocity components $u$, $v$ in the $x$, $y$ directions the equations for the velocity and temperature distributions are:

$$u\frac{\partial u}{\partial x}+v\frac{\partial u}{\partial y} = -\frac{1}{\rho}\frac{\partial p}{\partial x}+v\frac{\partial^2 u}{\partial y^2},$$

$$u\frac{\partial T}{\partial x}+v\frac{\partial T}{\partial y} = \kappa\frac{\partial^2 T}{\partial y^2}.$$

The equation for the temperature has a solution for which $T-T_1$ is proportional to $u-u_1$, where $u_1$ and $T_1$ are the velocity and temperature at some reference plane, provided that the conditions $\partial p/\partial x = 0$ and $\sigma = v/\kappa = 1$ are satisfied and provided also that the boundary conditions for $u$ and $T$ are analogous. The condition $\sigma = 1$ is approximately satisfied for some gases and the condition $\partial p/\partial x = 0$ is satisfied for flow along a flat plate and for wakes and jets. However, the analogy between heat transfer and skin friction has no special significance when the flow is laminar because the equations for the velocity and temperature can then be solved, at least approximately, in all important cases: this is always preferable to placing reliance on the imperfect analogy between heat transfer and skin friction. Further, the risk in using the analogy indiscriminately is well illustrated by considering conditions near the forward stagnation point of a round-nosed cylinder (§ 16); the skin friction vanishes at the stagnation point and near this point is proportional to the distance from it, whereas in contrast the heat transfer is uniform in the region.

The analogy between heat transfer and skin friction is much more important when the flow is turbulent because the equations for turbulent flow cannot at present be solved exactly. For turbulent flow when the mean velocity $U$ is a function of $y$ only, or alternatively is large compared with the component $V$, the equations for the velocity distribution are

$$U \frac{\partial U}{\partial x} + V \frac{\partial U}{\partial y} = -\frac{1}{\rho} \frac{\partial \overline{p}}{\partial x} + \frac{\partial}{\partial y} \left( \nu \frac{\partial U}{\partial y} + \overline{Lv} \frac{\partial U}{\partial y} \right) \tag{88}$$

on the momentum transfer theory, and

$$U \frac{\partial U}{\partial x} + V \frac{\partial U}{\partial y} = -\frac{1}{\rho} \frac{\partial \overline{p}}{\partial x} + (\nu + \overline{Lv}) \frac{\partial^2 U}{\partial y^2} \tag{89}$$

on the vorticity transfer theory, where $\overline{Lv}$ is a transfer coefficient or eddy viscosity (see Vol. I (1938), chap. v). When heat is being transferred the equation for the temperature, given by (74), is

$$U \frac{\partial T}{\partial x} + V \frac{\partial T}{\partial y} = \frac{\partial}{\partial y} \left( \kappa \frac{\partial T}{\partial y} + \overline{L_1 v} \frac{\partial T}{\partial y} \right). \tag{90}$$

In this equation the quantity $\overline{L_1 v}$ is a transfer coefficient or eddy conductivity which is not necessarily identical with the quantity $\overline{Lv}$ which appears in (88) and (89). There is, however, certainly a close relation between these quantities and in the following discussion we shall generally assume that they are identical, but it is desirable to emphasize that this is unproved. The effect of assuming that they are proportional instead of equal is considered in § 31 below.

Inspection of these equations shows that there is no direct correlation between velocity and temperature if the velocity distribution is controlled by the vorticity transfer theory. If, however, the momentum transfer theory is applied, so that $U$ satisfies (88), eqn. (90) has a solution for which $(T - T_1)$ is proportional to $(U - U_1)$ provided that the conditions $\partial \overline{p}/\partial x = 0$ and $\sigma = \nu/\kappa = 1$ are satisfied, in addition to the condition $\overline{L_1 v} = \overline{Lv}$, and provided also that the boundary conditions for $T$ and $U$ are analogous. With these assumptions we see that (86) and (87) are valid when the shearing stress $\tau$ and the rate of heat transfer $Q$ per unit area are given by

$$\tau = \mu \frac{\partial U}{\partial y} + \overline{Lv}\, \frac{\partial U}{\partial y}, \tag{91}$$

$$Q = -k \frac{\partial T}{\partial y} - \rho c_p\, \overline{L_1 v}\, \frac{\partial T}{\partial y}. \tag{92}$$

It follows that Reynolds's theory holds only under special conditions. The condition $\sigma = 1$ is of importance only when a region of laminar flow is present or a region in which the viscous stresses and molecular heat transfer are comparable with the Reynolds stresses and eddy heat transfer—for example, near a wall. Extensions of the theory in such cases for values of $\sigma$ not equal to unity have been given by Taylor, Prandtl, and von Kármán (see § 29 below).

Consideration of the extensions of Reynolds's analogy is given in the following paragraphs. The conclusion of our discussion so far is that the analogy in its simple form, as represented by eqns. (86) and (87), should only be used if a more thorough investigation is impracticable. Improvements on the formulae can be made, but a completely satisfactory analysis will only be possible when a better understanding of the mechanism of momentum and heat transfer in turbulent flow has been attained.

## § 29. Temperature distribution near a heated wall

A discussion of the conditions near a wall for isothermal flow is given in Vol. I (1938), chap. viii, § 153. It is there shown, by a dimensional argument, that the velocity distribution near a wall at which the shear stress is $\tau_0$ is given by

$$\frac{U}{U_\tau} = A + \frac{1}{K} \log_e y_\tau, \tag{93}$$

where $U$ is the velocity at a distance $y$ from the wall, $U_\tau = \sqrt{(\tau_0/\rho)}$ and is called the friction velocity, $y_\tau = U_\tau y/\nu$, and $A$ and $K$ are constants. This result is not valid very close to the wall, where the viscous stress is significant in comparison with the Reynolds stress. This viscous layer near the wall consists of a laminar layer adjoining the wall within which the Reynolds stress is negligible and a transition layer in which the viscous stress and the Reynolds stress are of the same order of magnitude. In the laminar layer the velocity distribution is determined by the equation

$$\tau_0 = \mu \frac{dU}{dy} = \rho U_\tau^2, \tag{94}$$

which has the solution

$$\frac{U}{U_\tau} = \frac{U_\tau y}{\nu} = y_\tau. \tag{95}$$

In general we may write for the velocity distribution throughout the region

$$\frac{U}{U_\tau} = f(y_\tau),$$

where the function $f$ is given by (95) for small values of $y_\tau$ and by (93) for large values of $y_\tau$. Measurements of the velocity distribution near a wall are shown in Fig. 282, and are in accordance with the representation of $U/U_\tau$ as a function of $y_\tau$. To obtain agreement with the experiments we take

$$\frac{U}{U_\tau} = 5 \cdot 5 + 2 \cdot 5 \log_e y_\tau$$

outside the viscous layer. This equation becomes valid for $y_\tau > 30$, which is therefore the thickness of the viscous layer. Eqn. (95) becomes valid for $y_\tau < 2$ and is a fairly good approximation up to $y_\tau = 5$, which may therefore be taken as the approximate thickness of the laminar layer.

Now suppose that the wall is heated to a temperature $T_1$ and that the rate of heat transfer per unit area normal to the wall is $Q_0$ and is constant throughout the region. The analysis is simplified if we introduce a temperature $T_\tau$ defined by the equation

$$\frac{Q_0}{\rho c_p} = U_\tau T_\tau.$$

The temperature $T_\tau$ will be called the friction temperature by analogy with the term 'friction velocity' for the quantity $U_\tau$, but it has no connexion with the kinetic temperature (§ 15). The heat transfer is related to the temperature gradient and the friction temperature by the eqn. (92), which gives

$$\frac{Q_0}{\rho c_p} = U_\tau T_\tau = -\kappa \frac{\partial T}{\partial y} - \overline{Lv} \frac{\partial T}{\partial y}, \tag{96}$$

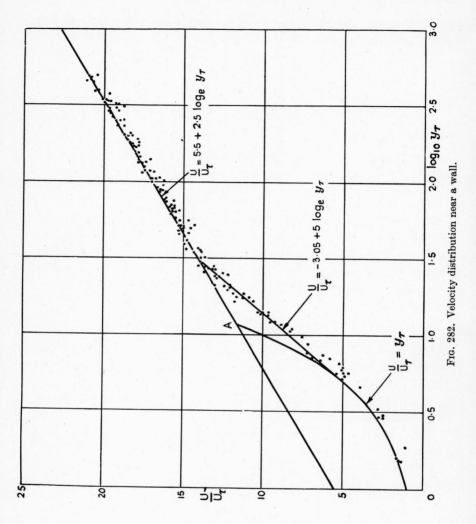

FIG. 282. Velocity distribution near a wall.

$$\frac{U}{U_\tau} = 5 \cdot 5 + 2 \cdot 5 \, \log_e y_\tau$$

$$\frac{U}{U_\tau} = -3 \cdot 05 + 5 \, \log_e y_\tau$$

$$\frac{U}{U_\tau} = y_\tau$$

where we have replaced $\overline{L_1 v}$ by $\overline{Lv}$, thereby identifying for the present the eddy conductivity with the eddy viscosity. Also

$$\frac{\tau_0}{\rho} = U_\tau^2 = \nu\frac{\partial U}{\partial y} + \overline{Lv}\frac{\partial U}{\partial y}.$$

If we now put $\qquad \dfrac{U}{U_\tau} = f(y_\tau), \qquad \dfrac{T_1 - T}{T_\tau} = g(y_\tau),$

and substitute for $U$ and $T$ in the last two equations, we obtain

$$f'(y_\tau) = \frac{\nu}{\nu + \overline{Lv}}, \qquad g'(y_\tau) = \frac{\nu}{\kappa + \overline{Lv}}. \tag{97}$$

Eliminating $\overline{Lv}$ we get

$$\frac{1}{g'} - \frac{1}{f'} = \frac{\kappa}{\nu} - 1 = \frac{1}{\sigma} - 1. \tag{98}$$

Eqn. (98) enables the temperature distribution function to be determined when the velocity-distribution function $f$ is known. For $\sigma = 1$ we obtain $g' = f'$ and hence $g = f$, since both $f$ and $g$ vanish at the wall, so that in this case

$$\frac{T_1 - T}{T_\tau} = \frac{U}{U_\tau}$$

and the velocity and temperature distributions are similar.

Following Taylor[†] and Prandtl[‡] we can derive a first approximation for the effect of the viscous layer at the wall by assuming that there is a sharp boundary between the laminar region of thickness $y_{\tau 1}$ in which momentum and heat are transferred purely by viscosity and conductivity, and the fully turbulent region in which only turbulent exchange is operative. In the laminar layer $\overline{Lv} = 0$, so that (97) becomes $\qquad f' = 1, \qquad g' = \sigma,$

giving $\qquad\qquad\qquad f = y_\tau, \qquad g = \sigma y_\tau$

for $0 < y < y_{\tau 1}$. In the fully turbulent layer we neglect $\nu$ and $\kappa$ in comparison with $Lv$ so that (97) gives $g' = f'$. Integrating we get

$$g = f + (\sigma - 1)y_{\tau 1}, \quad \text{for} \quad y > y_{\tau 1}, \tag{99}$$

choosing the constant of integration to make $g$ continuous at the junction between the two regions. From the measurements of velocity distribution given in Fig. 282 we see that the curves

† *Rep. Memor. Aero. Res. Coun.*, No. 272 (1919).
‡ *Phys. Zeitschrift*, **11** (1910), 1072.

representing pure laminar and fully turbulent flow intersect at the point $A$ for which $y_\tau = 11 \cdot 5$, and with this value (99) becomes

$$g = f + 11 \cdot 5(\sigma - 1).$$

The existence of a gradual transition between the laminar and the fully turbulent regions, which is shown in Fig. 282, allows some freedom of choice for the location of the boundary between the regions; the location recommended by Prandtl after an examination of the experimental data on heat transfer corresponds to $y_{\tau 1} = 5 \cdot 6$.

The assumption of a sharp boundary between the laminar layer at the wall and the fully turbulent region leads to satisfactory results for fluids such as air for which the Prandtl number does not differ much from unity. (For $\sigma = 1$ the temperature distribution is similar to the velocity distribution whatever the exact character of the flow near the wall.) But comparison between the theory and experiments on heat transfer for liquids such as water for which $\sigma$ is much greater than unity has indicated that the assumption of a sharp boundary between the laminar layer and the turbulent core is too drastic, and that it is necessary to make an allowance for the transition layer between the laminar layer at the wall and the fully turbulent region.† To calculate the effect of this transition layer on the temperature distribution we must use a representation of the velocity distribution function which is closer to the actual velocity distribution near the wall than the one used above. In the laminar layer we take

$$f(y_\tau) = y_\tau, \quad \text{for} \quad 0 < y_\tau < 5,$$

and in the transition layer

$$f(y_\tau) = -3 \cdot 05 + 5 \log_e y_\tau, \quad \text{for} \quad 5 < y_\tau < 30.$$

It is not essential to specify $f$ in the fully turbulent region, but for definiteness we take

$$f(y_\tau) = 5 \cdot 5 + 2 \cdot 5 \log_e y_\tau, \quad \text{for} \quad y_\tau > 30. \tag{100}$$

These expressions are shown in Fig. 282 and it will be seen that they represent the velocity distribution quite well. We proceed to insert them in eqn. (98) for the temperature distribution function $g$ and obtain the following results by straightforward integration:

*Laminar layer*     $g(y_\tau) = \sigma y_\tau, \quad \text{for} \quad 0 < y_\tau < 5. \tag{101}$

† von Kármán, *Proc. 4th Int. Congr. Appl. Mech. Camb.* (1934), 77–83; *Engineering*, **48** (1939), 210–13.

*Transition layer*

$$g(y_\tau) = 5\log_e\left(\frac{\sigma y_\tau}{5}+1-\sigma\right)+5\sigma, \quad \text{for} \quad 5 < y_\tau < 30. \qquad (102)$$

*Turbulent layer*

$$g(y_\tau) = f(y_\tau)+ \Sigma(\sigma), \quad \text{for} \quad y_\tau > 30, \qquad (103)$$

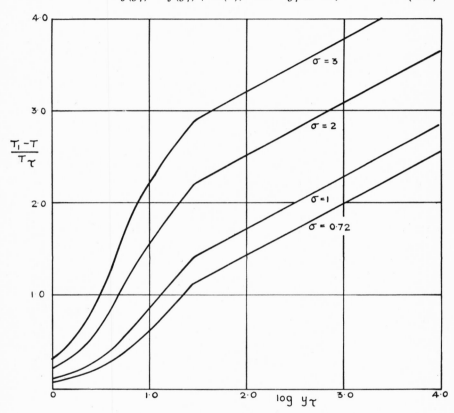

FIG. 283. Calculated temperature distribution near a heated wall.

where
$$\Sigma(\sigma) = 5\left[\sigma-1+\log_e\left(\frac{5\sigma+1}{6}\right)\right].$$

These results are due to von Kármán. Some values of $\Sigma(\sigma)$ are given in Table 9.

The temperature-distribution function given by these expressions is shown in Fig. 283 for several values of $\sigma$. There are no sufficiently reliable measurements of temperature near a wall to check the

calculations directly, but we shall show later that an indirect check
is provided by heat transfer data.

TABLE 9

| $\sigma$ | 0·01 | 0·72 | 1·0 | 2·0 | 3·0 | 5·0 | 7·0 | 10 | 100 |
|---|---|---|---|---|---|---|---|---|---|
| $\Sigma(\sigma)$ | −13·66 | −2·73 | 0 | 8·03 | 14·9 | 27·3 | 38·9 | 55·4 | 517 |

## § 30. Temperature distribution and heat transfer from a heated flat plate

As a preliminary to the consideration of flow in a circular pipe
we shall calculate the temperature distribution in the boundary layer
of a heated flat plate maintained at a temperature $T_1$ in a stream of
velocity $U_0$ and temperature $T_0$. We consider only the momentum
transfer theory since a satisfactory solution for flow near the wall
is not possible using the vorticity transfer theory. The procedure
follows that given for flow near a wall, and we obtain from eqn.
(103) the formula

$$\frac{T_1-T}{T_\tau} = \frac{U}{U_\tau} + \Sigma(\sigma) \tag{104}$$

for the temperature distribution just outside the viscous layer. Also
from the general discussion given in § 28 we know that the velocity
and temperature distributions are similar in the outer parts of the
boundary layer. Hence (104) will apply everywhere beyond the
viscous layer, although $U/U_\tau$ is not known except near the wall.
At the outer edge of the boundary layer $U = U_0$, $T = T_0$ so that,
from (104),

$$\frac{T_1-T_0}{T_\tau} = \frac{U_0}{U_\tau} + \Sigma(\sigma). \tag{105}$$

Eliminating $T_\tau$ between (104) and (105) we obtain

$$\frac{T-T_0}{T_1-T_0} = \frac{U_0-U}{U_0+U_\tau \Sigma(\sigma)}, \tag{106}$$

which enables the temperature distribution in the boundary layer
to be calculated if the velocity distribution is known.

We can also deduce a formula for the heat-transfer coefficient; we
have

$$c_f = \frac{2\tau_0}{\rho U_0^2} = 2\frac{U_\tau^2}{U_0^2}$$

and

$$K_S = \frac{Q_0}{\rho c_p U_0(T_1-T_0)} = \frac{U_\tau T_\tau}{U_0(T_1-T_0)}.$$

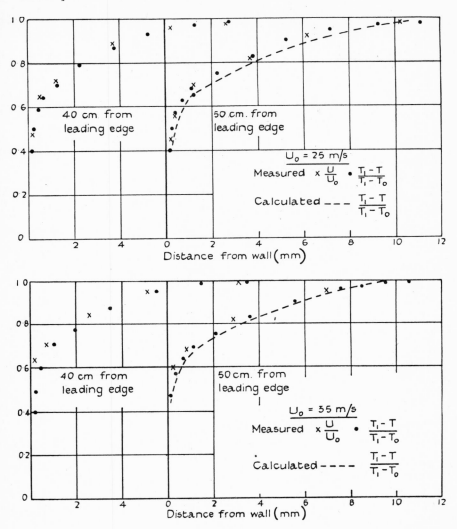

FIG. 284. Heated flat plate. Elias's tests.

Hence (105) is equivalent to

$$\frac{1}{K_S} = \sqrt{\left(\frac{2}{c_f}\right)}\left[\sqrt{\left(\frac{2}{c_f}\right)} + \Sigma(\sigma)\right]. \qquad (107)$$

This result was obtained by von Kármán, who applied it also to flow through pipes although this is not strictly justifiable.

Elias[†] has made measurements of the velocity and temperature distributions of a flat plate. Some typical results for a smooth plate with turbulent boundary layer are shown in Fig. 284. It will be seen that the velocity and temperature distributions are similar in shape, but that on the whole the temperature curves lie below the velocity curves. Temperature distributions calculated by means of (106) from the *measured* velocity distributions are also given in some of the cases and show trends in the same direction as the experiments. The accuracy of the measurements is not, however, sufficient to provide a proper check on the relation (106).

The calculation on mixture length theories of the velocity distribution for flow in a turbulent boundary layer along a flat plate was considered in Vol. I (1938), chap. viii, § 165, where a comparison with experiment was also shown. If the plate is heated the temperature satisfies the equation

$$U\frac{\partial T}{\partial x}+V\frac{\partial T}{\partial y}=\frac{\partial}{\partial y}\left(\overline{Lv}\frac{\partial T}{\partial y}\right),$$

neglecting molecular conductivity. The solution of this equation has been studied by Howarth,[‡] who replaced $\overline{Lv}$ by $l^2\partial U/\partial y$ on Prandtl's hypothesis, where $l$ is the mixture length, and assumed that the temperature distributions at different sections are similar.

## § 31. Reichardt's extended exchange theory

It has been assumed in all the detailed cases of turbulent flow considered in this chapter that the heat-exchange coefficient $\overline{L_1 v}$ is equal to the momentum exchange coefficient $\overline{Lv}$. On the introduction of the vorticity transfer theory by Taylor many years ago it was pointed out that this assumption is not necessarily true, but some corresponding assumption about the exchange coefficients for heat and vorticity was necessary.

Reichardt[§] has proposed that the exchange coefficient for heat and momentum should be assumed to be proportional instead of equal. We shall consider the consequence of this generalization in the present paragraph and begin with the temperature distribution near a heated plane wall. As in § 29 the rate of heat transfer per unit

---

[†] Loc. cit. on p. 782.
[‡] *Proc. Roy. Soc.* A, **154** (1936), 373–6.
[§] *Z. angew. Math. Mech.* **20** (1940), 297–328.

area $Q_0$ and the shear stress $\tau_0$ are related to the velocity and temperature by the equations

$$\frac{Q_0}{\rho c_p} = U_\tau T_\tau = -\kappa \frac{\partial T}{\partial y} - \overline{L_1 v} \frac{\partial T}{\partial y},$$

$$\frac{\tau_0}{\rho} = U_\tau^2 = \nu \frac{\partial U}{\partial y} + \overline{Lv} \frac{\partial U}{\partial y}.$$

Substituting as before

$$\frac{U}{U_\tau} = f(y_\tau), \qquad \frac{T_1 - T}{T_\tau} = g(y_\tau),$$

we obtain
$$f' = \frac{\nu}{\nu + \overline{Lv}}, \qquad g' = \frac{\nu}{\kappa + \overline{L_1 v}}.$$

Following Reichardt we now put $\overline{L_1 v} = \lambda \overline{Lv}$, where $\lambda$ is a constant, and eliminating $\overline{Lv}$ we obtain

$$\frac{1}{\lambda g'} - \frac{1}{f'} = \frac{\kappa}{\lambda \nu} - 1 = \frac{1}{\sigma_1} - 1, \tag{108}$$

where $\sigma_1 = \lambda \sigma$ and may be called the generalized Prandtl number. The case $\sigma_1 = 1$ is now a special case for which (108) gives

$$\lambda g' = f',$$

and hence
$$\lambda g = f,$$

since both $f$ and $g$ vanish at the wall, or

$$\frac{T_1 - T}{T_\tau / \lambda} = \frac{U}{U_\tau},$$

which shows that the velocity and temperature distributions are similar for $\sigma_1 = 1$. It will be seen that the introduction of the proportionality factor $\lambda$ can be allowed for by replacing $\sigma$ by $\sigma \lambda$, $T_\tau$ by $T_\tau / \lambda$, and $g$ by $\lambda g$ wherever they occur. For example in place of (101)–(103) for the temperature distribution near a heated wall we get:

*Laminar layer*
$$\lambda g(y_\tau) = \sigma_1 y_\tau, \quad \text{for} \quad 0 < y_\tau < 5.$$

*Transition layer*
$$\lambda g(y_\tau) = 5 \log_e \left( \frac{\sigma_1 y_\tau}{5} + 1 - \sigma_1 \right) + 5\sigma_1, \quad \text{for} \quad 5 < y_\tau < 30.$$

*Turbulent layer*

$$\lambda g(y_\tau) = f(y_\tau) + \Sigma(\sigma_1), \quad \text{for} \quad y_\tau \geqslant 30,$$

where
$$\Sigma(\sigma_1) = 5\left[\sigma_1 - 1 + \log_e\left(\frac{5\sigma_1 + 1}{6}\right)\right].$$

The presence of the undetermined factor $\lambda$ in these equations makes it easier to secure agreement between theory and experiment, which is otherwise difficult to attain in some cases. Further detailed study of the mechanism of exchange in turbulent flow may enable this factor to be predicted.

## § 32. Flow through a heated pipe. Temperature distribution

The application of (107) to pipe flow, with $K_S$ and $c_f$ based on the mean velocity and mean temperature difference, ignores several features which do not greatly affect the overall result but nevertheless are significant for the study of heat transfer in pipes. We shall consider the temperature distribution in a pipe of radius $a$ whose walls are maintained at a constant temperature gradient $A$ per unit length, limiting consideration to the momentum transfer theory.[†] Except in the viscous layer near the walls, momentum and heat are transferred predominantly by turbulent mixing, so that the heat transfer per unit area radially outwards is

$$Q = \rho c_p \overline{v_r T'} = -\rho c_p \overline{L_r v_r}\frac{\partial T}{\partial r},$$

and hence, from (84),

$$-\frac{Q}{\rho c_p} = \overline{L_r v_r}\frac{\partial T}{\partial r} = \frac{A}{r}\int_0^r U r\, dr,$$

where we have put $L_{1r}$ equal to $L_r$ and neglected the effect of molecular conductivity. The equation for the shear stress on the momentum transfer theory is

$$\frac{\tau}{\rho} = -\overline{L_r v_r}\frac{\partial U}{\partial r} = -\frac{r}{2\rho}\frac{\partial \overline{p}}{\partial x} = \frac{\tau_0 r}{\rho a},$$

where $r$ is measured from the centre of the pipe, so that $\partial U/\partial r$ is negative, and $\tau$ stands for the positive shear stress. Near the wall

† Taylor (*Proc. Roy. Soc.* A, **129** (1930), 25–30) worked out this problem for the particular case $R = 10^5$, $\sigma = 1$, and the investigation given here is a generalization of his work.

the shear stress and rate of heat transfer per unit area are $\tau_0$ and $Q_0$, and consequently

$$-\frac{Q_0}{\rho c_p} = U_\tau T_\tau = \frac{A}{a} \int_0^a U r\, dr, \qquad \frac{\tau_0}{\rho} = U_\tau^2,$$

where we have introduced the friction velocity $U_\tau$ and the friction temperature $T_\tau$ defined as above. If the walls of the pipe are heated $Q$ and $Q_0$ are negative and $T_\tau$ is positive. Hence

$$\frac{Q}{Q_0} = \frac{\overline{L_r v_r}}{U_\tau T_\tau}\left(\frac{\partial T}{\partial r}\right) = \frac{a}{r} \int_0^r U r\, dr \Big/ \int_0^a U r\, dr, \qquad (109)$$

and

$$\frac{\tau}{\tau_0} = -\frac{\overline{L_r v_r}}{U_\tau^2}\left(\frac{\partial U}{\partial r}\right) = \frac{r}{a}. \qquad (110)$$

Now it is known that $(U_c - U)/U_\tau$ is a universal function of $r/a$ for sufficiently high Reynolds numbers, where $U_c$ is the velocity at the centre of the pipe.† Hence we write

$$\frac{U_c - U}{U_\tau} = f\left(\frac{r}{a}\right), \qquad (111)$$

and by analogy we write

$$\frac{T - T_c}{T_\tau} = g\left(\frac{r}{a}\right), \qquad (112)$$

where $T_c$ is the temperature at the centre of the pipe. We shall find that the function $g(r/a)$ is independent of the conditions close to the wall but depends on the Reynolds number through the factor $U_\tau/U_c$. Substituting in (109) and (110) we get

$$\frac{\overline{L_r v_r}}{U_\tau a} g'\left(\frac{r}{a}\right) = \frac{(a/r) \int_0^{r/a} [U_c - U_\tau f(t)] t\, dt}{\int_0^1 [U_c - U_\tau f(t)] t\, dt},$$

and

$$\frac{\overline{L_r v_r}}{U_\tau a} f'\left(\frac{r}{a}\right) = \frac{r}{a}$$

where $f'(x)$ denotes the first derivative of $f(x)$. Elimination of $\overline{L_r v_r}$

† Vol. I (1938), chap. viii, § 154.

between these two equations gives, after some reduction,

$$\frac{dg}{df} = \frac{g'(r/a)}{f'(r/a)} = 1 + 2\left(\frac{U_\tau}{U_c}\right)\left[\frac{\int_0^1 f(t)t\,dt - \frac{a^2}{r^2}\int_0^{r/a} f(t)t\,dt}{1 - 2\frac{U_\tau}{U_c}\int_0^1 f(t)t\,dt}\right]. \qquad (113)$$

The second term of the right-hand side of this equation is a measure of the difference between the velocity and temperature distributions, since we should have $g = f$ if this term were missing.

Calculations of the temperature distribution function $g$ have been made from eqn. (113) for three values of $R = 2aU_m/\nu$, where $U_m$ is the mean velocity, using Stanton's measurements of the velocity distribution function $f$, obtained at $R = 9{\cdot}1 \times 10^4$. The results are given in Table 10 and also, for $R = 10^5$, in Fig. 285.

TABLE 10

| $R$ $U_c/U_\tau$ | | | $10^4$ 20·81 | | $10^5$ 25·80 | | $10^6$ 30·92 | |
|---|---|---|---|---|---|---|---|---|
| $(r/a)^2$ | $r/a$ | $f(r/a)$ | $g(r/a)$ | $\delta(r/a)$ | $g(r/a)$ | $\delta(r/a)$ | $g(r/a)$ | $\delta(r/a)$ |
| 0 | 0 | 0 | 0 | 0 | 0 | 0 | 0 | 0 |
| 0·2 | 0·447 | 1·78 | 2·24 | 0·46 | 2·13 | 0·35 | 2·06 | 0·28 |
| 0·4 | 0·633 | 3·32 | 4·09 | 0·77 | 3·91 | 0·59 | 3·80 | 0·48 |
| 0·6 | 0·775 | 4·90 | 5·91 | 1·01 | 5·67 | 0·77 | 5·52 | 0·62 |
| 0·8 | 0·895 | 6·97 | 8·19 | 1·22 | 7·90 | 0·93 | 6·72 | 0·75 |
| 0·9 | 0·949 | 8·52 | 9·84 | 1·32 | 9·32 | 1·00 | 9·33 | 0·81 |
| 0·98 | 0·99 | 11·60 | 13·01 | 1·41 | 12·67 | 1·07 | 12·47 | 0·87 |
| 1·0 | 1·0 | .. | .. | 1·42† | .. | 1·08† | .. | 0·88† |

† Extrapolated.

We can write the result of this calculation as

$$g(r/a) = f(r/a) + \delta(r/a), \qquad (114)$$

where $\delta(r/a)$ is a correction term which is given in Table 10; from (113) it can be shown that $\delta'(r/a) \to 0$ for $r/a \to 1$. Hence near the wall

$$g(r/a) = f(r/a) + \delta(1)$$

to a good approximation: this is equivalent to

$$\frac{T - T_c}{T_\tau} = \frac{U_c - U}{U_\tau} + \delta(1), \qquad (115)$$

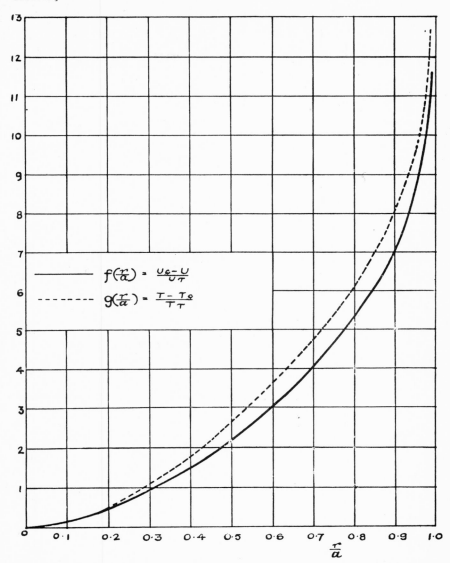

FIG. 285.  Flow in pipes.  Velocity and temperature distributions for $R = 10^5$.

which is valid near the wall.  But from our previous analysis of heat transfer in the viscous layer at a wall (§ 29) we obtained the result

$$\frac{T_1 - T}{T_\tau} = \frac{U}{U_\tau} + \Sigma(\sigma), \tag{116}$$

where $T_1$ is the wall temperature and $\Sigma(\sigma)$ is the function which is given in Table 9. From (115) and (116) we get by addition

$$\frac{T_1-T_c}{T_\tau} = \frac{U_c}{U_\tau} + \delta(1) + \Sigma(\sigma). \tag{117}$$

In general away from the wall (114) is equivalent to

$$\frac{T-T_c}{T_\tau} = \frac{U_c-U}{U_\tau} + \delta(r/a). \tag{118}$$

Hence from (117) and (118) the temperature distribution across a section of the pipe, expressed as a fraction of the temperature difference between the centre and the wall, is given by

$$\frac{T_1-T}{T_1-T_c} = \frac{U + U_\tau[\delta(1)-\delta(r/a)+\Sigma]}{U_c + U_\tau[\delta(1)+\Sigma]}.$$

As an example we consider the case of the flow of air ($\sigma = 0.72$) through a heated pipe at $R = 10^5$. We obtain the calculated temperature distribution given in Table 11. Measurements have been made by Pannell† and Lorenz‡ and in Fig. 286 the calculations are compared with experimental results of Lorenz‡; it will be seen that fair agreement is obtained.

TABLE 11

*Calculated Temperature Distribution for Air flowing through a Heated Pipe for $R = 10^5$*

| $(r/a)^2$ | $(r/a)$ | $U/U_c$ | $\dfrac{T_1-T}{T_1-T_c}$ |
|-----------|---------|---------|--------------------------|
| 0         | 0       | 1·0     | 1·0                      |
| 0·2       | 0·447   | 0·931   | 0·912                    |
| 0·4       | 0·663   | 0·871   | 0·838                    |
| 0·6       | 0·775   | 0·810   | 0·761                    |
| 0·8       | 0·895   | 0·730   | 0·673                    |
| 0·9       | 0·949   | 0·670   | 0·606                    |
| 0·98      | 0·99    | 0·589   | 0·476                    |
| 1·0       | 1·0     | 0       | 0                        |

Closer agreement could be obtained by rejecting the assumption that the eddy conductivity $\overline{L_{1r}v_r}$ is equal to the eddy viscosity $\overline{L_r v_r}$. If instead we take $\overline{L_{1r}v_r} = \lambda\overline{L_r v_r}$, as in § 31 above, with $\lambda = 1.25$,

† *Rep. Memor. Aero. Res. Coun.*, No. 243, Part II (1916–17).
‡ *Z. Tech. Phys.* **15** (1934), 376–7.

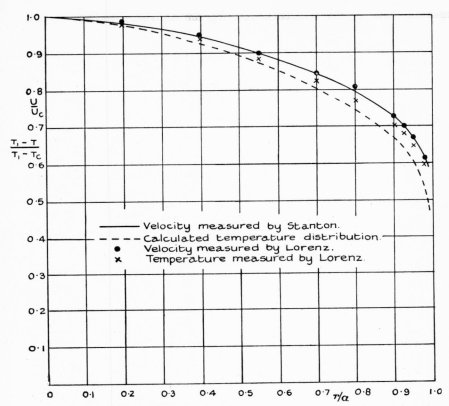

FIG. 286. Flow of air in heated pipes at $R = 10^5$. Comparison between theory and experiment.

and hence $\sigma_1 = \lambda\sigma = 0.9$ for air, close agreement can be obtained, but this may not be the only way of explaining the data.

## § 33. Flow through a heated pipe. Rate of heat transfer from the walls

The difference of the heat content in the fluid passing any two sections of the pipe is equal to the heat transferred from the walls between these two sections. Applying this to two sections very close together we obtain an expression for the rate of heat transfer per unit area $Q_0$ from the walls in the form

$$Q_0 = \frac{\rho c_p}{a}\frac{d}{dz}\left[\int_0^a U T r\, dr\right] = \tfrac{1}{2}\rho c_p\, a U_m \frac{dT_M}{dz},$$

where the 'mixing-cup' mean temperature $T_M$ is defined by the equation

$$T_M = \frac{\int_0^a T U r \, dr}{\int_0^a U r \, dr},$$

and the mean velocity $U_m$ by the equation

$$U_m = \frac{2}{a^2} \int_0^a U r \, dr.$$

The heat-transfer coefficient is defined by the equation

$$K_S = \frac{Q_0}{\rho c_p \, U_m (T_1 - T_M)},$$

and from the definition of $T_\tau$ we have

$$\frac{Q_0}{\rho c_p} = U_\tau T_\tau.$$

Hence 
$$K_S = \frac{1}{4} \left( \frac{dT_M}{dz} \right) \frac{d}{(T_1 - T_M)} = \frac{U_\tau T_\tau}{U_m (T_1 - T_M)},$$

where $d = 2a$ is the diameter of the pipe.

From (111) and (112) $T_M$ is related to the temperature at the centre of the pipe by the equation

$$\frac{T_M - T_c}{T_\tau} = \frac{\int_0^1 g(t) [U_c - U_\tau f(t)] t \, dt}{\int_0^1 [U_c - U_\tau f(t)] t \, dt}.$$

In addition we may require the mean temperature $T_m$ defined by

$$T_m = \frac{2}{a^2} \int_0^a T r \, dr,$$

which can be calculated from the formula

$$\frac{T_m - T_c}{T_\tau} = 2 \int_0^1 g(t) t \, dt.$$

From the data given in Table 10 numerical calculations have been made of $T_M$ and $T_m$ and these are given in Table 12. For the velocity distribution in Table 10 we find also that

$$\frac{U_c - U_m}{U_\tau} = 4{\cdot}60, \tag{119}$$

where $U_m$ is the mean velocity. We may therefore express the results in Table 12 in the form

$$\frac{T_M - T_c}{T_\tau} = \frac{U_c - U_m}{U_\tau} - \delta_M + \delta(1), \tag{120}$$

where $\delta_M$ is a correction factor which is calculated from (119) and the values of $(T_M - T_c)/T_\tau$ given in Table 12 and which is also given in Table 12. Hence from (117) and (120) we obtain

$$\frac{T_1 - T_M}{T_\tau} = \frac{U_m}{U_\tau} + \delta_M + \Sigma(\sigma).$$

This is equivalent to

$$\frac{1}{K_S} = \sqrt{\left(\frac{2}{c_f}\right)} \left[ \sqrt{\left(\frac{2}{c_f}\right)} + \delta_M + \Sigma(\sigma) \right], \tag{121}$$

where $K_S$ is the Stanton number $Q_0/\rho c_p U_m (T_1 - T_M)$ and $c_f$ is the skin-friction coefficient $2\tau_0/\rho U_m^2$.

TABLE 12

| $R$ | $10^4$ | $10^5$ | $10^6$ |
|---|---|---|---|
| $\dfrac{T_M - T_c}{T_\tau}$ | 4·94 | 4·84 | 4·78 |
| $\dfrac{T_m - T_c}{T_\tau}$ | 5·43 | 5·23 | 5·11 |
| $\delta_M$ | 1·08 | 0·84 | 0·70 |
| $\dfrac{U_m}{U_\tau} = \sqrt{\left(\dfrac{2}{c_f}\right)}$ | 16·11 | 21·10 | 26·22 |

It will be seen from eqn. (121) that the only result of this laborious calculation is to show that there is a correction term $\delta_M$ to be applied to von Kármán's formula (107) which is in practice small compared with $\Sigma(\sigma)$, the term depending on the Prandtl number (except when $\sigma$ is nearly equal to unity); for example, for $R = 10^5$, $\sigma = 2{\cdot}0$ we have $\delta_M = 0{\cdot}84$, $\Sigma = 8{\cdot}03$. However, it is useful to know the order of magnitude of the correction which has hitherto been uncertain, except for the example $R = 10^5$, $\sigma = 1{\cdot}0$; this was calculated by

Taylor,[†] who found that $1/K_S = 1{\cdot}04(2/c_f)$, in good agreement with the result given by the present calculations using eqn. (121) and Table 12.

If instead of taking the eddy conductivity $\overline{L_1 v}$ equal to the eddy viscosity $\overline{Lv}$, we put $L_1 v = \lambda \overline{Lv}$, then, as explained in § 31, we must everywhere replace $\sigma$ by $\sigma_1 = \lambda\sigma$, $T_\tau$ by $T_\tau/\lambda$, and $K_S$ by $K_S/\lambda$ to obtain the corresponding results.

In the above calculations we have assumed that the wall of the pipe is maintained at a constant temperature gradient. If, however, the pipe wall is maintained at a constant temperature and if further the shape of the temperature distribution curve has reached its final form, then the axial temperature gradient at any point varies over any cross-section from zero at the walls to a maximum at the centre of the pipe, instead of being constant. Allowance for this effect has been made by Reichardt,[‡] and it appears that its principal effect is to change the magnitude of the correction term $\delta_M$ in eqn. (121) somewhat. The conclusion that the effect of this correction term is normally not large remains, however, unaltered.

## § 34. Comparison between theory and experiment for flow in pipes

The experimental values obtained for heat transfer from pipes to fluids flowing through them are mostly rather scattered owing to difficulties of measurement. These difficulties arise: (1) from the effect of the entry length, in which the temperature distribution has not settled down and in which the rate of heat transfer is higher than the final value, and (2) from the variation of the properties of fluids with temperature, which results in the heat-transfer coefficient for a finite rate of heat flow being different from the coefficient for an infinitesimal rate. The theoretical formulae apply only to the coefficient for an infinitesimal rate of heat flow. For gases the variation with temperature of the Prandtl number $\sigma$ is not large; but further errors may be caused by the convection currents which arise from the variation of density with temperature. For water the variation of $\sigma$ with temperature is important as shown in Table 1 (p. 762).

Eagle and Ferguson[§] have made a complete series of experiments on the heat transfer from pipes to water flowing through them, in

[†] Loc. cit. on p. 832.                    [‡] Loc. cit. on p. 830.
[§] *Proc. Roy. Soc.* A, **127** (1930), 540–66.

which the difficulty of the variation of $\sigma$ with temperature was surmounted by measuring the heat transfer at three different rates of heat flow and extrapolating the results to obtain the heat-transfer coefficient for an infinitesimal temperature difference. The effect of the entry length was eliminated by heating the tube electrically, so that a linear distribution of temperature along the pipe was obtained, and choosing the section for which the heat flow was measured at such a distance from the beginning of the heated section that the entry effects had died away. The experiments extended over a range of values of $\sigma$ from 3 to 10, and a range of Reynolds numbers from $5.10^3$ to $2.10^5$. Eagle and Ferguson proposed an empirical formula to fit their experimental results, of the form

$$\frac{1}{K_S} = \frac{2}{c_f}[\alpha + \beta(\sigma - 1) - \gamma(\sigma - 1)^2],$$

where $\alpha$, $\beta$, $\gamma$ are functions of the Reynolds number and $c_f$ is the skin-friction coefficient $\tau_0/(\tfrac{1}{2}\rho U_m^2)$. The experimental values of these quantities are given in Table 13 together with the values of $2/c_f$ deduced by Eagle and Ferguson from the experiments of Stanton and Pannell.[†]

TABLE 13

| log $R$ | $2/c_f$ | $\alpha$ | $\beta$ | $100\gamma$ |
|---|---|---|---|---|
| 3·7 | 207 | 1·483 | 0·480 | 0·59⁵ |
| 3·8 | 220 | 1·414 | 0·439 | 0·56⁵ |
| 3·9 | 234 | 1·343 | 0·411 | 0·53⁵ |
| 4·0 | 250 | 1·284 | 0·390 | 0·51 |
| 4·1 | 266 | 1·237 | 0·372 | 0·48⁵ |
| 4·2 | 284 | 1·202 | 0·358 | 0·46 |
| 4·3 | 303 | 1·175 | 0·345 | 0·43⁵ |
| 4·4 | 323 | 1·152 | 0·333 | 0·41 |
| 4·5 | 344 | 1·133 | 0·324 | 0·39 |
| 4·6 | 366 | 1·118 | 0·316 | 0·37 |
| 4·7 | 388 | 1·105 | 0·311 | 0·35⁵ |
| 4·8 | 411 | 1·094 | 0·307 | 0·34 |
| 4·9 | 434 | 1·084 | 0·305 | 0·33 |
| 5·0 | 457 | 1·075 | 0·303 | 0·32 |
| 5·1 | 480 | 1·069 | 0·302 | 0·31⁵ |
| 5·2 | 503 | 1·064 | 0·302 | 0·31 |
| 5·3 | 524 | 1·060 | 0·301 | 0·30⁵ |

The values of $K_S$ are based on the mean water temperature as obtained by the 'mixing-cup' method and are therefore to be com-

† *Philos. Trans.* A, **214** (1914), 199–224.

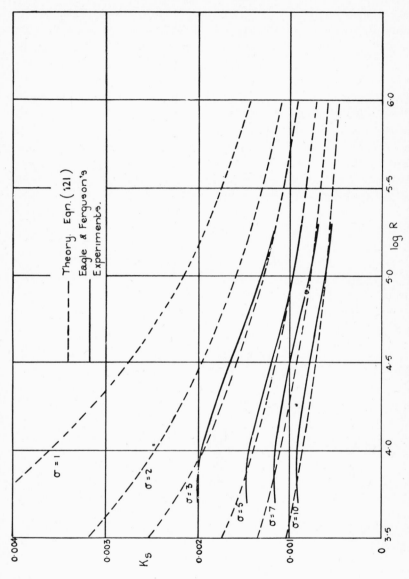

FIG. 287. Comparison between theory and experiment for heat transfer from pipes.

pared with the values given by (121) in which the inclusion of the factor $\delta_M$ represents an improvement in von Kármán's formula (107). The comparison is shown in Fig. 287 and good agreement is obtained for the range $3 \leqslant \sigma \leqslant 10$ which was investigated by Eagle and Ferguson.

The results of tests at larger values of $\sigma$ show a considerable scatter and von Kármán's theory ceases to be a good approximation for $\sigma > 25$. In these cases most of the temperature drop occurs in the viscous layer and the variation of viscosity with temperature may be significant. Reference may be made to McAdams's book[†] for a discussion of the various empirical formulae which have been proposed for heat transfer if $\sigma$ is large.

Reichardt[‡] has concluded from his analysis of the experimental data that the best agreement between theory and experiment is obtained by taking the ratio of the heat-exchange coefficient to the momentum-exchange coefficient to be equal to 1·1.

Heat transfer to mercury flowing in pipes is of interest because the Prandtl number of mercury is of order 0·01, which is much lower than for other fluids. There is, however, lack of agreement between the different sets of measurements,[§] which may be due to the liquid wetting the walls in some cases but not in others.

## § 35. Flow at high speeds in pipes

Experiments to measure the rate of heat transfer from the walls of a pipe to air flowing through it at high speeds have been made by McAdams and others.[‖] Since kinetic temperature effects are important under these conditions it is necessary to define the Stanton number in the form

$$Q = K_S \rho_m c_p S U_m [T_1 - (T_0 + \Delta T)]$$

as in § 19 above, where $\rho_m$, $U_m$ are the mean density and velocity respectively so that $\rho_m U_m$ is the mean mass flow per unit area, $T_1$ is the wall temperature, $T_0$ is the stream temperature, and $\Delta T$ is the kinetic temperature. The experiments gave the result that

$$\Delta T = 0.88 \frac{U_m^2}{2c_p}$$

---

† *Heat Transmission*, New York (1942).　　　　　‡ Loc. cit. on p. 830.
§ Styrikovitch and Semenorker, *J. Tech. Phys. U.S.S.R.* **10** (1940), 1324–30; Bailey, Cope, and Watson, *Rep. Aero. Res. Coun.*, No. 12,391 (1949).
‖ *Tech. Notes Nat. Adv. Comm. Aero.*, No. 985 (1945); also *Trans. Amer. Inst. Chem. Engrs.* **42** (1946), 907–25.

over a range of Mach numbers from 0·2 to 1·0, the coefficient 0·88
being a mean of values between 0·85 and 0·90. This is in agreement
with results for flat plates (Fig. 267). The measurements of heat
transfer and a comparison with the results of other experimenters
showed that, for air,

$$K_S = 0·033 R^{-0·23},$$

where

$$R = \frac{\rho_m U_m d}{\mu_m}$$

and $\mu_m$ is the viscosity at the mean static temperature of the stream.

## § 36. Calculation of heat transfer from cylinders and aerofoils

For the calculation of heat transfer from cylinders and aerofoils
with turbulent boundary layers, it is necessary to rely on the formulae
calculated by von Kármán for the flat plate, due to the lack of a more
satisfactory theory. We take therefore the relation (105) as applying
to a cylinder or aerofoil in the form

$$\frac{T_1 - T_0}{T_\tau} = \frac{U_1}{U_\tau} + \Sigma(\sigma),$$

where $T_1$ is the surface temperature, $T_0$ the stream temperature, and
where we have replaced $U_0$, the main stream velocity, by $U_1$, the
velocity at the edge of the boundary layer. In terms of the coefficients $c_f$ and $K_S$ as in § 30 this gives

$$\frac{1}{K_S} = \sqrt{\left(\frac{2}{c_f}\right)} \left[ \frac{U_1}{U_0} \sqrt{\left(\frac{2}{c_f}\right)} + \Sigma(\sigma) \right],$$

where $U_1/U_0$ varies along the surface of the cylinder, $c_f = 2\tau_0/(\rho U_0^2)$,
and $K_S = Q_0/[\rho c_p U_0(T_1 - T_0)]$. If required, we can allow for kinetic
temperature effects as explained in § 19.

## § 37. The temperature distribution between rotating cylinders

The velocity and temperature distributions for air between rotating cylinders at different temperatures have been investigated
by Taylor.† If the cylinders are kept at a constant temperature
difference, the rate of heat transfer $Q$ per unit length is constant.
Also

$$Q = -2\pi \rho c_p \overline{L_r v_r} r \frac{dT}{dr},$$

where $r$ is measured radially from the axis of the cylinders. The
results of Taylor's experiments are shown in Fig. 288, where the temperature is plotted against $\log_{10}(r/r_1)$, where $r_1$ is the radius of the

† *Proc. Roy. Soc.* A, **151** (1935), 494–512.

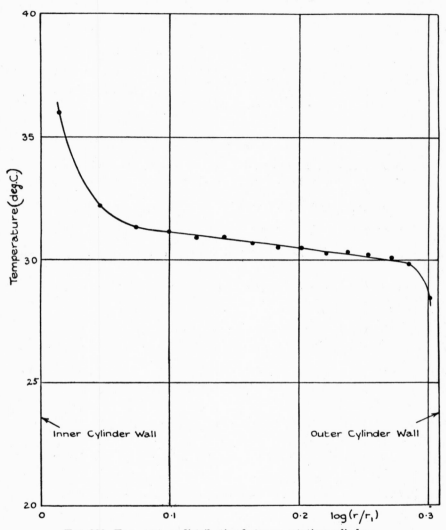

Fig. 288. Temperature distribution between rotating cylinders.

inner cylinder. A linear distribution in the central region is obtained, indicating that the eddy conductivity $\overline{L_r v_r}$ is constant in this region. Near the walls the velocity and temperature distribution could not be defined closely owing to difficulties of measurement, but they showed the rapid increase in gradient with approach to the wall which is characteristic of flow near walls.

# APPENDIX I

## *Derivation of the Energy Equation in the form* (10)

FOR the present purpose it is convenient to work with coordinates $x_\alpha$ and velocities $v_\alpha$ ($\alpha = 1, 2, 3$), and to make use of the summation convention whereby repeated indices are summed over the three values. Then the equations of motion are, in this notation (eqn. (57) of Chap. II)

$$\rho \frac{Dv_\alpha}{Dt} = \rho X_\alpha - \frac{\partial p}{\partial x_\alpha} - \frac{2}{3} \frac{\partial}{\partial x_\alpha} (\mu \Delta) + \frac{\partial}{\partial x_\beta} \left[ \mu \left( \frac{\partial v_\alpha}{\partial x_\beta} + \frac{\partial v_\beta}{\partial x_\alpha} \right) \right],$$

where the external force has components $X_\alpha$ per unit mass and $\Delta$ stands for $\partial v_\alpha / \partial x_\alpha$. We next multiply this equation by $v_\alpha$ and sum, thereby obtaining

$$\rho \frac{D}{Dt} \left( \frac{q^2}{2} \right) = \rho v_\alpha X_\alpha - v_\alpha \frac{\partial p}{\partial x_\alpha} - \tfrac{2}{3} v_\alpha \frac{\partial}{\partial x_\alpha} (\mu \Delta) + v_\alpha \frac{\partial}{\partial x_\beta} \left[ \mu \left( \frac{\partial v_\alpha}{\partial x_\beta} + \frac{\partial v_\beta}{\partial x_\alpha} \right) \right]. \qquad \text{(i)}$$

The energy eqn. (9) in this notation is

$$\rho c_p \frac{DT}{Dt} - \frac{Dp}{Dt} = \frac{\partial}{\partial x_\alpha} \left( k \frac{\partial T}{\partial x_\alpha} \right) + \Phi, \qquad \text{(ii)}$$

where

$$\Phi = \mu \left[ -\frac{2}{3} \Delta^2 + \frac{1}{2} \left( \frac{\partial v_\alpha}{\partial x_\beta} + \frac{\partial v_\beta}{\partial x_\alpha} \right) \left( \frac{\partial v_\alpha}{\partial x_\beta} + \frac{\partial v_\beta}{\partial x_\alpha} \right) \right].$$

Adding (i) and (ii) we get

$$\rho \frac{D}{Dt} \left( c_p T + \frac{q^2}{2} \right) - \frac{\partial p}{\partial t} = \rho v_\alpha X_\alpha + \frac{\partial}{\partial x_\alpha} \left[ k \frac{\partial T}{\partial x_\alpha} + \mu \frac{\partial}{\partial x_\alpha} \left( \frac{q^2}{2} \right) \right] + \chi, \qquad \text{(iii)}$$

where

$$\chi = \Phi - \mu \frac{\partial v_\alpha}{\partial x_\beta} \frac{\partial v_\alpha}{\partial x_\beta} - \tfrac{2}{3} v_\alpha \frac{\partial}{\partial x_\alpha} (\mu \Delta) + v_\alpha \frac{\partial}{\partial x_\beta} \left( \mu \frac{\partial v_\beta}{\partial x_\alpha} \right)$$

$$= \frac{\mu}{3} \Delta^2 + \frac{v_\alpha}{3} \frac{\partial}{\partial x_\alpha} (\mu \Delta) + \mu \left[ \frac{\partial v_\alpha}{\partial x_\beta} \frac{\partial v_\beta}{\partial x_\alpha} - \frac{\partial v_\alpha}{\partial x_\alpha} \frac{\partial v_\beta}{\partial x_\beta} \right] + \frac{\partial \mu}{\partial x_\beta} \left( v_\alpha \frac{\partial v_\beta}{\partial x_\alpha} - v_\beta \Delta \right).$$

Now the dilatation term $\Delta$ is usually not large (see § 7) and products of it with $\mu$ are small, so that the first two terms in the last expression may be neglected. The middle term in the above expression for $\chi$ is also small; this can best be seen by considering its value in various special cases. For example, its value in two-dimensional flow, reverting to $x$, $y$, $z$ coordinates, is

$$2\mu \left[ \frac{\partial u}{\partial y} \frac{\partial v}{\partial x} - \frac{\partial u}{\partial x} \frac{\partial v}{\partial y} \right].$$

For flow in a boundary layer of thickness $\delta_u$, $\partial u/\partial x$ and $\partial v/\partial y$ are $O(1)$, $\partial u/\partial y$ is $O(\delta^{-1})$, and $\partial v/\partial x$ is $O(\delta_u)$, so that the term in square brackets is at most $O(1)$; since $\mu$ is small the whole term is therefore small. By similar arguments it may be shown that the last terms in the above expression are small.

We shall therefore neglect the terms contained in the expression $\chi$ and if we limit consideration to flow with no body forces ($X_\alpha = 0$) eqn. (iii) becomes

$$\rho \frac{D}{Dt} \left( c_p T + \frac{q^2}{2} \right) - \frac{\partial p}{\partial t} = \frac{\partial}{\partial x_\alpha} \left[ k \frac{\partial T}{\partial x_\alpha} + \mu \frac{\partial}{\partial x_\alpha} \left( \frac{q^2}{2} \right) \right].$$

Putting the total temperature $T_H$ equal to $T + q^2/2c_p$ this equation may be written

$$\rho c_p \frac{DT_H}{Dt} - \frac{\partial p}{\partial t} = \frac{\partial}{\partial x_\alpha}\left[k\frac{\partial}{\partial x_\alpha}\left(T_H + \frac{(\sigma-1)}{2c_p}q^2\right)\right],$$

where $\sigma = \mu c_p/k$. For steady flow the term $\partial p/\partial t$ vanishes.

If the flow is turbulent we may still neglect the residual viscosity term $\chi$ because it is smaller than the more important of the terms depending on viscosity and conductivity which are themselves unimportant in turbulent flow except near walls.

# APPENDIX II

## Diffusion and its Analogy with Heat Transfer

### 1. The equations of mass transfer for a mixture

WE give here an elementary account of the theory of diffusion in so far as it is necessary to understand the analogy between heat transfer, diffusion, and skin friction. This analogy has recently gained an added interest in aerodynamics in relation to chemical methods of locating the transition from laminar to turbulent flow.

If we have a mixture of two gases of molecular weights $m_1$ and $m_2$ and densities $\rho_1$ and $\rho_2$ the number of molecules of the first gas crossing an element of area $\delta S$ in unit time is $-j_{12}\dfrac{\partial}{\partial n}\left(\dfrac{\rho_1}{m_1}\right)\delta S$, where $n$ is the normal drawn in the direction considered, $\rho_1/m_1$ is the number of molecules of the first gas in unit volume, and $j_{12}$ is the diffusion coefficient for the pair of gases.† Similarly the number of molecules of the second gas crossing the elementary area is

$$-j_{12}\frac{\partial}{\partial n}\left(\frac{\rho_2}{m_2}\right)\delta S.$$

Consider the conditions in a small parallelepiped of fluid with centroid at $P(x_1, x_2, x_3)$ of sides $\delta x_1$, $\delta x_2$, $\delta x_3$ and volume $\delta\tau$ through which diffusion is occurring. Then the rate of transfer of molecules of the first gas by diffusion into the element is calculated as for heat conduction (Chap. II) to be

$$\delta\tau \frac{\partial}{\partial x_\alpha}\left(j_{12}\frac{\partial}{\partial x_\alpha}\right)\left(\frac{\rho_1}{m_1}\right),$$

where the summation convention for Greek suffixes is in operation. The rate of convection of molecules of the first gas into the element is shown, again similarly to heat transfer (Chap. II), to be

$$-\delta\tau\frac{\partial}{\partial x_\alpha}\left(\frac{\rho_1 v_\alpha}{m_1}\right).$$

The rate of increase of the number of molecules of the first gas in the element is

$$\delta\tau\frac{\partial}{\partial t}\left(\frac{\rho_1}{m_1}\right),$$

† See, for example, Jeans, *Kinetic Theory of Gases*, Cambridge (1940), or Kennard, *Kinetic Theory of Gases*, New York (1938).

and this must be equal to the net inflow.  Hence

$$\frac{\partial}{\partial t}\left(\frac{\rho_1}{m_1}\right)+\frac{\partial}{\partial x_\alpha}\left(\frac{\rho_1 v_\alpha}{m_1}\right) = \frac{\partial}{\partial x_\alpha}\left[j_{12}\frac{\partial}{\partial x_\alpha}\left(\frac{\rho_1}{m_1}\right)\right],$$

which may be written

$$\frac{D\rho_1}{Dt}+\rho_1\Delta = \frac{\partial}{\partial x_\alpha}\left(j_{12}\frac{\partial\rho_1}{\partial x_\alpha}\right), \tag{i}$$

where $\Delta$ is the dilatation (Chap. II, § 4).  Similarly for the second gas

$$\frac{D\rho_2}{Dt}+\rho_2\Delta = \frac{\partial}{\partial x_\alpha}\left(j_{12}\frac{\partial\rho_2}{\partial x_\alpha}\right).$$

These two equations replace the equation of continuity for a single gas. Summing them we obtain an equation for the overall density $\rho = \rho_1+\rho_2$,

$$\frac{D\rho}{Dt}+\rho\Delta = \frac{\partial}{\partial x_\alpha}\left(j_{12}\frac{\partial\rho}{\partial x_\alpha}\right), \tag{ii}$$

which is of the same form as the equations for the components.

## 2. The equation of state for a mixture

The equation of state for the mixture has the form

$$p = p_1+p_2 = \bar{R}\left(\frac{\rho_1}{m_1}+\frac{\rho_2}{m_2}\right)T, \tag{iii}$$

where $p_1$ and $p_2$ are the partial pressures of the components.

## 3. Approximate theory of diffusion for a gas of small concentration

It is our object to develop only an approximate theory and we shall from this point in general limit consideration to the diffusion of a gas of small concentration in air, ignoring the diffusion of the air into the gas. We assume also that the general motion is slow so that the density variations in the field are not large; the right-hand side of (ii) can then be neglected and the equation of continuity for the mixture can be reduced to its old form

$$\frac{D\rho}{Dt}+\rho\Delta = 0. \tag{iv}$$

Substituting from (iv) in (i) we obtain

$$\frac{D\rho_1}{Dt}-\frac{\rho_1}{\rho}\frac{D\rho}{Dt} = \frac{\partial}{\partial x_\alpha}\left(j\frac{\partial\rho_1}{\partial x_\alpha}\right),$$

where we have replaced $j_{12}$ by $j$ which stands for the coefficient of diffusion of the contaminating gas in air. This equation is approximately equivalent to

$$\frac{D}{Dt}\left(\frac{\rho_1}{\rho}\right) = \frac{\partial}{\partial x_\alpha}\left[j\frac{\partial}{\partial x_\alpha}\left(\frac{\rho_1}{\rho}\right)\right], \tag{v}$$

if we neglect some derivatives with respect to $\rho$ which are multiplied by $j$; this is consistent with our neglect of the right-hand side of (ii). We now put $\rho_1/\rho$ equal to $n$, which is called the concentration of the contaminating gas, and also assume that the coefficient of diffusion $j$ is a constant. Eqn. (v) becomes

$$\frac{Dn}{Dt} = j\nabla^2 n. \tag{vi}$$

## 4. Analogy between heat transfer and diffusion

We are now in a position to consider the analogy between heat transfer and diffusion. The approximate eqn. (8) determining the temperature distribution in the case of slow motion is

$$\frac{DT}{Dt} = \kappa \nabla^2 T.$$

This is similar to eqn. (vi) for the concentration with the replacement of the coefficient of diffusion $j$ by the thermometric conductivity $\kappa$. The first condition for the validity of the analogy is therefore that these two quantities shall be equal. This is approximately true for the important case of water vapour diffusing in air,† but it is not generally valid. However, even if the two coefficients are not equal there may be a qualitative similarity between the temperature and concentration fields. The second condition for the validity of the analogy is that the boundary conditions for the heat transfer and diffusion problems shall be similar. When both these requirements are satisfied the solutions of the equations for temperature and concentration are related by the equation

$$\frac{n-n_0}{n_1-n_0} = \frac{T-T_0}{T_1-T_0},$$

where $n_0$, $T_0$ and $n_1$, $T_1$ are the concentration and temperature at a pair of corresponding stations.

By analogy with the heat-transfer coefficients $K_N$ and $K_S$ we can introduce mass transfer coefficients $K_{Nd}$ and $K_{Sd}$ defined by the equations

$$\left. \begin{array}{l} G = K_{Nd}\,\rho Sj(n_1-n_0)/d \\ G = K_{Sd}\,\rho SU(n_1-n_0) \end{array} \right\}, \qquad\qquad \text{(vii)}$$

where $G$ is the rate of transfer of mass of the diffusing gas across an area $S$ in unit time. Then if the conditions for the validity of the analogy are satisfied we shall obtain the results‡

$$K_N = K_{Nd},$$
$$K_S = K_{Sd}.$$

One further point about the boundary conditions requires notice; these may be affected by the diffusion process, because there is a normal velocity directed towards the surface of an absorbing body at which the concentration is known.§ In the corresponding heat-transfer problem there is no flow towards the surface of a body maintained at a fixed temperature. This reinforces the requirement that the concentration shall be small everywhere if the analogy with heat transfer is to hold.

If the Reynolds number is large there is a vapour boundary layer at the surface of a body in a stream, corresponding to the temperature and velocity

---

† The International Critical Tables give the value of $j$ for water vapour diffusing into air as $0 \cdot 22$ cm.²/sec. at $0°$ C. The value of $\kappa = k/\rho c_p$ for air at $0°$ C. is $0 \cdot 183$ cm.²/sec. using the value of $k$ given in § 4.

‡ First given in a different form by W. K. Lewis, *Mech. Eng.* **44** (1922), 145. See also E. Schmidt, *Gesundheits-Ingenieur*, **52** (1929), 525–9.

§ If the concentration at the wall is high the velocity normal to a surface from which evaporation is proceeding may be appreciable. Solutions in such cases have been given by Schuh (*Z. angew. Math. Mech.* **25/27** (1947), 54–60, translated as *Tech. Memor. Nat. Adv. Comm. Aero.*, No. 1,275 (1950).)

boundary layers. There is no need to discuss the vapour boundary-layer conditions here as they follow closely the conditions in the temperature boundary layer.

## 5. Examples

We proceed to consider some examples of diffusion. We begin with the case of a flat plate of length $l$ with a wet surface which is held along wind in a stream of air of velocity $U$ at infinity. It is assumed that the boundary layer is laminar. The air at the surface of the plate is saturated with water vapour so that the concentration $n$ is equal to $n_1$ (say) at the plate and is equal to $n_0$ (say) at infinity. By analogy with the corresponding problem of the flat plate maintained at a temperature above the stream temperature, which is discussed in § 13, we can write down the solution of the diffusion problem as

$$K_{Nd} = \alpha_1(\sigma_d)R^{\frac{1}{2}} \doteqdot 0 \cdot 664\sigma_d^{\frac{1}{3}}R^{\frac{1}{2}}, \qquad \text{(viii)}$$

where $\alpha_1(\sigma)$ is the function given in Table 2, $\sigma_d = \nu/j$ is the diffusion number which corresponds to the Prandtl number in heat transfer, and $R$ is the Reynolds number $Ul/\nu$. The diffusion coefficient $K_{Nd}$ is related to the mass $G$ diffusing from the surface $S$ of the plate per second by eqn. (vii), if we take the representative length $d$ as equal to the length $l$ of the plate.

In the above example the evaporation from the surface requires a continuous supply of heat to the plate to provide the latent heat of evaporation of the water. We are at liberty to postulate the existence of an internal source of heat of sufficient strength to ensure that the temperature of the plate is maintained equal to that of the stream, and if such a source is present, there will be no temperature variations in the field. In practice such a source will not usually be present and the temperature of the plate will fall just enough for the transfer of heat from the stream to the plate to be sufficient to provide the necessary latent heat of evaporation of the water. The diffusion of vapour from the surface and the transfer of heat to the surface may be assumed to proceed independently of one another, provided that the temperature and concentration near the surface do not differ too much from their values in the free stream. The amount of heat required per second to evaporate a mass of water of $G$ units per second is

$$Q = LG, \qquad \text{(ix)}$$

where $L$ is the latent heat of unit mass of water. The solution of the problem of the transfer of heat to the plate at a sufficient rate to provide for the evaporation of the water may be written

$$Q = K_N kS(T_0 - T_1)/l, \qquad \text{(x)}$$

where $T_1$ is the unknown temperature of the surface and $T_0$ is the temperature at infinity. The solution of this heat transfer problem is given in § 13 and may be written

$$K_N = \alpha_1(\sigma)R^{\frac{1}{2}} \doteqdot 0 \cdot 664\sigma^{\frac{1}{3}}R^{\frac{1}{2}}. \qquad \text{(xi)}$$

Eliminating $Q$ and $G$ between (vii)–(xi) we obtain

$$L = \frac{K_N}{K_{Nd}} \frac{k}{\rho j} \frac{T_0 - T_1}{n_1 - n_0} = c_p \left(\frac{\kappa}{j}\right)^{\frac{2}{3}} \left(\frac{T_0 - T_1}{n_1 - n_0}\right), \qquad \text{(xii)}$$

putting $k/(\rho c_p) = \kappa$ and $\sigma_d = \nu/j$, $\sigma = \nu/\kappa$. This equation determines the surface temperature if the concentrations are known but it can also be used to determine the concentration of water vapour in the air by the measurement of the temperature. Eqn. (xii) is the basis of the use of the wet-bulb thermometer.

It is probable that $\kappa$ and $j$ are nearly equal, for the diffusion of heat and water vapour in air, and if this is assumed to be exactly true (xii) reduces to the simple form

$$L = c_p \left( \frac{T_0 - T_1}{n_1 - n_0} \right). \tag{xiii}$$

In the wet-bulb thermometer the air adjacent to the bulb is assumed to be saturated with water vapour and (xiii) is used to determine $n_0$, the relative humidity, from measurements of $T_0$ and $T_1$ and from a knowledge of $n_1$, the saturation concentration of water vapour in air at the temperature $T_1$. The above analysis is given by Nusselt[†] and Whipple.[‡]

A corresponding theory for evaporation with turbulent boundary layers can be constructed by analogy with the theory for heat transfer given in § 30.

Another related example is the free evaporation from a wet vertical plate in still air.[§] In this case the air close to the plate is saturated with water vapour, and its density is reduced so that it tends to rise. On the other hand, the reduction in temperature of the air near the surface due to the evaporation produces an increase in density and this tends to cause a downward movement. Under atmospheric conditions the final motion is downwards and the flow near the plate resembles the free convection from a vertical plate which is maintained at a lower temperature than the surrounding air. As in the previous example there is similarity between the temperature and concentration fields if the diffusivity and the thermometric conductivity are equal. This leads to the same relation (xii) between the temperature and concentration at the plate and far away from it as was obtained in the previous example of forced convection and evaporation. The effect of draughts and of radiation are more important in the case of free evaporation and consequently for accurate measurements of the wet-bulb temperature it is usual to induce air flow by a fan.

The above discussion refers to the flat plate, but it is probable that the conclusion applies, at least approximately, to bodies of other shapes.

[†] *Z. angew. Math. Mech.* **10** (1930), 105–21.
[‡] *Proc. Phys. Soc.* **45** (1933), 307–19. Whipple states that this theory of the wet-bulb thermometer is due to G. I. Taylor.
[§] See Schmidt, loc. cit. on p. 849, who describes some preliminary experiments.

## ADDITIONAL REFERENCES

*Treatises and collected works*

FISHENDEN and SAUNDERS, *Introduction to Heat Transfer*, Oxford (1950).
McADAMS, *Heat Transmission*, New York (1942).
GRÖBER and ERK, *Die Grundgesetze der Wärmeübertragung*, Berlin (1933).
ECKERT, *Introduction to the Transfer of Heat and Mass*, New York (1950).
SCHUH, 'Temperature boundary layers', *M.A.P. Völkenrode Rep. R. & T.*
     No. 1,007 (1948).

McAdams, 'Some recent developments in heat transfer', *Bull. Engng. Purdue Univ.*, No. 104 (1948).
ten Bosch, *Die Wärmeübertragung*, Berlin (1936).

*Flow in pipes*

(a) *Laminar flow*

Kraussold, 'Die Wärmeübertragung bei zähen Flüssigkeiten in Röhren', *Forschungsh. Ver. dtsch. Ing.*, No. 351 (1931).
Sherwood, Kiley, and Mangsen, 'Heat transmission to oil flowing in pipes', *Industr. Engng. Chem.* **24** (1932), 273–7.
Jacob and Eck, 'Über den Wärmeaustausch bei der Strömung zäher Flüssigkeiten in Röhren', *Forsch. IngWes.* **3** (1932), 121–6.

(b) *Turbulent flow*

Mattioli, 'Theorie der Wärmeübertragung in glatten und rauhen Röhren', *Forsch. IngWes.* **11** (1940), 149–58, translated as *Tech. Memor. Nat. Adv. Comm. Aero.*, No. 1,037.
Martinelli, 'Heat transfer to molten metals', *Trans. Amer. Soc. Mech. Engrs.* **69** (1947), 947–59.
Bailey and Cope, 'Heat transmission through circular, square, and rectangular pipes', *Rep. Memor. Aero. Res. Coun.*, No. 1,560 (1934).
Bühne, 'Die Wärmeübertragung in zähen Flüssigkeiten bei turbulenter Strömung', *Jb. dtsch. Luftfahrtforsch.* **2** (1937), 57–66.
Hall and Tsao, 'Heat transfer at low temperatures between tube walls and gases in turbulent flow', *Proc. Roy. Soc.* A, **191** (1947), 6–21.
Jung, 'Wärmeübergang und Reibungswiderstand bei Gasströmung in Röhren bei hohen Geschwindigkeiten', *Forschungsh. Ver. dtsch. Ing.*, No. 380 (1936); also *Z. Ver. dtsch. Ing.* **81** (1937), 496–8.

*Forced convection*

Latzko, 'Der Wärmeübergang an einem turbulenten Flüssigkeits- oder Gasstrom', *Z. angew. Math. Mech.* **1** (1921), 268–90.
Denis, 'On convective cooling in liquids', *Phil. Mag.* (6), **47** (1924), 1057–92.
Kalikhman, 'Heat transmission in the boundary layer', *Prikl. Mat. Mekh.* **10** (1946), translated as *Tech. Memor. Nat. Adv. Comm. Aero.*, No. 1,229 (1948).

*Kinetic temperature*

Schirokow, *J. Tech. Phys. U.S.S.R.* **3** (1936), 1020–7.
Brun, *Publ. Sci. Tech. Min. Air*, No. 112 (1937).

*Analogy between heat transfer and skin friction*

Cope, 'Friction and heat transmission coefficients', *Proc. Instn. Mech. Engrs.* **137** (1947), 165–94.
White, 'Fluid friction and its relation to heat transfer', *Trans. Inst. Chem. Engrs.* **10** (1932), 66–80.
Colburn, 'A method of correlating forced convection heat transfer data and a comparison with fluid friction', *Trans. Amer. Inst. Chem. Engrs.* **29** (1933), 174–209.

BOELTER, MARTINELLI, and JONASSEN, 'Remarks on the analogy between heat transfer and momentum transfer', *Trans. Amer. Soc. Mech. Engrs.* **63** (1941), 447–55.

### Analogy between heat transfer and diffusion

LOHRISCH, 'Bestimmung von Wärmeübergangszahlen durch Diffusionsversuche', *Forschungsarb. Ver. dtsch. Ing.* **6** (1935), 293–304.

### Free convection

NUSSELT, 'Die Wärmeabgabe eines wagrechtliegenden Rohres oder Drahtes in Flüssigkeiten und Gasen', *Z. Ver. dtsch. Ing.* **73** (1929), 1475–8.

WEISE, 'Wärmeübergang durch freie Konvektion von quadratischen Platten', *Forsch. IngWes.* **6** (1935), 281–92.

JOUKOVSKY and KIREJEW, 'Optische Methode zur Untersuchung des Temperaturfeldes in der Umgebung umströmter Zylinder', *J. Tech. Phys. U.S.S.R.* **3** (1936), 754–66.

# AUTHOR INDEX

Abdurahiman, P. V., ii. 609.
Ackeret, J., i. 3, 221, 285, 323, 333, 335, 464–5, 470, 473; ii. 481, 482, 626–7, 629, 638, 648, 669.
Ackermann, G., ii. 790.
Adamson, D., ii. 617, 626.
Aihara, T., i. 278.
Albers, L. U. J., ii. 609.
Allen, H. J., ii. 521.
Ashkanas, H., i. 464, 468, 474; ii. 503, 551, 570.
Atkin, A. O. L., i. 175, 178; ii. 607.

Bailey, A., ii. 606.
Bailey, D. L. R., ii. 843, 852.
Bailey, F. J., i. 221.
Baird, E. G., ii. 605.
Bairstow, Sir Leonard, ii. 720–1.
Baranoff, A. von, ii. 523.
Bardsley, O. A., i. 475.
Barnes, N. F., ii. 593.
Barry, F. W., i. 475; ii. 611.
Bartels, R. C. F., i. 324.
Batchelor, G. K., i. 271, 272; ii. 606–7.
Bäuerle, H., ii. 554–5, 574–5.
Beavan, J. A., ii. 528, 561, 566, 570, 606, 614, 616, 617, 631, 633, 643, 660, 663, 680.
Becker, R., i. 124–5; ii. 545.
Beckmann, W. von, ii. 801, 803, 805, 807–8, 810.
Bell, R. W., ii. 514, 530.
Bellinger, S. L., ii. 593.
Bethe, H. A., i. 126, 129–30.
Bingham, E. C., ii. 762.
Binnie, A. M., i. 21; ii. 547, 605.
Biot, M. A., i. 362.
Bitterly, J. G., ii. 605.
Black, J., i. 3, 9.
Blasius, H., i. 402, 405, 410, 412, 420, 442; ii. 799.
Boelter, L. M. K., ii. 853.
Böhm, H., ii. 608.
Boltzmann, L., i. 67.
Borbely, S. von, i. 339.
Bosch, M. ten, ii. 852.
Boussinesq, J., ii. 765.
Bowling, A. G., ii. 500.
Brainerd, J. G., i. 403, 418, 423, 440, 442.
Bratt, J. B., i. 368, 369, 374; ii. 578.
Bright, P., i. 24.
Britten, K. H. V., ii. 609.

Broderick, J. B., i. 313.
Browne, S. H., i. 324.
Brun, E., ii. 852.
Bühne, W., ii. 852.
Bumstead, N., ii. 680.
Burnett, J., i. 69.
Burrows, P. M., ii. 663.
Burstall, F. H., ii. 602.
Busemann, A., i. 24, 79, 84, 116, 172, 176, 221, 266, 286–7, 297, 402, 403, 418; ii. 605, 607, 637–9, 668–9, 677–8, 788.
Byrne, R. W., ii. 608.

Calder, P. H., i. 210.
Callendar, G. S., i. 49; ii. 762.
Carrier, G. F., i. 266, 364.
Castagna, A., ii. 607.
Chambré, P., ii. 546.
Chang, C. C., i. 266.
Chaplygin, S., i. 228, 229, 231, 237.
Chapman, D. R., ii. 800.
Chapman, S., i. 37, 38, 39, 41, 66, 68, 69, 124.
Charlesworth, M. P., i. 3.
Charnley, W. J., ii. 626, 629.
Cheers, F., ii. 606.
Cherry, T. M., i. 246, 264, 265, 266.
Chinneck, A., i. 368, 374; ii. 559, 578, 641, 756.
Church, A. H., ii. 608.
Coburn, N., i. 104.
Codd, J., i. 27; ii. 613, 639, 641.
Cohen, H., ii. 546.
Cohen, H. G., i. 266.
Colburn, A. P., ii. 852.
Cole, J. A., i. 456.
Cole, J. D., i. 266, 464, 468, 474.
Collar, A. R., i. 333, 335, 374; ii. 607, 608.
Cope, W. F., i. 68, 221, 389, 418, 423, 431, 432, 433, 434, 439, 456, 457, 458, 459; ii. 546, 549, 572, 606, 701, 746, 756, 843, 852.
Courant, R., i. 71, 75, 76, 97, 102, 137, 138, 143, 157.
Cowling, T., i. 37, 38, 39, 41, 66, 68, 69, 124.
Craggs, J. W., i. 253, 260, 264.
Crocco, L., i. 63, 66, 69, 70, 77, 131, 266, 400, 403, 404, 406, 409, 410, 417, 418, 419, 420, 421, 422, 423, 426; ii. 505.

Dale, T. P., ii. 579.

C c

# SUBJECT INDEX

Accelerated motion, i. 362–3.

Ackeret–Collar ('quasi-stationary') derivatives, i. 333.

Adiabatic flow:
defined, i. 40, 194.
*See also* Homentropic flow.

Adiathermal flow, one-dimensional, i. 194; at constant cross-sectional area with friction, i. 212–16.

Adjustable walls for wind tunnels, ii. 528–30.

Aerodynamic centre, definition of, ii. 666.

— derivatives (unsteady motion), i. 364–74; (Ackeret–Collar derivatives), i. 333.

Aerofoil:
accelerated, i. 362–3.
at incidence, i. 29–31.
bulging of surface of, effects of, ii. 633–7.
camber, *see* Aerofoil section shape.
double-wedge, i. 182–5.
downwash from, i. 329–32, 341.
drag of: at subsonic speeds, i. 270–4, 350–6, ii. 641–55; at supersonic speeds, i. 282–96, 332–50, ii. 668–77; 'basic', ii. 652–4; effect of boundary-layer suction on, ii. 653–5; effect of camber on, ii. 644–7; effect of incidence on, ii. 643–8; effect of leading-edge radius on, ii. 648; effect of position of maximum thickness on, ii. 647–8; effect of Reynolds number on, ii. 648–52; effect of surface roughness on, ii. 648; effect of sweepback on, ii. 677–82; effect of thickness/chord ratio on, ii. 644–5.
flow past, i. 24–33, ii. 612 et seq.; at high speeds (formation of shock waves), ii. 612–14; at high subsonic speeds, ii. 616–37; at low subsonic speeds, ii. 614–16; at supersonic speeds, ii. 637–41.
forces and moments on: in subsonic flow, i. 270–4, 350–6, 364–71, ii. 641–64; in supersonic flow, i. 282–96 332–50, 371–4, ii. 668–73.
in heat-transfer calculations, ii. 797–801, 844.
incidence effects on: i. 29–31; on drag,

ii. 643–8; on pressure distribution, ii. 631.

Joukowski, i. 276.
leading edge of: flow around, ii. 639–41; radius of, effect on drag, ii. 648.
lift on, i. 270–4, 282–96, 332–56, 364–74, ii. 655–64, 668–77; effect of camber on, ii. 663–4; effect of Mach number on, ii. 655–60, 661–4; effect of surface roughness on, ii. 664; effect of sweepback on, ii. 677–82; representation by vortices for calculation of wind-tunnel corrections, ii. 520, 521.
oscillating, theory of, i. 325 et seq.
pitching moment on: at subsonic speeds, i. 270–4, 350–6, 364–71, ii. 664–8, 673–6; at supersonic speeds, i. 282–96, 332–50, 371–4, ii. 668–73, 676–7; determination from pressure distribution, ii. 560; direct measurement of, ii. 575–7.
pressure distribution on, i. 270–4, 282–96, 332–56, ii. 614–41; effect of bulging of surface on, ii. 633–7; effect of sweep-back on, ii. 677, 679, 681, 682.
'roof-top', ii. 616, 617, 621–3.
section shape: effect on drag, ii. 643–8; effect on lift, ii. 655–60, 663–4; effect on pitching moment, ii. 664–8; effect on pressure distribution, ii. 629–31.
semi-infinite, in unsteady motion, i. 354.
shock-waves on: development of, ii. 617–27; effect of bulging of surface on, ii. 633–7.
swept-back, i. 31–33, ii. 677–82.
symmetrical, at zero incidence, i. 24–29.
theory: quasi-stationary, supersonic flow, i. 332–6; steady motion, i. 270–4, 282–96; three-dimensional: (steady motion, subsonic flow), i. 273–4, (steady motion, supersonic flow), i. 290–302, (unsteady motion, subsonic flow), i. 354–6, (unsteady motion, supersonic flow), i. 341–50.
thickness-chord ratio of: effect on drag, ii. 643–4; effect on lift, ii. 656, 658; effect on pitching moment, ii. 666–7.

Wind tunnel: (*cont.*)
  methods of driving, ii. 507–9.
  — of drying the air in, ii. 481–2.
  model span and length, effects of, ii. 526–7.
  — supports, effects of, ii. 536.
  nozzle design, i. 88–93, 175–8, ii. 485–500, 607.
  — profiles, ii. 492–500.
  pressure ratios, ii. 506, 510.
  relaxation-time effects in, ii. 539.
  Reynolds number in, ii. 478.
  special, ii. 531.
  supersonic: auxiliary nozzle in, effect on condensation, ii. 550; nozzle design for, i. 88–93, 175–8, ii. 485–500.
  throats, *see* Nozzles.
  transonic testing in, ii. 534–5.
  turbulence in, effect on flow, ii, 551.
  uncertainties arising in tests in, ii. 516 et seq.
  walls: adjustable, ii. 528–30; slotted, ii. 531; velocity increments at, ii. 530.
  working fluid, factors which may cause its behaviour to depart from that of perfect gas, ii. 537–41.
  — section, design of, ii. 500–1.
  *See also* Pressure measurement; Measuring techniques; Shock tube; Visualization.
Wing-flow method for transonic flow, ii. 516.
Wing:
  delta: i. 301; of 'mixed' planform, unsteady supersonic flow over, i. 334; of 'simple' planform, unsteady supersonic flow over, i. 346.

  of finite aspect ratio: subsonic theory for, i. 272–4, 354–6; supersonic theory for, i. 290–6, 341–50.
  of infinite aspect ratio: derivatives for (unsteady motion), i. 364–74; general subsonic theory for, i. 269–72, 350–4; general supersonic theory for, i. 282–90, 332–41.
  of 'mixed' planform, supersonic theory for (unsteady motion), i. 347–50.
  of 'simple' planform, supersonic theory for (unsteady motion), i. 343–7.
  of small aspect ratio on slender body of revolution, in steady motion, i. 313–16.
  quarter-infinite, in unsteady motion, i. 347.
  theory, supersonic, quasi stationary, i. 332–6.
  *See also* Aerofoil.
Wool tufts, ii. 578.
Working fluid, behaviour of, departure from that of perfect gas, ii. 537–41.

X-rays, density measurements with, ii. 599–600.

Yawed aerofoil, i. 31–33, ii. 677–82; experimental results, ii. 680–2.
Yawed body of revolution: base pressure on, ii. 720; drag of, i. 302–13, ii. 746; head shock on, ii. 720; force system on, i. 302–13, 356–60; ii. 726; measuring techniques for, ii. 736–44; pressure distribution on, i. 302–13, 356–60, ii. 715–21; skin friction on, ii. 720; theory of, i. 302–13, 356–60, ii. 727–35.
Yawmeters, ii. 572–5.